16

Priscilla
Bacchus

LIFE SERIES

Visions and Dreams

Level 15
Seventh-day Adventist Readers

Patricia A. Habada

Gary B. Swanson

Sally J. McMillan

LuWana J. Kumalae

Acknowledgments

Grateful acknowledgment is made to the following:

Ginn and Company for assistance in the preparation of this book: and to Rosly Walter, Ginn staff editor, for guidance.

Reading steering committee members: George Babcock, chairman; Patricia Habada, secretary: Frances Clark, Southwestern Union; Malcolm Graham, Canadian Union; Marion Hartlein, General Conference; Erna Hauck, Columbia Union College; Sandra Herndon, Northeastern Conference; Elizabeth Hudak, Florida Conference; Erma Lee, North Pacific Union; Norwida Marshall, Southern Union; Lorraine Miller, Oregon Conference; Joyce Morse, Southern California Conference; Esther Novak, Wisconsin Conference; Desmond Rice, Southern Missionary College; Aleene Schaeffer, Union College.

Canadian consultants: Herbert Penney-Flynn, Newfoundland; Frances Schander, Saskatchewan; George Unger, Ontario.

Special consultants: Margaret Hafner, New York; Betty McCune, Loma Linda University; Millie Youngberg, Andrews University.

Grateful acknowledgment is made to the following publishers, authors, and agents for permission to use and adapt copyrighted materials:

Abingdon Press for "Praying Hands" adapted from *Pictures that Preach* by Charles Nelson Page. Copyright 1924.

Addison-Wesley Publishing Company for "Inventor for Safety," adapted from *Eight Black American Inventors,* Copyright © 1972, by Robert C. Hayden. Reprinted by permission of Addison-Wesley Publishing Company, Inc., Reading, Massachusetts 01867.

George Allen & Unwin Publishers, Ltd., for the poem "Roads Go Ever Ever On" from *The Hobbit* by J. R. R. Tolkien. Copyright 1966. Used by permission of George Allen & Unwin Publishers, Ltd.

Associated Press for "Power Failure Darkens Northeast." News bulletin dated November 10, 1965. Used by permission of the Associated Press.

Fern Babcock for "Bamboo Beds and Running Water" by Fern Babcock.

William Blackwood Publishers for "My Father and the Hippopotamus" by Leon Hugo. From *Blackwood's Magazine,* February, 1960. Used by permission of William Blackwood Publishers.

Broadside Press for the poem "Martin Luther King, Jr." by Gwendolyn Brooks. Used by permission of Broadside Press.

The Canadian Press for "Large Ontario Section Plunged in Darkness." News item dated November 10, 1965. Used by permission of The Canadian Press.

City Lights Books for the poem "To Paint the Portrait of a Bird" from *Paroles* by Jacques Prevert, translated by L. Ferlinghetti. Copyright © 1947 by Les Editions du Point du Jour. Reprinted by permission of City Lights Books.

Eleanor Clymer for "Lillian Gilbreth Engineer" from *Modern American Career Women* by Eleanor Clymer and Lillian Erlich. Copyright 1959. Used by permission of Eleanor Clymer.

Joan Daves for "I Have a Dream" excerpted from *I Have a Dream* by Martin Luther King, Jr. Reprinted by permission of Joan Daves. Copyright © 1963 by Martin Luther King, Jr.

Dodd, Mead & Company, Inc., for "Thomas Jefferson's Dream House" from *Thomas Jefferson: His Many Talents* by Johanna Johnston. Copyright © 1961 by Johanna Johnston. Used by permission of Dodd, Mead & Company, Inc.

Doubleday & Company, Inc., for "A Road to Independence," adapted from *Call the Darkness Light* by Nancy Zaroulis. Copyright © 1979 by

6

Illustrations were provided by the following: Corrine Borja (233, 235); Linnea Carlson (123, 125, 127, 165); Churchmouse Graphics/Annie Lunsford (179, 180-181, 183, 192, 350-351); David Cunningham (504-505, 517, 531, 547, 563, 577); Jeffrey L. Dever (130, 131, 132, 211, 358); Evergreen Graphics/Nancy Beatty Gleeson (39, 41, 43, 347); Nathan Greene (239, 242, 405, 407, 494); Dennis Hockerman (197, 198, 199, 471); Richard Keane (138-139); Kenneth Krafchek (157, 159, 162); Jared D. Lee (168, 169); Catherine Meindl (170, 172, 175, 177, 278, 279, 282); Charles Mitchell (267, 268, 272-273, 453); Yoshi Miyake (100-101, 102, 106, 108, 109, 112, 289, 295, 298, 303, 309); Angela M. Moizio (152, 155, 220, 225, 228, 261, 264); Pat Morrison (213, 216-217, 311, 312-313); Bradley O. Pomeroy (29, 30-31, 34, 37, 185, 186-187, 190, 338, 344-345, 353, 416, 421); Steffi Rubin (376, 448, 451); Bob Russo (250, 253, 257); Jim Schaefer (466, 469); Larry Simmons (55, 57, 61); Richard Steadham (15, 18-19, 25, 26, 201, 203, 206, 318, 321); Lowell Stumpf (362, 365); Jack Wallen (145, 147).

Photographs were provided by the following: Albertina Museum (499); American Heart Association (374); James L. Ballard (12, 13, 137); Anne LaBastille, Ph.D. (141); The Bettmann Archive, Inc. (66, 70, 72, 238); Raimondo Borea (398); Art Buchwald (192); Margaret Bourke-White, Life Magazine © 1936 Time, Inc. (463); Dr. E. R. Degginger (286, 287, 330-331, 332-333); Gene Dekovic (65); Margaret Durrance/Black Star (336, 337); E. P. Dutton, Inc. (141); Gretel Ehrlich (81, 82, 83); James L. Fly (440); Gary Gilbert (90-91, 92, 93, 94, 95); Leonard Freed/Magnum Photos, Inc. (14); Burt Glinn/Magnum Photos, Inc. (98, 99); Houghton Mifflin Company (443, 444); Jerry D. Jacka (472); Keystone Press Agency, Ltd. (426, 427); The Library of Congress (402); Loma Linda University (409, 412, 414, 415); Lowie Museum of Anthropology, University of California, Berkeley (63); Louis Lubeski/Taurus Photos (122); Thomas McAvoy, Life Magazine © 1955 Time, Inc. (115, 118); Peter Menzel/Stock, Boston (166, 167); The Metropolitan Museum of Art, Roger's Fund, 1949 (457); Dan Morrill (244, 245); NASA (363); Review and Herald Publishing Association (46, 89); H. Armstrong Roberts (246, 502-503); The Smithsonian Institution (349, 402, 422); Lynn M. Stone (79); Thomas Jefferson Memorial Foundation (377, 378, 379, 380, 381); United Press International (323, 325, 328, 387, 392, 394); Wide World Photos, Inc. (390, 396).

Cover design by Tom Dunbebin. Cover photograph by H. Armstrong Roberts. Harry Knox and Associates, Inc. provided consultation services in art and design.

Every effort has been made to trace the ownership of all copyrighted material in this book and to obtain permission for its use.

Contents

BOLD JOURNEYS

There are many different reasons for traveling and many different ways to go. Some journeys take us far, some only into the interior of our minds. What do the journeys accomplish for the characters you will read about?

THE NEW COLOSSUS

Emma Lazarus

ENGRAVED ON A PLAQUE IN THE STATUE OF LIBERTY

Not like the brazen giant of Greek fame,
With conquering limbs astride from land to land;
Here at our sea-washed, sunset gates shall stand
A mighty woman with a torch, whose flame
Is the imprisoned lightning, and her name
Mother of Exiles. From her beacon-hand
Glows world-wide welcome; her mild eyes command
The air-bridged harbor that twin cities frame.
"Keep, ancient lands, your storied pomp!" cries she
With silent lips. "Give me your tired, your poor,
Your huddled masses yearning to breathe free,
The wretched refuse of your teeming shore.
Send these, the homeless, tempest-tost to me,
I lift my lamp beside the golden door!"

Don't Count Your Bears...

Michael H. Milts

How do you move bears across town? Or more specifically how do you move them across New York City? Very carefully!

In the spring of 1977, plumbing problems cropped up at the Central Park Zoo. The pool in one of the bear enclosures was clogged and, if left to stagnate, could be a health hazard for the three elderly bears that lived there.

Making house calls is the plumber's stock in trade. But making a den call is something else again. The bears would have to be relocated before the pools could be drained and the maintenance work done.

At just that time the Prospect Park Zoo in Brooklyn happened to have very nice, and very empty, facilities for bears. What could be more logical than bundling up the bears and moving them out there? But the Prospect Zoo was twenty miles from Central Park. The bears would have to be trucked past millions of people and thousands of cars, and they were not the lovable honey-hunters so often seen in the movies. They were grizzlies.

15

The grizzly is a subspecies of that giant North American predator, the brown bear. This magnificent silver-tipped creature is more ferocious, more unpredictable, and just as omnivorous. Like the polar bear, it will eat anything.

In this country we are more familiar with the North American black bear, generally shy unless a cub is threatened. But the grizzly is a dangerous, and now endangered, animal. It is quite likely that within the next few decades, it will follow its relative, the Mexican grizzly, into virtual extinction. So although our bears were beyond the age of breeding, they were quite valuable from a number of viewpoints. Our job was to anesthetize them and move them over local streets, expressways, and bridges.

Even the stage directions for our little play, which would soon be splashed across the centerfolds of the New York newspapers, were a problem. The Central Park Zoo had been designed at the turn of the century and was considered a marvel of construction. But the architect had no way of knowing that at some vague time in the future, a handful of men would have to shuttle three eight-hundred-pound bears through its narrow hallways.

All the public ever sees is the outside enclosure where the pool is. The den, where the bears sleep, is low-ceilinged and covers about the area of an average kitchen. To gain entrance to the den requires going up two small flights of stairs, then down a long, narrow corridor, approximately fifty yards long, poorly lit, and wide enough for two humans (or a single bear) to navigate.

A parks recreational van and an enclosed pickup truck, along with a police car for escort, waited at the exit. Judging the floor areas of the transport vehicles, we found there was only room to move two of the bears on the first trip. The third would have to wait in line for the next bus to Brooklyn.

An official brain trust gathered to plan the move. It included Jim Dooley, an engineer and expert on zoo facilities, the Assistant Parks Commissioner, John Fitzgerald and other zookeepers, and several policemen armed with .38 caliber handguns. Impressive weaponry if you are patrolling Fourty-second Street, but very nearly useless against a creature as large and powerful as a grizzly.

Peering down the cramped corridor, I wondered if bears, like people, were generally smaller three-quarters of a century ago. Or maybe they had moved the bears in as cubs, and they had just grown. Whichever, it was going to be like getting a model ship out of a bottle.

The safest way to proceed would be to anesthetize the bears, crate them up, move them, then give them another injection to wake them up. But they were elderly bears, and I was leery about giving them too strong a preliminary shot of M-99, the anesthetic we were using. The crating and uncrating would take too much time, and the necessity for an extra injection would be almost guaranteed. I had to weigh the safety of the animals against the possible risk to human life. My own included.

M-99 is a very strong narcotic drug. If you use it on an animal and don't give him the antidote, he's going to die. The antidote, administered intravenously, presents another problem. The animal revives almost instantly. You can easily wind up staring into the eyes of a totally conscious grizzly who is wondering: Why is this person sticking a needle into me? Used on the large herbivores like the rhinoceros, it's a different matter. They are lumbering, slower, and have to get to their feet to attack.

An intravenous shot of M-99 would have been ideal, if I could have walked up to one of the bears, wrapped a strand of rubber around its arm, and said, "Squeeze your fist." But the shot had to be from a tranquilizer gun, intramuscularly, which meant that it would be absorbed at a slower rate. And sometimes the syringes don't go off perfectly, or they bounce away from the ani-mal, and you have no idea whether you have actually injected 8 ml, 10 ml, or even 18 ml. All we could do was take an educated guess at the dosage and hope for the best.

As we debated, I filled several syringes. I had once hit a bear with M-99 and then gone into the cage to do some dental work on him. He happened to be stretched out between me and the cage door, and in the middle of the operation he sat up and raised his paw over my head. It's strange how vividly you recall moments like that. It had been raining all day; I was drenched and annoyed to begin with, and my first reaction was to look up at him and tell him to quit being a pest and lie down so I could finish. The dental equipment jutted from his mouth like toothpicks, and his yellow teeth were clotted with blood. Then I distinctly remember thinking, *I really didn't know I was going to die when I got up this morning.*

The bear got to his feet while I knelt there, knowing that any move I made would only serve to focus his attention on his dentist. I couldn't say whether he was awake or asleep at the time, but he immediately lay back down and closed his eyes. Perhaps he was just having a bad dream. I know I've had several since that encounter.

Two by two, we walked down the hallway and opened a steel

door. An inner doorframe, set with steel bars, stood between us and the bears. The male and one of the females were in the den, a few feet from us. The other female was outside pacing methodically by the pool. Although they were aging bears, it was spring and they were itchy.

Fitzgerald turned a large, creaking wheel that lowered the grill between the outside enclosure and the den. The two isolated bears stirred. As soon as I started firing the tranquilizer gun, they began hurling themselves against the bars, singly at first, then in tandem. The shots echoed loudly in the hallway, and the sudden high cracks didn't improve their dispositions. At the peak of their anger, they were standing side by side, smashing at the bars with their paws.

I was aiming for their legs, reloading in the semidarkness and shooting as fast as possible. Two of the darts misfired, and it was a good forty-five minutes before either of the bears went down.

The tremendous amount of fatty tissue in the leg muscle slowed the absorption of the anesthetic considerably, and later, when we returned for the third bear I made sure to shoot for the arm muscles.

Their increased heart rate helped pump the M-99 through their systems, and the force of their blows began to lessen. The female dropped to her forepaws. She lurched against the wall and collapsed. The male redoubled his efforts, eyes blazing with fury. Then his equilibrium faltered. He grabbed at the bars a final time, missed, and dropped.

Although deafened by the shots and chilled by the ferocity of the attack, we swarmed into the den when John opened the inner door. Eight of us grabbed the male and converged on the narrow hallway. One supported the monster head, one on each leg, and the others half-dragged the deadweight body. The air was soon filled with muttered speech as knuckles and elbows, backs and buttocks were scraped along the cement walls.

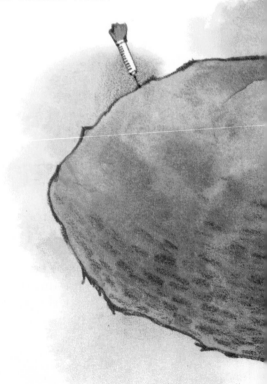

The same routine was repeated with the second bear, the female. She was a bit lighter, six hundred pounds or so, but we managed to scrape and bruise whatever areas of our bodies we had missed on the first passage. The bears were loaded, one in the parks van, the other in the pickup.

As a precaution, Bill Dooley and I went back to the den to make sure none of the tranquilizing darts had been left lying around. We got them all, and, as we left, I slammed the inner door behind me. The hinges creaked, then snapped. After three-quarters of an hour of continuous pounding by the bears, metal fatigue and sheer age had destroyed them.

We stood silently for a moment, both envisioning what surely would have happened if the bears had struck it one more time.

"You'd better get that door fixed," I said.

"Next time you want to shuttle some bears around," he said quietly, "count me out."

Dooley is an incredibly dedicated person and has spent many days with me on the Wednesday rounds as we discussed the health and natural habitat of various animals. He does a remarkable job, working within a limited city budget, to upgrade the zoo facilities. But, quite reasonably, he had second thoughts about risking his life.

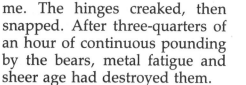

We split into two groups, manned the vehicles, and pulled out. With any luck, we had about thirty minutes to get the bears into the Prospect Park Zoo before I would have to give them the antidote. The countdown started.

Bill Webster, who had been with me for eleven years and has an almost uncanny feeling for the disposition of the animals, joined me in the back of the pickup. We squeezed in around the inert body of the male grizzly. The cab of the truck was packed with officials.

We were halfway to Brooklyn before the bear sat up. I never realized you could fit so many people under a dashboard.

For a moment, it looked as if I had grossly underestimated the amount of narcotic that the animal required. But he was still disoriented and only beginning to elbow his way around when I injected a small shot of the drug. He was sedated quickly, and dropped back into a prone position. Just to be safe, or relatively safe, Bill hog-tied him with heavy rope.

"You ought to get a job in a rodeo," I said.

He smiled knowing as well as I that even a groggy bear, in the confines of a pickup truck, would be a disaster. I could imagine someone coming in late for work and trying to explain to his boss how he was driving along, right on time, and suddenly a giant grizzly had burst through the side of a passing truck.

A week before the move was scheduled, we had tried to arrange to borrow a couple of paddy wagons from the Police Department. But the bureaucratic lines of communication got fouled up, so the vehicles we used were not exactly bear-proof to start with. After the second injection, however, things went fine until we got to Brooklyn, a spiderweb of angling cross-streets that tend to confuse all but its legendary natives.

I glanced through the window to check our progress. I had driven out to Prospect Park every Wednesday for several years and was quite familiar with the most direct route. My stomach began to sink as a row of unfamiliar street signs flashed by. Whoever had been giving directions to our driver had made a mistake.

The blare of the police siren up ahead made conversation difficult, so I motioned toward the small window with my head and shrugged at Bill. He frowned. If the caravan was delayed very long, another shot of M-99 would be necessary—and probably fatal—for the bear.

We had no idea, of course, how the bear in the other van was holding up. We learned, later, that she had slept peacefully throughout the trip. M-99, even though it seemed to work well on a variety of species, was still a relatively new anesthetic. And, as always, there was the uncertainty as to the exact physiological status of a particular animal's detoxification mechanisms.

It always amazes me to watch them anesthetize large animals on the popular wildlife television shows. They always seem to administer the perfect dose, the animal always drops, and there is never any trouble with the antidote. What you don't see are the animals that crash off into the bush and don't survive, or the ones that need a second shot, or the ones that wake up a little too fast. Film editors, I suppose, have to keep in mind the fact that most of those shows are scheduled for after-dinner viewing.

I knocked on the front window. The driver nodded hastily, already aware that we were off course. Everyone in the cab seemed to be talking at the same time. We began to zigzag, looking for Flatbush Avenue, which leads directly to the park. Minutes dragged by. I kept hoping that the police car leading us would pull over and ask a native how to get to the zoo.

We felt the truck shift into high as it wheeled around a corner and knew the driver must have located Flatbush. Within minutes, we roared into Prospect Park with all the subtlety of an armored tank attack.

Midafternoon strollers scattered as we poured out of the trucks. Being of a more modern design than Central Park, the Prospect bear den was easily accessible—no narrow, endless corridors to deal with. Hastily, we manhandled the sedated animals into the safety of their new home. I injected the antidote shots into both of them and they regained consciousness—dazed at first, then lapsing into their usual ill humor while they explored the unfamiliar den.

Our battered crew assembled outside the bear enclosure, while various cuts and scrapes were treated. By mutual consent, we decided to wait until the next day to move the final grizzly.

With a slightly larger dose of M-99, she passed out more rapidly than the others had, and there was no trouble during the move. I was confident that when it came time to return them to Central Park, we would have smooth sailing. It is a fallacy to count your bears before they're caged.

When the pool had been drained and repaired, John Fitzgerald and I met with Mr. Kinzig of the Prospect Zoo to plan the return of the bad news bears.

The midafternoon traffic, we agreed, had been a little heavier than expected on the first trip. I suggested we try it in the early morning. Kinzig thought five

21

o'clock would be a good time, but John said four would be even better.

Being a night person by habit, I knew the only conceivable way I could do anything at four in the morning would be to stay up all night, and I really didn't want to move grizzlies without sufficient sleep. We settled on five, which would give us plenty of time to beat the morning rush hour.

I met Dr. Woods in front of the office well before sunup, and we were joined by several volunteers—student vets who were anxious to gain practical experience in handling large animals. They were full of excitement and anticipation, convinced that the adventure would be fun. I often felt the same way, but rarely at that hour. We pulled into Prospect Park at exactly five o'clock.

Fitzgerald was already there with the police escort. We shuffled around in the predawn darkness. Dr. Woods began filling syringes while our assistants went off to check on the bears. They were awake, they reported, and as content as grizzlies ever get.

Kinzig arrived shortly with the first bad news. There had been a mixup between park and police officials. The policemen who were there to escort us were scheduled to go off duty within the hour.

We hurried to the administration building, opened the switchboard, and started calling offi-

cials. It was nearly 5:30. No one could be reached who could sanction an extension of the policemen's shift. And about the last thing we needed was to drive through half of Manhattan without an escort.

The chief of police was out of town. The parks commissioner wasn't in yet. The mayor was at a convention. We got a busy signal on the governor's hotline. As we neared the end of our list of official sanctioners, the policemen themselves got together and talked it over. They decided to stick with us, unauthorized and without pay, until the job was done. It wasn't the world's most enticing assignment, especially for the officer who would be riding shotgun with us, but they were extremely cooperative and understanding.

From outside the enclosure we lured two of the bears to a narrow section and penned them there to restrict movement. The third refused to fall for any offers of food or companionship. She had evidently taken a liking to Brooklyn and was in no mood to travel. We came to the conclusion that Prospect Park really needed a grizzly, and Kinzig was delighted. We had a larger parks van this time, one that would accommodate two bears. Only one trip would be necessary.

Because I had more room to move around and place my shots, the bears succumbed with a minimum of earthshaking roars. Loading them seemed like a piece of cake, even though the cake weighed nearly eight hundred pounds. Dr. Woods monitored one bear with a stethoscope, a syringe full of antidote and another syringe full of M-99 handy. I did the same with the other.

The last person to climb into the back of the van was a policeman from the special tactical squad carrying a shotgun. He was very calm and matter of fact, obviously not the type who would use a weapon unless there was a drastic emergency. Assuming that their systems would stand the drugs, we felt the bears would sleep throughout the trip. But if one of them awoke, and we couldn't sedate it quickly enough, he would have to open fire. At that range, one shot would probably take out both the bears, plus the people, the van, and about half a block of downtown Brooklyn.

Flatbush Avenue was nearly deserted when we pulled out. The screaming police car was in the lead, then the parks van, followed closely by my own car, which I almost had to leave in Prospect Park. I think New York has the highest percentage of nondrivers in any city in America. I'm not sure whether that's a tribute to the efficiency of the Metropolitan Transit Authority, or an indication of the scarcity of parking spaces. Just before we left, I asked if anyone would volunteer to drive my car into Manhattan, behind the procession. Out of the dozen people present, I found only four who knew how to drive, and none of them had ever driven a stickshift car. I had to enlist the aid of a park chauffeur who had come into work early.

We bullied our way through the gradually increasing traffic. We got some odd looks from the drivers who pulled over to let us pass. Motorcades are usually reserved for visiting dignitaries in limousines.

By the time we had crossed the Manhattan Bridge and turned onto F.D.R. Drive, it began to look like we'd make it with no trouble. Then the bear I was monitoring stopped breathing.

Dr. Woods must have seen me tense up. We both looked at the syringe full of antidote, then at the shotgun in the policeman's hands. There was no time to rehash alternatives. Quickly, I injected 2 ml, hoping it would be enough to revive breathing, but not enough to wake him up.

The special forces officer sat there, stony cool, quite aware of what could easily happen in the next few seconds. I concentrated on the stethoscope, trying to block everything else from my mind.

The bear's heart fluttered. He gasped, then exhaled. The jaws opened. He labored. Another gasp. I nodded to Dr. Woods. A regular pattern returned as his breathing slowed and steadied. He was alive and asleep. We relaxed.

We turned west on Fifty-seventh Street and three minutes later were in Central Park. I heard our driver ask someone, "What's going on?" The reply was drowned out by the squeal of brakes as we came to a halt.

The back door of the van flew open and we jumped out, blinking in the sunlight. We hadn't expected a reception committee; the shuttling about of dangerous predators is not as well publicized as the arrival of movie stars. But, within fifty yards of us, there was a mob.

Park administrators, press photographers, and groups of curious citizens were walking toward our vehicles. In the confusion, we learned that some sort of early morning dedication ceremony was scheduled in front of the next building, and the photographers obviously thought we were part of that event.

Police officers from our escort car, aided by park workers, formed a line between the van and the entrance to the bear den. The female was closest to the rear of the van, so we eased her out first. Once she came into view, the crowd began to grow. People deserted the ceremony site in droves.

Everyone seemed to have suggestions about the best way to carry a sleeping bear. Children fought to get through the police line for a better view. A circus atmosphere prevailed. Among the onlookers, anyway.

The van was closed and we trundled the female into the corridor leading to the den. It was comforting to see that they had replaced the doorframe that had been so badly battered weeks before.

We returned to the van, discussing how we could get the larger male grizzly through the hallway without suffering another bout of bruises and cuts. He took care of the problem for us.

I was standing a few feet from Fitzgerald when he opened the van. Suddenly he was backing toward me, and I threw up my hands to avoid a collision. The small amount of antidote I had given the bear had been totally absorbed and had worked too well. The bear rolled out of the van and stood up in the middle of Central Park.

There was a panic.

Some of the officials must have remembered that they had urgent letters to dictate. They fled. Women plucked their children from the front lines and headed for parts unknown. Flashbulbs turned the scene incandescent as the normally fearless photographers fired away, backpedaling all the while.

The policemen, relieved of the duty of holding back a curious crowd, turned toward us and began to draw their weapons. The grizzly was not fully awake, but even in a dazed condition he towered fearsomely over his rapidly disappearing audience.

It had all happened so quickly that my only thought was for the safety of the bear. "It's okay," I yelled at the policemen, "everything's under control! Don't shoot!"

They didn't look very convinced. I don't imagine I sounded very convincing.

Several zookeepers moved forward and surrounded him. The groggy beast stumbled and staggered a few feet. The circle widened and they kept just out of his reach. He regained his balance and began to take note of his environs.

Expecting to hear a volley of shots at any moment, I raced for the van and grabbed a syringe of M-99. The shouts and screams of the retreating mob only served to make him more alert.

My hands were trembling as I entered the circle of zookeepers, slightly on his flank. He had lowered his arms and was standing motionless, getting his bearing. I jabbed.

The bear huffed as the needle went in. He turned toward me. His eyes began to glaze, and within moments he was off in another world—one inhabited by his ancestors, perhaps, where there were no cages and no scuttling little bipeds to annoy him.

"Is he out?" asked Fitzgerald.

"I think so," I said, "but he probably won't go down for another couple minutes."

"Maybe we can get him to walk."

"Worth a try," I said. If it worked, it would certainly shorten the time the bear would have to spend under the second full dose of anesthetic and would enhance his chances of surviving it.

The volunteer assistants, zookeepers, Dr. Woods, John, and myself—ten of us in all, started pushing and pulling him in the general direction of his den. Like a giant reluctant dog, he moved. Up the stairs, then into the hallway. His musky odor filled the air. I had visions of him collapsing and falling on those of us who were crawling over each other to push from behind.

Because of our slow progress, the journey seemed endless. Several times he stopped and staggered backwards before we could shift his momentum. Eventually someone up ahead broke away and we heard the cage door opening. With a final shove, we sent him weaving into the den.

The female was curled in the corner, dead to the world. But the male, securely back in his own familiar territory, turned to face us again. Dr. Woods left immediately and was soon back with syringes of antidote.

"Let's bring them around," I said.

Fitzgerald and I stepped into the den. We edged around to the female and injected her. Then John walked boldly up to the male and waved his hands in front of its face. I approached from the rear and emptied the syringe into it. Without waiting for a reaction, we exited.

Two of the grizzlies are now living in Central Park with a pool drainage system, which we hope will function for many years to come. The third, a loner by nature, seems quite content in Brooklyn. There are no plans in the works for ever moving any of them again.

The spectacular photographs of a grizzly loose in Central Park made all the local papers. Reading the stories, I realized how exciting the lives of people who deal with such animals must seem. There is rarely any notice of the hard work and drudgery that goes into the maintenance of a zoo and the care of its animals.

With no time to celebrate our success, the zoo attendants went back to their regular jobs, the policemen finally went off duty, and I wound up late for my office hours.

Two of my clients wanted to know why they had to be kept waiting, after making early appointments. After all, if they could show up on time, didn't I have the courtesy to do the same?

I apologized, treated their pets, and said I'd try to see that I wasn't late next time.

What Do You Think?

1. Dr. Milts said he had to "weigh the safety of the animals against the possible risk to human life." What did he mean by this? Do you think he made the proper choices? Support your answers.
2. What is it about this story that qualifies it for inclusion in a unit titled Bold Journeys?
3. Can you think of a safer way to repair the pools in the bear cages?
4. The humor in this story is subtle. For example, in describing the method of anesthetizing the bears the author says it would have been easy if "I could have walked up to one of the bears, wrapped a strand of rubber around its arm, and said, 'Squeeze your fist.'" What makes this humorous? Find at least three other instances of subtle humor.

Taking a Closer Look

1. What problems arose in the out-of-date zoo that made it necessary to move the bears?
2. What does the writer say is inaccurate about television accounts of anesthetizing animals?
3. How did the newspaper account of the bear incident give a false impression of caring for animals?
4. Why is the use of narcotics dangerous to animals?
5. What made moving the bears difficult?

Putting Ideas to Work

Look for information on the training of a veterinarian or do some research on grizzlies—the behavior of grizzlies toward humans they encounter in the wild. Prepare a short written report to share with the class.

The Great Chicago Fire

Eddie Foy and Alvin F. Harlow

Fire! Dry brush, dry timbers, and wind fed the flames that kept
Eddie on the run.

I was fifteen when the great Chicago fire occurred. That was a strange and terrible autumn we had in Chicago in 1871.

We were all at home at the time. My oldest sister, Catherine, had been married, but her husband had died shortly afterwards, leaving her with a baby who was about eighteen months old at the time of the fire.

Chicago was a wooden city then. I suppose that more than ninety-nine percent of the homes, business buildings, and factories were of wood. The bridges across the river were all of wood, and so were nearly all of the sidewalks. Even miles and miles of the streets had wooden-block pavement, though many other miles had no pavement at all.

For nearly fifteen weeks we hadn't had enough rain to lay the dust. The sprinkling wagons did their best, but we were choking with dust and gasping from heat from late June until October. The sun blazed and the hot winds blew off the prairies until the whole city was as flammable as dry grass.

We were living near the South Branch of the Chicago River. On Saturday evening, October 7, there was a big fire just a few blocks below us. It burned over about six blocks of lumberyards, sawmills, and other small factories and homes. We watched it from the Madison Street bridge, and it made such a big blaze that we grew a little uneasy until the firemen finally put it out. Had the wind been blowing as strong as it was on the following evening, the great disaster might have happened then and there.

The next evening—Sunday—a high wind was blowing, a regular gale. I turned in between nine and ten o'clock and was sound asleep immediately. Just about that time the bells were ringing for a fire farther south than the blaze of the night before.

There's no certainty as to how the fire began. It is said to have started in a stable, but whether Mrs. O'Leary's cow was to blame is, I think, an open question. Anyhow, I slept peacefully all through the early part of it.

But about midnight I was awakened by my mother shaking me vigorously. She had to fairly haul me out of bed. But when she got it through my head that the fire was coming and I saw the red glow through the windows, I was on my feet in a hurry.

Mother and the girls had known before ten o'clock by the glare in the sky that a big fire was raging. It was on the other side of the river, however. Though the wind was bringing it north, everybody thought—or at least, hoped—that the burned district of the night before would stop it. Still Mother was a little uneasy, as the fire didn't seem to grow less but rather increased. She stayed up, watching it. Along toward midnight she learned that it had leaped across the river to a lumberyard. Now it was rushing up our side of the stream before that terrible gale, spreading not only northward but eastward toward the lake. The firemen were powerless.

Wagons and drays were already passing north and west, moving household goods and valuables from the vicinity of the fire. Mother was a strong-willed woman, and she fought stubbornly against the possibility that our own home might be burned. Nevertheless, she asked an old drayman who lived near us about removing our goods if it became necessary. Little did she think how soon it would become necessary. Other people in the neighborhood were becoming badly frightened and were moving out.

We debated what to do, and finally Mother said to me, "Eddie, you take Bernard (the baby) and go up to Mr. Jackson's till the fire's over. If our own house doesn't burn, come back here in the morning. If it does, we'll see you at Mr. Jackson's."

The Jacksons were friends who lived at the corner of Lake and Dearborn Streets, near the business section. Mother sent me up there because she thought that place would be perfectly safe. She thought she was protecting the baby. To reach the Jacksons' the fire would have to burn through the main business area of the city, and it never occurred to her or to anyone else that this could possibly happen. The firefighters would undoubtedly find some way to stop it—and besides, most of the big downtown buildings were brick and stone and iron. They would doubtless stop the fire dead in its tracks. But they didn't! Until then, no one knew what a fire could do if conditions were right for it, as they were that night in Chicago.

Catherine clung to the baby a bit anxiously as she kissed him good-by. But neither she nor Mother were seriously worried over the separation. They had a lot of faith in me. Had they had any idea of what the history of that night would be, they never would have let me go.

It was three blocks north and

four east to Lake and Dearborn. I trudged north, carrying the baby and turning at every three or four steps to look back to the red sky. Presently I could see the tips of the flames leaping into the air. The farther I went, the more badly I was scared. I had not yet reached Lake Street when I realized that the fire was coming faster than any of us had judged. Why, it looked as if it might be almost to our house already. No such area of a city, I believe, was ever burned over so quickly. It overwhelmed fire companies, destroyed their apparatus, perhaps killed some of their firefighters, and swept on. The flame ran along the plank sidewalks as if through prairie grass.

When I turned east and reached Wells Street, there were dozens of vehicles hurrying north toward the bridge across the main river, loaded with furniture, bedding, and goods which merchants were trying to save from their stores. I could look south and see the fire coming—so near that I thought it must be among the big downtown buildings already. The tumult around me was growing worse at every step. Some people along Lake Street were already moving their furniture out of their houses, and men were hurrying about, looking for wagons. When I reached the Jacksons' home, they were moving out too.

"What are you doing here with that baby?" cried Mr. Jackson. "Get across the river or down to the lakefront, quick! We're going to move across the river."

He and his family were so absorbed in their own troubles that they had no time to think of me. I stood around for several minutes. I hated to separate myself from friends—that is, from people who had always been friendly before. It was evident, however, that they felt they couldn't be bothered with me. The danger was increasing at every moment. Blown by the wind, the flames reached forward and in moments caught building after building in their path. Meanwhile sparks and bits of flaming wood were carried far ahead by the wind and started new fires. Several square miles of Chicago were burning simultaneously that night.

I might have begged to go with the Jacksons across the river. Though they were stacking their furniture on the sidewalk, they had not yet found a wagon, and I wasn't sure they ever would. So it was pretty clear that if the baby were to be saved, I would have to do it unassisted.

I finally turned away and hurried east on Lake Street, thinking to cross the river either at the State or Rush Street bridge, or else to reach the lakeshore. But at State Street the turmoil was terrible. The bridges were narrow—not half the width of the streets—and this one was jammed with a tangle of wagons and drays. People on foot swarmed and struggled around them, screaming and crying and fighting. I dared not venture into that mob with the baby, so I kept on eastward. I had now decided to go to the lake.

Every street was crowded with vehicles, the drivers utterly reckless of people on foot. I risked both our lives at every crossing. People were begging for wagons—offering twenty-five, fifty, a hundred dollars a load to anyone who would haul it. Many wagoners were demanding outrageous prices. Some desperate people were seizing vehicles by force.

The sidewalks were becoming almost as dangerous as the streets. People crazed by fear ran wildly, some staggering under loads of plunder or their own worldly goods. Trying to shield the baby, I was knocked this way and that, and once I went down to my knees but got up again quickly. Looters were smashing the doors and windows of stores and making away with whatever they could carry.

The destroyer was now so close that I fancied I could hear its roar above all of the other din. Its glare was already lighting up the streets. Sparks and burning embers were falling in showers around us. I was continually afraid some of them would set the baby's clothes on fire or burn his face. I pulled a flap of his cloak well up over his head to protect him. He was crying at the top of his voice from terror. I couldn't hear him with the uproar around me, but I knew he was crying because his mouth was wide open and his eyes shut. He was getting terribly heavy too, but I was nearing Michigan Avenue and the lakefront.

My own home must be gone by now, I thought. What had become of my mother and sisters? And if they were still alive, what would they think had become of Bernard and me? How would we ever find each other again?

As I reached Michigan Avenue, I saw great sections of shingles and weatherboarding from the roofs and sides of houses, all ablaze, flying through the air above me. A wagonload of household goods passed in full gallop toward the Rush Street bridge. The driver, lashing the horses, was unaware that the load, fired by a spark, was blazing behind him. Watching my chance, I dived across the avenue with a group of people, through the throng of wagons and galloping horses, and at last was on the lakeshore. There was a place there, just south of the mouth of the river, where the beach was much wider than elsewhere. North and south of us the beach was very narrow. There many people were driven by the heat far out into the water, and some were drowned.

Merchants near the lakefront were carrying goods out on the beach—bolts upon bolts of silk, woolen, and linen cloth, and even some cotton. They brought men's clothing, women's cloaks, furs, hats, jewelry, silverware, and even a few groceries. Some of the people who got there first were resentful at the crowds who came later and at the merchants for filling up the space with their goods. There was much confu-

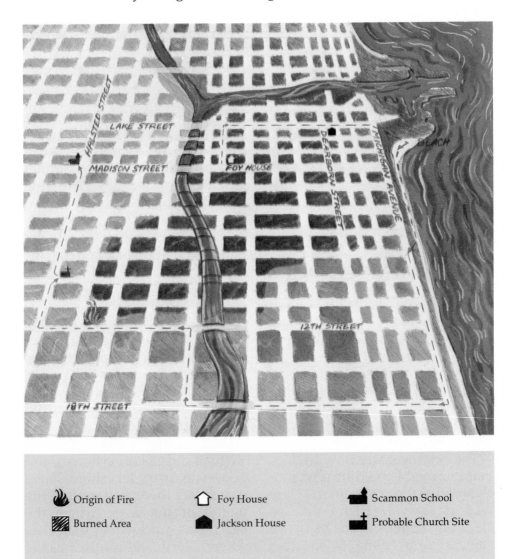

🔥 Origin of Fire	⌂ Foy House	Scammon School
Burned Area	Jackson House	Probable Church Site

sion, excitement, and terror on that little patch of ground.

There we sat and watched the fire march by. When it was at its nearest point, just opposite us, the heat was so great that we had to retreat to the farther edge of the beach. Some waded into the water or were pushed in.

Before sunrise the flames had crossed the river. Many citizens from the north side of the city had come down to the river to see the fire. They suddenly discovered to their horror that the waterworks and other buildings were burning, nearly a mile behind them.

About dawn I went to sleep with my head pillowed on a bolt of cloth. Bernard slumbered beside me, lying on a pile of men's suits. I must have slept for two or three hours. When I awoke, such a pall of smoke was hanging over us that the sun could only be seen dimly through it, a sort of dull red ball. Piles of ruins were still blazing and smoking in all directions.

One of the things I remember best about the great fire is the wonderful fellowship, sympathy, and kindness of people. A woman who had brought a bottle of milk for her baby gave half of it to Bernard. Somebody else gave me a little bread and meat. With that snack we had to get along until late in the day. The hours dragged by until about the middle of the afternoon when some people began to drift south on Michigan Avenue, hoping to reach friends or relatives. Nobody tried to go north, for the bridges across the river were gone, the boats were burned, and the whole North Side was a dreary waste, much of it still burning.

It was reported that the South Side had been spared. I decided to go around that way, cross the river, and return to where our home had been. I wanted to learn the fate of my mother and sisters—to find somebody to share with me the terrible responsibility of the baby. If I had found them dead, I wouldn't have been much more dazed and shocked than I was already.

Of course, it was impossible to cross the business section yet. Even some of the frame structures were still glowing. Great piles of red-hot brick, stone, marble, and iron from the big downtown buildings were still spouting flames. So I went south on Michigan Avenue, even then compelled to keep on its outer edge near the lake because of the heat.

Zigzagging along the edge of the burned district, I saw thousands of others wandering like myself. There were also hordes of curious sightseers. Many wagons still hauled those pitiful loads of household goods which, perhaps, hadn't yet found a resting place. A slow rain had begun to fall—too late to save the city—and it added to our discomfort. I was very much afraid Bernard would catch cold, so I wrapped my coat around him. I was very tired and ravenously hungry, and of course he was too. He cried almost incessantly.

I learned by questioning people on the way that our home neighborhood had certainly been burned over. How in the world would I ever learn the fate of Mother and my sisters? I thought that they would most likely have dashed across the river by the Madison Street bridge and would, therefore, be somewhere on the West Side. I could not reach the bridge at Madison, so I had to walk blocks out of my way to reach one at Eighteenth Street. By that time I was pretty well exhausted.

Having crossed the river, I turned north on the west side, but I realized I couldn't go much farther. I had stopped several times under porches and awnings and set the baby down to rest myself. My arms felt as if they were nearly paralyzed, and my back was getting weak. I was soaking wet from the rain which continued to fall slowly, and I was afraid Bernard might be ill from the exposure.

I noticed that the churches were headquarters for refugees, and I decided to stop at the next one I saw. I had walked between four and five miles, I suppose, when I came to a big church where the lamps were lighted and many people were going in and out. I staggered and sank down on the steps, exhausted.

Kind women gathered around me immediately, took Bernard out of my arms, and led me inside to a big stove, where I dried myself and grew drowsy. I do not know how many people were being sheltered in the church, but there were scores, perhaps hundreds of them. The good Christians in the church—most of whose homes had been spared by the fire, but many of whom had lost their businesses—were working their heads off and giving all to aid the sufferers. Bernard was cuddled and given a bottle of milk, and I was given a good supper—all I could eat. I fell asleep before I had finished it. They laid me on a cushioned church bench, and I slept for twelve hours.

When I awoke the next morning, I could see stacks of sandwiches on a bench nearby. I felt like a new man already, but my first thought was for Mother and the girls. After eating breakfast, I asked one of the women to look after Bernard while I went to seek my family in our old neighborhood.

"No, you stay right here," she commanded. "We'll try to do that for you. Your folks probably aren't anywhere near your old home, and you'd never find them by wandering around." She then went on to explain that the citizens were already beginning to organize an identification service in an effort to get families together and find out how many lives had been lost. They took my name and my mother's and our home address, and cautioned me not to stray far from the church, as they might have news for me at any time.

All day I waited and worried. Messengers were bustling in and out, and the volunteer workers were busier than bees. But to us refugees, the time dragged frightfully.

Night came and I slept on the bench again. The next morning a man with a paper in his hand came towards me and said, "Is this Eddie Fitzgerald?"

"Yes, sir," said I.

"Your mother and sisters are at the Scammon School," said he. "Corner of Madison and Halsted."

It was only about thirty-six hours after the halting of the fire. As I look back on it and remember the chaos that followed the disaster, it seems marvelous to me that they found my people as quickly as they did. There were no telephones then. All news and instructions had to be carried by messenger.

A place was made for the baby and me on a wagon, and I rode up to the Scammon School. I found a number of tents set up in the yard and learned that Mother and the girls were being sheltered in one of them. Supposing that they had heard news of me, I burst in on them without warning and gave them the shock of their lives. Then we kissed each other and wept in chorus—all, that is, save Bernard who, well-fed and glad to be in the family circle again, very sensibly laughed.

What Do You Think?

1. What bad sides of human nature did Eddie see in the behavior of the people of Chicago during the fire? What good sides of human nature did he see? Do you think Eddie was impressed more with the bad or with the good? Explain.
2. How do you think Eddie felt when the Jacksons paid little attention to him and the baby? List at least five words describing his feelings.
3. Why do you think some of the people of Chicago were helpful and kind during the fire and others were not?
4. Why do you think Eddie never panicked, even though many others did? What does this tell you about his character?
5. What do you think would have happened to Eddie and Bernard if their family had been lost in the fire?

Taking a Closer Look

1. What conditions contributed to the fire?
2. Why did Eddie's mother send only Eddie and the baby to the Jacksons' house?
3. Why did Eddie leave the Jacksons and set out on his own?
4. What story is most often repeated about the origin of the fire?
5. Where did Eddie find safety from the fire?
6. Explain in your own words how Eddie and Bernard were reunited with the family.

Putting Ideas to Work

Develop a plan for reuniting your family should you be separated during a disaster.

I Meet Money

Prince Modupe

Prince Modupe[1] was born in the early 1900s in a village in French Guinea. His grandfather was chief of the So-So people, and Prince Modupe was to become chief after his grandfather.

Throughout his childhood, Prince Modupe's life was exactly like that of all the other children of the So-So people. He had taken part in certain rituals, and finally, to prove his manhood, had single-handedly killed a leopard.

But then a great change took place in Prince Modupe's life. Paul Boolama came to his village. Boolama, a member of the neighboring Bambara people, had become a Christian. He had come to the So-So people to prepare the way for a missionary, who was to come later. Prince Modupe's grandfather was so impressed by the Christian way of life, that he decided to send his grandson to the coast to study this new religion.

The villagers stood on the bank of the Scarcis to see me off to the world outside. Kende stood beside my mother in the front ranks. The pain of parting, especially from those two, almost made me change my mind. Would they ever see me again? They feared not. In one way, they were right. When I returned several years later, I was not the same person who had left.

Muddy-tan water lapped at the sides of the dugout. Mapam, an older warrior, sat in front; I at the stern. A few strokes and we were in midstream. Although I was busy with my *batai,*[2] the paddle, I saw through tear-blur their gallant efforts to wave. The dugout swept easily around a bend, and we were out of sight.

---

[1] Modupe (mō dü′ pā)

[2] batai (bä tī′)

A trip down the Scarcis is not easy. There are mud flats studded with crocodiles, there is quicksand, and in my day it was the vast playground of the huge river horses, the hippopotamuses. They are not man-eaters, but they love to frolic, and when any creature of almost elephant size gets playful with a human, it is dangerous. They love to submerge and surface, cavorting with the zest of a child. If one comes up under the canoe or even brushes the side of the shell-frail craft, over it goes. The crocodiles grin as they wait and watch with small evil eyes.

The first hippo we saw crossed directly in front of us. Others followed into the water, diving and breaking surface. There were too many of them to be traceable. All we could do was to alert ourselves and hope. One of them came up so close to us that my *batai* struck him at the finish of the stroke. Mapam and I ceased paddling; our full concern was to balance the craft by throwing our weight to one side. It steadied, settled. We bent again to our paddles.

It was important to go as far as possible by daylight. There were few places on the bank where it seemed safe to stop. Reeds grew in the shallow water near shore. The banks were lined with huge trees, thick and twisted with lianas, making a screen and a mystery of what lay behind. Brilliant birds perched on overhanging limbs like noisy flowers. Monkeys played on the lianas, chattering defiance at our dugout.

Toward evening we spied game at land's edge, antelope, chevrotain. We heard an elephant trumpet in the distance. For the most part, the day slipped away as quietly as the dugout glided. Yet it seemed more adventurous to me than anything which had happened previously because of the unknown quality of life ahead. Those things which had gone into making me an adult—the Bondo training, the test of manhood, the judgment poisonings, and the sacrificial executions I had witnessed—were the expected shapes and colors of life in the bush. I had been prepared for them since birth. For the unknown ahead, I had no qualification except a burning desire to know.

When night fell, we lit a palm-oil lamp in the dugout and continued to paddle in the moonless darkness. Crocodiles lie up on mud banks and sand flats at night. If we were lucky enough to avoid going aground on one of those, we would be all right. The hazard of the river was less than the dangers of the unknown, jungle-choked shore. We ate some food we had brought with us and continued downstream.

The morning of the next day we reached the village where it had been arranged on the drums that Paul Boolama was to wait for me. As I stepped from the dugout, he grasped my hand and wrung it, laughing at the startled expression on my face. Shaking hands was, he

explained, the Christian mode of greeting a friend. I tucked this bit of information away for future use. I believe it would be safe to say that during my early years as a Christian, I was one of the most persistent of all handshakers. I shook the hand of everyone I met, man, woman, or child, often to the surprise or annoyance of the shakee. To thrust forward the hand was my first lesson in the rituals of·Western civilization, learned on the bank of the muddy Scarcis.

After we had rested, Mapam started back toward Dubricka alone, paddling against the current. A great pang clutched my heart as I watched him slowly disappear from view. Paul Boolama and I prepared to go in the other direction. The other direction! The river flows to the sea. Tides push it back upon itself for a space, then the tide reverses, is with the current, and all is swept before it. The waters of rivers merge with the sea.

A warrior sat in the front, another in the back of the new dugout. Paul Boolama and I sat between them. This was a larger boat. I asked for a *batai.* Paul explained that we would talk and the others would row. This seemed strange to me because I seemed to be the youngest member of the party, but then I supposed I would have to get used to all sorts of reversals of custom.

Boolama was highly pleased that he was able to bring a protégé to his big-father, the missionary with whom he lived. He explained that after we reached Konakry, he would send word to Freetown and arrange for my passage in a huge boat. The big-father in Sierra Leone would meet my boat in Freetown. He tried to make me understand that the message would be sent by something called a telegram rather than by talking drums, but I could make nothing of that. For one thing, I was too appalled at the news that Boolama was not going the entire journey with me. He had to visit more villages in Guinea before he came back to Freetown. He was a Bambara and so the logical one to attend to the work in Guinea. I would be perfectly safe on the big coastal boat, he explained.

It was the beginning of a clear night when we approached Konakry. The water was choppy with tide wash and breeze. We swung around a bend. There before my eyes was the dazzling sight of the lights of the coastal city. The grandeur of those lights to my eyes, accustomed to palm-oil lamps, balks any effort of description. Thrill and disbelief quivered through me. The lights were shut off for a moment by a bend in the river. I thought they had been an illusion. They reappeared and were constantly visible like a skyful of stars snared in a net and brought to earth. Nothing in the missionary's kit of pictures conveyed the lovely sublimity of heaven as did those twinkling lights in front of me.

We passed the blurred outlines of houses of such size as I had never dreamed possible. In the wide span of water before us, huge canoes, with smoke coming out of their round tops, lay offshore. The dugout was turned toward the docks. These high piles of wooden structure frightened

me as did all else. Only Paul Boolama's presence at my side gave me courage to keep my eyes open.

I was wearing my jungle attire. I was nude to the waist and had my spear and knives and bow and arrows. These were sufficient equipment to meet any unknown or known danger in the bush. I clutched them tighter, wondering whether they would be adequate to the dangers of the world. The dugout was steadied for us. Boolama climbed out and I followed. People on the dock stared at me and pointed. I had my full growth and was well muscled from an active life. The dock loungers could not have known that my heart pommeled my ribs with hard-knocking fear.

Boolama left me for a moment to find a conveyance, telling me to stay where I was and wait for him. Nearby I saw an African woman seated on the ground. Beside her was a calabash filled with *akara*,[3] fried bean bread. I was hungry, and it was good to see a familiar kind of food. She held some up to me, speaking in a language I did not understand. I accepted it and began eating. She spoke out sharply and held up her empty hand. I did not understand. This must be some other ritual of the hands in the outer world. A small crowd gathered quickly as she screamed at me. I would have run except that Boolama had told me with emphasis to stay where he left me.

---

[3] akara (ä kä′ rə)

42

A white-uniformed man came over and spoke sharply to me. I could not understand him either. He gestured for my weapons. I was not about to give those up without a struggle. I kept on eating because I was hungry and because I reasoned that if something terrible was about to happen to me, it would only be worse on an empty stomach. The uniformed man put a whistle to his lips and blew on it. Two more men came riding up on shiny-wheeled affairs. The crowd thinned at the sweep of their hands.

Paul Boolama came running to me just in time. He said something to the policemen which satisfied them, and he drew something shiny out of his pocket which satisfied the African woman.

We went to Boolama's friends in an affair which seemed like a small hut on wheels. On our way he tried to make me understand what money was. Food was not given for nothing in the Western world. In fact, almost nothing one wanted could be had without money. It was the most important single thing to have and to know about. I was baffled. In our village everything we needed for food, clothing, shelter, entertainment, weapons, religion, was furnished by the Great Mother Earth. If there was some small thing we lacked, such as a Foulah pot, we traded something we had to obtain it. I had met money, but I did not understand it. All I understood was

an implication of the terrors of needing it and not having it.

Paul Boolama showed me a coin and explained how much rice it would purchase. My father had brought home similar coins from his trips to the coast. They were viewed by the women in our household as suitable source material for bangles to wear at the neck. Our village had no other use for silver. How was one ever to learn the relative value of these shiny little disks. The only thing we had that was in any way comparable was the cowrie shell, and a big one was not worth more than a slightly smaller one. From this to-do about money, I began to suspect that Western civilization was complicated. I was shaken by a great fear that I would never be able to master the complications.

At the home of Boolama's friends, clothes were brought for me. He helped me bathe and dress. The thing in which I bathed repulsed me because the used water stayed right there until one had finished, instead of sliding away like the stream water at home. The clothes seemed too many, too heavy, too tight. And the shoes! It took years for me to get accustomed to shoes. What torture! I knew I would have to get used to strange customs, but I did not expect any punishment as harsh as having to encase my feet in pinching leather.

Dinner was a nightmare. Was this food, this stuff laid out on a flat dish, a little green here, a little dab of red there, something yellow in one corner? At home everything was cooked together and cooked thoroughly. Most frightening of all was the sharp, shiny pronged thing they called a fork. Were these people not at one with each other that they did not eat with their hands from a common bowl?

I tried to do what Boolama did. I stuck my tongue with the fork. The food tasted awful. I needed seasoning, much hot pepper. In the bush it is indication of enmity not to eat proffered food, so I forced it all down, hating every bite, relieved that the portions were what would have seemed meager at home. Perhaps these people ate sparsely because the food was so unpalatable.

Shortly after we arose from the table, I had to go into the little room where I had bathed. My stomach would not agree to keep the food I had made it accept.

I took off the leather which was torturing my feet and the socks which made them so hot. I sat, thinking about the hardships which seemed to go with being a Christian.

Boolama came looking for me, calling my name. I stood up dizzily and replied. He took one look at me and led me to a cot in the next room. Just as I was I fell asleep. I dreamed of converging policemen blowing whistles and swinging clubs because I lacked something called money. Thus passed my first twenty-four hours in Western civilization.

What Do You Think?

1. What other seemingly insignificant, everyday kinds of things, do you think may have led to Prince Modupe's confusion as he learned the ways of the Europeans?
2. Prince Modupe says that the dangers on the river at night were not as great as on the jungle-choked shore. Why do you think this is so?
3. Why was it necessary for Prince Modupe to learn new ways of obtaining goods?
4. Why do you think Prince Modupe felt uneasy when Paul Boolama left him alone?

Taking a Closer Look

1. In what way were Kende and Prince Modupe's mother right in fearing that they would never see him again?
2. What led Prince Modupe to the conclusion that Western civilization was too complicated? Do you think it is complicated? Explain your answer.
3. Why did Prince Modupe take so readily to the practice of shaking hands?
4. What misunderstanding arose over the fried bean bread?
5. Why did Prince Modupe think it strange that he did not have to row the canoe with the warriors?
6. What kinds of admirable things does this story tell about Prince Modupe's people?

Putting Ideas to Work

Imagine that you are Prince Modupe and you ride in an automobile for the first time. Describe the ride in terms the prince might have used.

Crossing the Sea

Crossing Through the Red Sea, by Fred Collins

Then the Lord said to Moses, "Tell the Israelites to turn back and encamp near Pi Hahiroth, between Migdol and the sea. They are to encamp by the sea, directly opposite Baal Zephon. Pharaoh will think, 'The Israelites are wandering around the land in confusion, hemmed in by the desert.' And I will harden Pharaoh's heart, and he will pursue them. But I will gain glory for myself through Pharaoh and all his army, and the Egyptians will know that I am the Lord." So the Israelites did this.

When the king of Egypt was told that the people had fled, Pharaoh and his officials changed their minds about them and said, "What have we done? We have let the Israelites go and have lost their services!" So he had his chariot made ready and took his army with him. He took six hundred of the best chariots, along with all the other chariots of Egypt, with officers over all of them. The Lord hardened the heart of Pharaoh king of Egypt, so that he pursued the Israelites, who were marching out boldly. The Egyptians—all Pharaoh's horses and chariots, horsemen and troops—pursued the Israelites and overtook them as they camped by the sea near Pi Hahiroth, opposite Baal Zephon.

As Pharaoh approached, the Israelites looked up, and there were the Egyptians, marching after them. They were terrified and cried out to the Lord. They said to Moses, "Was it because there were no graves in Egypt that you brought us to the desert to die? What have you done to us by bringing us out of Egypt? Didn't we say to you in Egypt, 'Leave us alone; let us serve the Egyptians'? It would have been better for us to serve the Egyptians than to die in the desert!"

Moses answered the people, "Do not be afraid. Stand firm and you will see the deliverance the Lord will bring you today. The Egyptians you see today you will never see again. The Lord will fight for you; you need only to be still."

Then the Lord said to Moses, "Why are you crying out to me? Tell the Israelites to move on. Raise your staff and stretch out your hand over the sea to divide the water so that the Israelites can go through the sea on dry ground. I will harden the hearts of the Egyptians so that they will go in after them. And I will gain glory through Pharaoh and all his army, through his chariots and his horsemen. The Egyptians will know that I am the Lord when I gain glory through Pharaoh, his chariots and his horsemen."

Then the angel of God, who had been traveling in front of Israel's army, withdrew and went behind them. The pillar of cloud also moved from in front and stood behind them, coming between the armies of Egypt and Israel. Through the night the cloud brought darkness to the one side and light to the other side; so neither went near the other all night long.

Then Moses stretched out his hand over the sea, and all that night the Lord drove the sea back with a strong east wind and turned it into dry land. The waters were divided, and the Israelites went through the sea on dry ground, with a wall of water on their right and on their left.

The Egyptians pursued them, and all Pharaoh's horses and chariots and horsemen followed them into the sea. In the morning watch the Lord looked down from the pillar of fire and cloud at the Egyptian army and threw it into confusion. He made the wheels of their chariots swerve so that they had difficulty driving. And the Egyptians said, "Let's get away from the Israelites! The Lord is fighting for them against Egypt."

Then the Lord said to Moses, "Stretch out your hand over the sea so that the waters may flow back over the Egyptians and their chariots and horsemen." Moses stretched out his hand over the sea, and at daybreak the sea went back to its place. The Egyptians were fleeing toward it, and the Lord swept them into the sea. The water flowed back and covered the chariots and horsemen—the entire army of Pharaoh that had followed the Israelites into the sea. Not one of them survived.

But the Israelites went through the sea on dry ground, with a wall of water on their right and on their left. That day the Lord saved Israel from the hands of the Egyptians, and Israel saw the Egyptians lying dead on the shore. And when the Israelites saw the great power the Lord displayed against the Egyptians, the people feared the Lord and put their trust

in him and in Moses his servant.
Then Moses and the Israelites sang this song to the Lord:

"I will sing to the Lord,
  for he is highly exalted.
The horse and its rider
  he has hurled into the sea.
The Lord is my strength and my song;
  he has become my salvation.
He is my God, and I will praise him,
  my father's God, and I will exalt him.
The Lord is a warrior;
  the Lord is his name.
Pharaoh's chariots and his army
  he has hurled into the sea.
The best of Pharaoh's officers
  are drowned in the Red Sea.
The deep waters have covered them;
  they sank to the depths like a stone.

"Your right hand, O Lord,
  was majestic in power.
Your right hand, O Lord,
  shattered the enemy.
In the greatness of your majesty
  you threw down those who opposed you.
You unleashed your burning anger;
  it consumed them like stubble.
By the blast of your nostrils
  the waters piled up.
The surging waters stood firm like a wall;
  the deep waters congealed in the heart of the sea.

"The enemy boasted,
  'I will pursue, I will overtake them.
I will divide the spoils;
  I will gorge myself on them.
I will draw my sword

and my hand will destroy them.'
But you blew with your breath,
    and the sea covered them.
They sank like lead
    in the mighty waters.

"Who among the gods is like you, O Lord?
    Who is like you—
        majestic in holiness,
        awesome in glory
        working wonders?
You stretched out your right hand
    and the earth swallowed them.

"In your unfailing love you will lead
    the people you have redeemed.
In your strength you will guide them
    to your holy dwelling.
The nations will hear and tremble;
    anguish will grip the people of Philistia.
The chiefs of Edom will be terrified,
    the leaders of Moab will be seized with trembling,
the people of Canaan will melt away;
    terror and dread will fall upon them.
By the power of your arm
    they will be as still as a stone—
until your people pass by, O Lord,
    until the people you bought pass by.
You will bring them in and plant them
    on the mountain of your inheritance—
the place, O Lord, you made for your dwelling,
    the sanctuary, O Lord, your hands established.
The Lord will reign
    for ever and ever."

—Exodus 14, 15:1-18 NIV

Using an Atlas

A geographical atlas is a book that contains all kinds of map information. Some atlases highlight certain map details through *map keys, distance scales,* and *population indexes.* These categories help the reader to better understand and use the maps.

If you do not live in Hawaii and want to visit there, it would be wise first to see what the fiftieth state looks like on a detailed map. The map here shows the position of the eight largest Hawaiian Islands. This map information shows a small part of an atlas entry. It will give you an idea of what makes up an atlas.

Note the *scale of distances* (miles or kilometers). Cut a strip of paper the same length. Check the compass rose for direction. Then locate Kauai Island at the northwestern part of the state, and Hawaii Island at the southeastern part of the state. Use your distance scale (the cut strip of paper) to find the distance between these two islands. It should measure a little more than three lengths, or about 260 miles.

One other special atlas feature is the *fact key.* It tells some interesting facts about Hawaii. It names the highest point (Mauna Kea), the state flower (red hibiscus), plus other details that may be useful—and fun—to know.

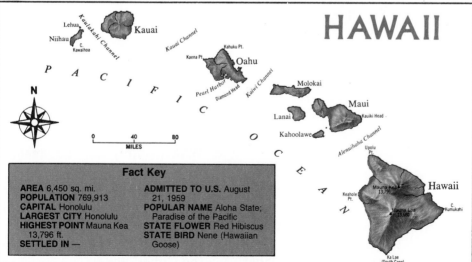

HAWAII

Fact Key

AREA 6,450 sq. mi.
POPULATION 769,913
CAPITAL Honolulu
LARGEST CITY Honolulu
HIGHEST POINT Mauna Kea 13,796 ft.
SETTLED IN —

ADMITTED TO U.S. August 21, 1959
POPULAR NAME Aloha State; Paradise of the Pacific
STATE FLOWER Red Hibiscus
STATE BIRD Nene (Hawaiian Goose)

The next map section shows the island of Oahu. Check the *key*, which shows the symbols for the state capital and the county seats. Use the symbol key to find the state capital on Oahu. (Sometimes there is more than one key. Each key tells different information.) After you have located Honolulu, measure the distance between that point and Kahana Bay (look N). Use kilometers this time (a new strip of paper). The distance between these two points is about 30 kilometers.

Hawaii has five counties. Counties are important and are listed first on the *index*. The index is a very useful feature of an atlas. Look at the population index for Hawaii. A partial list of cities and towns follows the counties. The number after each name is its population, or number of people who live there. This index also gives the zip code, written in front of the name. Scan the alphabetical list until you find Waikiki. The number following the name is its population.

Population Index

COUNTIES

Name	Population
Hawaii	63,468
Honolulu	629,176
Kalawao	172
Kauai	29,761
Maui	45,984

CITIES and TOWNS

Zip	Name/Pop.
96701	Aiea, 12,560
96821	Aina Haina, 15,000
96703	Anahola, 638
96706	Barbers Point Housing, 1,947
96704	Captain Cook, 1,263
96705	Eleele, 758
96706	Ewa, 2,906
96706	Ewa Beach, 7,765
96701	Foster Village, 3,755
96714	Haena, 75
96708	Haiku, 464
96709	Haina, 333
96710	Hakalau, 742
96788	Haikoa, 1,050
96731	Haleiie, 80
96791	Haleiwa, Oahu, 4,047
96792	Hanaee, 3,302
96793	Haihee, 346
96793	Haikapu, 598
96815	Waikiki, 35,000
96748	Haliau, 300
96710	Hailea, 315
96746	Hailua, 1,379
96793	Hailuku, 7,979
96701	Haimalu, 2,982
96795	Hailmanalo, 2,081
96795	Waimanalo Beach, 3,045
96743	Waimea (Kamuela), Hawaii, 756
96796	Waimea, Kauai, 1,569
96712	Waimea, Oahu, 200
96772	Waiohinu, 200
96797	Waipahu, 22,798
96786	Waipio Acres, 2,146
96786	Whitmore Village, 2,015
96801	Woodlawn, 5,569

Map copyright of Hammond Incorporated, Maplewood, N. J.

Here are some atlas questions. Give the answers, and tell which feature (key, scale, index) you used to find each one.

1. Name the capital of Hawaii.

2. What is the population of Waikiki?

3. Approximately how far is it between Kahoolawe and Oahu Islands?

4. Is Ewa Beach more populated than Waipio Acres? Calculate the difference.

5. What is the "popular name" for Hawaii?

6. Which county has the smallest population?

7. On Oahu, how many kilometers are there between Nanakuli (west) and Mokapu (east)?

8. When was Hawaii admitted to the United States?

To the Edge of the World

Theodora Kroeber

Changes in the world around us
sometimes force people to make
journeys. How does Ishi's journey
change him?

Ishi was the last survivor of an American Indian tribe called the *Yahi*. For years, he and a few remaining tribespeople lived in hiding. They found it harder and harder to escape the notice of the changing civilization growing up around them, people with "firesticks" and "monsters" that moved through the land on iron tracks. One by one, Ishi's companions died, and he was left alone. There was no one who spoke his language. He was the last of his tribe.

For as long as Ishi could remember, the *saldu,* or white people, had been his enemies. Now, weakened and dazed from loneliness and starvation, Ishi stumbles into the *saldu* world.

Darkness overtook Ishi; nights of no moon. He could no longer see where he stepped, where he stood.

He had expected to be on the broad Trail long before now.

It is no matter. The journey is begun. I will find the trail soon; it cannot be much farther.

Weak from hunger and tired in his bones and in his heart, he lay down and slept. His was an uneasy sleep. In his dreams he continued his journey which took him into a wild, strange land. Loose rocks rolled under his feet, tripping him. Worst of all, winged demons pecked at his face and pulled at his arms and tried to push him off the trail. At first dawn, their screeching woke him.

He looked around, one quick look before the demons were on him again. There was no sign of the trail he was looking for; the hills, dark against the rising sun, were not the hills he knew. He lay on the ground, crumpled against a corral fence; the bitter stench of slaughtering filled his nostrils, and he smelled saldu and saldu dogs.

Hanging over the fence were cattle hides and on the other side of the corral was a saldu slaughterhouse. Yapping, whining and threatening him was a ring of dogs. Beyond the dogs were five or six saldu, also threatening him with their firesticks. Ishi did not move.

Why do those demons not explode their firesticks? I am without even the hunting bow of my father.

But the saldu beat the dogs off. Careful not to come too close to Ishi, they kept their firesticks pointed at him.

For what do they wait? They wish to hang me? Let them! Let them take my scalp. . . . Su, su! They show fear. What can they fear from the last Yahi? He has no knife, no bow; he is already half-dead. It will soon be over, their fear and mine.

Ishi closed his eyes, opening them only when some time had passed and a wagon drove up bringing more saldu. One of the newcomers was a Headman; the others addressed him as "Sheriff." The sheriff walked directly to Ishi, spoke to him in a quiet voice, helped him up from the ground, and without roughness, fastened his wrists together with rings of a hard material. He then brought an apron which had been worn by someone while butchering—it was dirty and bloodstained—and put it around Ishi's shoulders.

The sheriff nodded toward the wagon. Between fright and weakness and the smell of stale blood and saldu sweat, Ishi was lightheaded. He stumbled, but the sheriff steadied him, holding his arm, and helped him to the high wagon seat beside him. The wagon lurched as the horses started, and Ishi almost fell off. The sheriff stopped the horses long enough to free his wrists so that he could hold on. The others, in the seat behind, grumbled when he did this, but he spoke sharply to them, and they said no more.

Ishi had seen wagons drawn by horses, but this was the first time he was ever in a wagon. Down the road ahead, he saw a large oak tree, and beyond the tree, houses at the edge of a saldu village. The sheriff slowed the horses to a walk.

We come now to the hanging tree, the oak which is an acorn oak.

But the sheriff did not stop under the tree; he continued into the village and down its main street. He went slowly because people came out of the houses and gathered around the wagon, talking and staring. The sheriff had to order them away from the wheels in order to keep moving.

My uncle has told me this is how the saldu behave at a hanging. They press close, women, children, the Old Ones, everyone, as at a Feast or a Round Dance.

They stopped in front of a large house, the sheriff's house. The

sheriff motioned Ishi to come with him into the house. Inside, he took him to a small room without windows and separated from a larger room by bars.

The outer room filled almost at once with the crowd which had followed the wagon. Men leaned on the bars staring at Ishi and saying words to him which he could not understand. When he answered, "Nize ah Yahi"—I am of the People, a Yahi—they laughed. The sheriff's helper brought a tray on which was a cup of coffee, a bowl of soup and bread. He offered it to Ishi, who shook his head.

The food and drink are probably poisoned. In any case, I do not eat while these saldu of no manners, these noisy demons, stare at me.

Ishi moved as far away from the bars as he could. He sat on the stone floor, leaned his head against the wall, and closed his eyes and his mind from the saldu who stared at him. He tried to recall the nights before.

What Mechi-Kuwi, Demon Doctor, guided my feet to this land? Did I walk while I slept? Where am I now? How shall my spirit, when they finish with me here, find its way back to the Trail?

Through the wall there came to Ishi's ears a faint familiar breathy call, Whu-HOOH-huu! The call was repeated, plainer, nearer. With a noise as of falling rocks, the Monster passed just outside the Sheriff's house.

The house shook and settled; the Monster slowed and stopped. Ishi could hear its deep, panting breath. After some moments, its breathing became heavier and it moved away, going out of sound.

Ishi shook himself. He was surprised to see that the house stood, that all was as it had been. *Su, su. I*

55

am within the Dream! Was it Kaltsuna and Jupka who led me, sleeping, off the Trail? Do they mean me to cross the Great Valley to the River Daha and to follow it to Outer Ocean?

More saldu crowded into the room, put their faces against the bars and tried to make Ishi talk. They laughed and spat tobacco juice. The air was thick and foul. After some hours the sheriff came with more food, but Ishi shook his head.

Will he say I must eat? It is no matter; I cannot.

Someone laughed when Ishi turned away from the offered food. The sheriff said some words; he did not raise his voice, but the room became quiet. He pointed toward the outside. At first no one moved; he spoke again; the crowd began to move draggingly toward the entrance. There were a few underbreath comments. This time when the sheriff spoke, his hand moved toward the firestick in his belt. There was a rush as of stampeding deer, then the room was empty except for the sheriff, his helper, and Ishi.

The sheriff turned to Ishi and said something of which Ishi understood the meaning if not the words. "This is better?"

His eyes were kind when he spoke. Ishi answered, "Aiku tsub!"[1] And he recollected his un-

cle's words, spoken long ago in the watgurwa[2] in Tuliyani, "Not all saldu are bad. Remember this in the moons to come when I am no longer with you."

The sheriff smiled, and, slowly, Ishi returned the smile.

The helper went out, coming back with a clean saldu shirt and pants. He motioned to Ishi to put them on. Ishi made signs to him that he wished to wash, and the helper placed a bucket of water and a towel in the room, at the same time taking away the dirty apron Ishi had been wearing. Ishi washed as well as he could.

This is like Grandfather and Grandmother with their one basket of water in Wowunupo.

When he was clean and had rid himself of the worst of the smell of the slaughterhouse, he put on the clumsy saldu clothes. *This stuff is such as the walls and tops of wagons are made of. Su—it is in any case clean. And the Headman seems pleased that I wear it.*

Once again, the sheriff offered Ishi something to eat. *This man has not the eyes of a poisoner. He is kind and it is a rudeness to refuse.*

Ishi ate a few mouthfuls of the strange food and drank some water. Again the sheriff smiled and said some pleasant words. Ishi, too, smiled. "Aiku tsub!"

The sheriff let a few people

---

[1] aiku tsub (ī'kü zäb): it is well; it is good
[2] watgurwa (wăt gə'r wă): home

come in. They tried to talk to Ishi and he tried to answer, but they could not understand each other. *They know nothing of the tongue of the People. It is no matter except the Headman is disappointed.*

Then the Monster returned. *Never has there been such a noise! It is as when Waganupa shakes and boulders roll into the canyons. It is also as the coming of a noisy friend. I wish I might see the Earth-Shaker! This watgurwa has not even a smokehole.*

Before leaving for the night, the sheriff brought a cup of coffee which Ishi drank. Then he pointed to the frame of pine wood with wagon cloth stretched across it, which stood in one corner of the room. Ishi lay down on the strange bed.

He was tired, tired. He listened to the saldu sounds in the dark: the tramp of booted feet; loud laughter; the explosion of a firestick. The

saldu sounds grew fewer and died away; there were only familiar night sounds: a mouse gnawing in the wall; crickets singing in a tree and the distant screech of an owl.

So ended Ishi's first day in the Saldu World. When the sheriff looked in to say goodnight, Ishi's eyes were closed and he did not open them. He was slipping into sleep; he did not wish to rouse himself.

Perhaps my Dream will lead me back to the lost Trail.

But his Dream did not lead Ishi to the Trail. He wakened the next morning in the room with the bars and it was the voice of the Monster which wakened him.

Later in the morning, a stranger came to the sheriff's house. Ishi observed him closely; he was different from any saldu he had seen. *The Headman appears pleased to see him. They grab each other's right hands. It is thus the saldu greet each other. This one comes from a distance—he carries a travel bundle. His clothes are not clumsy; they follow the line of the body. He wears the hair on the face, but it appears to be trimmed with a sharp knife or other tool. He does not spit tobacco juice . . . . His eyes are different, without the coyote look of those who stare through the bars. He carries no knife or firestick in his belt. He and the Headman speak together; they speak of me. Now the Headman brings him to me. Su! I shall do the handgrabbing since it is expected.*

No! He sees I do not wish to handgrab. He sits beside me. His smile is good; he does not have the strong saldu smell. He reaches into his pouch and brings out pieces of white bark, with blue markings on them like little birds' footmarks in the dust . . . . Now he looks closely at the markings, and he says something to me . . . .

What should I answer?

He looks again at the bird tracks and says something else. The sounds remind me of the sounds which Grandfather learned from people who lived on the far side of Waganupa before the saldu came. Now he speaks as the Lost One once told me the People to the north of Yuna Creek spoke.

Aii! What does the saldu say? Siwini?

Ishi spoke for the first time since the Stranger came into the room.

He repeated the word, siwini, and patted the frame of the bed.

The Stranger nodded, yes. "Siwini, pine."

The Stranger said, "Auna, fire." Ishi repeated, "Auna," and made the motion of lighting a quick-fire stick.

The Stranger laughed and nodded, yes, again. Ishi studied the pieces of white bark. *I make nothing of the saldu magic, but it is powerful. These bird tracks cause the Stranger to speak in the tongue of the People. Perhaps it is a trick? Perhaps I am dawana[3] and dream I hear the Tongue again after the many moons of silence? I shall try speaking to him.*

Said Ishi, "Moocha?"

The Stranger looked down his line of bird tracks, then he repeated, "Moocha," and, taking out a pouch, opened it. "Moocha?— tobacco?" Ishi nodded.

Said the Stranger, "Hildaga."

Ishi pointed to the Sky World, spreading his fingers to mean many hildaga, many stars.

Said Ishi, "Wakara?"

The Stranger pointed upwards and cupped his hands. "Wakara, moon."

Then he said, "Daana." Ishi held his arms as if cradling a baby, a daana.

Ishi said, "Wowi." The Stranger pointed around the small room. "Wowi, home."

Ishi shrugged, and they both

---

[3]dawana (dä wă'nă): crazy, wild

58

smiled when he said, "Wowi." *Is this place of no smokehole my home? . . . . Ayii! It is no matter; the Stranger and I say words to each other.*

After a while the single words grew to short questions and answers. *We speak the Tongue! Even my Dream did not reveal such magic! My strength returns as I speak again! There are many unsaid words which have choked me since the morning the Lost Ones went out of sight down the tetna trail; since my mother slept off during the white night.*

Now the unsaid words poured out faster than the Stranger could mark them down or find them in his lists: words of loneliness, of searching, of hunger, of cave-living alone. *The Stranger listens. Sometimes he knows the words; sometimes he understands by signs and by what my voice tells him beyond the words. And because he understands, I cannot stop speaking . . . . But now after much speaking, I am very tired.*

Ishi lay down on the bed, unable to say anything more. The Stranger left him for a while, making him understand he would be back when sun was straight overhead in the Sky World.

Ishi half-slept, half-dreamed; the word siwini, siwini, siwini weaving through his dream.

The Stranger came back as he said he would. They spoke together now slowly, quietly. By the end of the day they had traded many words; they were beginning to speak as friends who talk together.

I no longer think of firesticks and the hanging tree and food into which poison has been put. I wait to speak the Tongue, to hear this Stranger speak it.

Ishi's sleep was dreamless that night. He wakened to the first faraway Whu! of the Monster. That morning the mush and the muddy drink, coffee, tasted good to him.

With the Stranger's help, the sheriff talked to Ishi. He asked him if he wished to return to the Yahi World. And he said he would help him find it if he wanted to go there. Ishi shook his head.

To the Stranger he said, "The kind saldu Headman does not know that World is no more."

Then, asked the sheriff, would he like to go to a Reservation? Some of the People who used to live in the Valley would be there.

Again Ishi shook his head. To the Stranger he said, "He speaks of the Fat Ones of short memory and full stomachs, the Forgetters of the Way."

Said the Stranger, "Come to my house with me. It is a museum-watgurwa. I think you will like it there."

"Is it far away?"

"Haxa, yes. It is where the River Daha and other rivers empty into outer Ocean."

Aii-ya! This is the Dream. Surely the Stranger does not speak of the Edge of the World? "One reaches the museum-watgurwa by wagon?"

"No, by train." The stranger imitated the breathy Whu-

HOOH-huu of the Monster.

"The—train—draws a wagon?"

Ishi sounded so unbelieving, the Stranger asked, "You have seen the train?"

"Many times. But from far away, from Lookout Point and from Black Rock. Even from Waganupa. I have known it since I walked the trails alone . . . . It enters my dreams; it is my friend."

"I wish also to enter your dreams; to be your friend. Will you come with me in the train?"

Ishi touched the Stranger's shoulder lightly. "You speak the Tongue of the People; you are my friend, Majapa, museum-Majapa. I will go with you to your watgur-wa."

The next day, Ishi was up before daylight. The sheriff helped him dress: underwear, shirt, tie, stockings, shoes. Ishi looked down at himself when he was dressed. "Tck. Tck. A saldu-Yahi!" He walked up and down the room several times. Then he sat down and took off the shoes and stockings and handed them back to the sheriff.

Majapa came just then, and Ishi said to him, "Now I know— nothing is wrong with saldu feet. It is what you call shoes that are wrong." He looked at Majapa's shoes. "How do you know where you walk when your feet do not touch the earth?"

"We mostly do not know where we walk."

"I think I am turning into a saldu. The night I came here my feet did not know where they walked."

Majapa laughed. "Do not fear, you will not turn into a saldu. But I thank your feet for bringing you where I could find you . . . . You know, I looked for you before; but to tell you of this I must first learn to speak more words of Yahi."

This is a strange one, this new Friend. What does he mean? He is like the Power Dream, not to be known or understood at once.

Ishi, the sheriff and Majapa walked to the railway station. And there, beside the station, the Monster stood panting. It was bigger and more powerful than Ishi had imagined anything could be. After a moment of hesitation, he moved closer to it, drawn by his old and friendly feeling for it. He measured his own height against the great wheels. He looked at its smoking head. To Majapa he said, "Truly it is the Smoky One. The smoke pours as from a God's pipe. The head and face are those of an Earth-Shaker. Jupka and Kaltsuna were right to turn my feet toward this wonder."

The sheriff shook hands with Ishi and said, "Good luck!" Ishi said, "Good luck!" and followed Majapa into the train. Almost as soon as they were seated, the Monster began to pull the train, slowly, then faster and faster into the Dream, deeper and deeper into

60

the World of the Saldu.

The plik, plikety plik of wheels rolling over rails fitted an old Yahi song which Ishi used to sing with his bow:

Yahina-weh,
Yahina-ini,
Yahina-weh,
Yahina-ini.

He sang it soundlessly, to himself now; it helped him to look past the passengers who stared at his burned-off hair, at his bare feet.

Ishi looked out the window. On all sides spread the great valley, of which he had seen narrow glimpses from Black Rock and Lookout Point. He drew in his breath with wonder.

The Great Valley is broader than the largest meadow. Not one, but many rivers flow in bends and curves across it. The acorn oaks grow tall and heavy with acorns here. And the ripening grasses cover the earth! Once the Valley People and the valley deer grew fat here and there were many of them. Now the saldu and their cattle fatten here. Many saldu! They are everywhere . . . too many saldu!

Yahina-weh, Yahina-ini! The telegraph poles streamed by in time to the song, in time to the wheels' plikety plik! The pictures in the window changed so fast that horses and houses and telegraph poles and people blurred and melted into one another.

Sun had almost finished his day's trip over the sky when the Monster came to the gathering of waters where two rivers, the Daha the larger of them, flowed together, and became one. Ishi smelled the distant salty smell of Outer Ocean. He and Majapa and the other passengers left the Monster, and rode on something Majapa called a ferryboat.

The ferryboat floats on the waters of the rivers as the newly fished-up World must once have floated on Outer Ocean.

"This is Outer Ocean?" Ishi asked Majapa.

"This is the bay." Majapa pointed west across the water to two headlands. "Beyond the headlands is Outer Ocean."

"It is larger than I remember. In my Dream I was swimming and there was much I did not see."

Ishi and Majapa leaned over the railing to look at the water rolling, wave after wave beneath and beyond the boat. Sun left the edge of the earth, plunging into the ocean. Said Ishi, "This water is not like the water of Banya Creek."

"No, this water is salty."

Ishi nodded. "The salt of Outer Ocean is different also from the salt of our meadows."

There came the shrill, thin call of seagulls; the lost moan of fog-horns. Sun's plumes disappeared beneath the waves; the waves turned green-black as they rolled on and on between the headlands and were swallowed up in Outer Ocean.

The rock-glass, green-black waves of Waganupa! The mountain which was the center of the World, the canyons and creeks of home floated before Ishi's eyes, awakening a homesickness which made him dizzy. *The rock-glass waves go on forever, too big, too many . . . Su, su! To be safe in Ancestor Cave, where there is no sound, no brightness—a dead world.*

Stiff with weariness, Ishi followed Majapa off the ferryboat, and into a trolley car which took them far, far into the City. The trolley car jolted and jerked; it fitted no song Ishi knew. The City was a strange shining place of stars fallen from the Sky World, lighting up endless broad trails as far as the eye could see.

Then they were off the trolley car, and Majapa was holding Ishi's arm, guiding him up a long flight of stone steps. Before them was a heavy door. Majapa found his keys and unlocked the door of a house of stone.

"This is Flint Man's House?"

"This is the museum-watgur-wa."

Majapa led the way through many rooms and upstairs, switching on a light as they entered a room and switching it off as they left it. At last Majapa put down the bag he was carrying.

"This is your room." He opened the curtains, turned back the covers of the bed. "Here is the clothes closet; here the bathroom."

He helped Ishi to undress, to get into the large bed. He pulled the blankets up over him. "You will be all right?"

"All right."

"Look, here is the switch. To make your room dark, push the dark button. To bring the light, push the white button. Shall I turn the light out for you?"

"Out."

"I will come for you in the morning. Sleep well—good night."

"Good night."

Ishi knew his Yahi world was gone and he remained in the saldu world with his new friend Majapa. Ishi's museum-watgurwa was the Museum of Anthropology at the University of California. Here, Ishi worked for many years on a Yahi exhibition room. He fashioned Yahi tools and other artifacts. At least once, he returned to the land of his Yahi ancestors, but only to visit, since only memories remained. Ishi, the last of his tribe, died at the museum in 1916, but he left behind a record of his people.

What Do You Think?

1. Why do you think the people who first found Ishi were so frightened of him?
2. How do you think Majapa knew words from Ishi's language?
3. How do you think Ishi felt when he first heard words from his own language?
4. Do you feel it is important to record and remember the ways of lost tribes like the Yahi? Why or why not?
5. Many happenings in the story are told as Ishi had seen them. List some ordinary happenings that seem extraordinary because of this view.

Taking a Closer Look

1. Who were the *saldu?*
2. What was the "Monster" that came near to where Ishi was being kept?
3. At first Ishi wouldn't eat the strange food brought to him. Why? What caused him to change his mind?
4. Who took Ishi from the jail cell where he was being kept? Where was Ishi taken?
5. How was the Stranger, Majapa, different from the other *saldu?*
6. How did Ishi and Majapa reach Majapa's home? List some of the things Ishi experienced on this trip.

Putting Ideas to Work

Suppose you were going to try to communicate with someone like Ishi, who understood neither your language nor your world. Which words do you think it would be most important to communicate first? Select the first ten words you would choose to teach and explain the importance of each one.

THE LOST TRIBE

Ruth Pitter

How long, how long must I regret?
I never found my people yet;
I go about, but cannot find
The blood-relations of the mind.

Through my little sphere I range,
And though I wither do not change;
Must not change a jot, lest they
Should not know me on my way.

Sometimes I think when I am dead
They will come about my bed,
For my people well do know
When to come and when to go.

I know not why I am alone,
Nor where my wandering tribe is gone,
But be they few, or be they far,
Would I were where my people are!

A Road to Independence

The beginning of manufacturing in factories changed the way many people lived. What problems must Sabra overcome in her journey toward self-reliance?

Nancy Zaroulis

She picked up her trunk and began to walk again.

"Please, Sir, how many miles to Lowell?"

Perhaps it was the unaccustomed "Sir," or perhaps it was the sight of her pale, thin face and her rain-soaked shawl; at any rate, the peddler pulled up his horse and looked down at her from his seat in his empty wagon.

"Fifty. Fifty-five."

It seemed the saddest news she had ever heard. She wiped a droplet from her cheek, but whether it was rain or tears he could not tell.

"Thank you." She bent to pick up her small trunk and without a further glance at him began to walk. It was a far way to go. Too far . . .

"Wait!" He clucked at his horse. In a moment he was at her side. "Get in. You can take the stage at Amoskeag."

She hesitated. He would not have harmed her, but she did not know that. "I have no money for the stage."

Despite her woeful appearance, her voice was clear and sweet, not like the jarring twang of so many upcountry Yankees. Her eyes—he could not tell their color—were large, and her features well-formed, if a trifle small. He could not judge from her wrapped shawl, but she seemed too thin by far.

"Get in anyway. In back. Plenty of room."

The girl hesitated a moment longer, and then obeyed.

For three days they traveled south, hardly speaking, the girl riding in the wagon like the peddler's goods. After the first night, when she understood that he would not harm her, she came to trust him enough to smile at him and tell him her name. She told him, too, that she was 18 (she looked younger, he thought, not more than 16) and that she came from Darby, some miles north.

He in turn introduced himself as Jacob Goldschmidt (his real name) and laughed when she was pert enough to ask his age, which, as he told her, was 31. And so they formed an easy bond although they spoke little, each absorbed in private thought.

Late in the afternoon of the third day the peddler stopped on a rise overlooking a wide river. Beyond it, she saw a red-brick town; the far bank was lined with long, many-storied brick buildings larger than any she had ever seen. A train whistle wailed through the sparkling air; a puff of white steam showed its route. A faint sound trembled like a swarm of countless bees. Sunlight glinted on white belfries; church spires rose like stalagmites. Here and there a smokestack spewed a black stain upon the clear blue sky. The scene enchanted her. It seemed a delightful town—a glistening toy town resting peacefully down beside the river.

The peddler, who had been there many times, was less

enthralled. He pointed to the road ahead of them; it led to a bridge which crossed the river just below a high, broad waterfall.

"I'll take you across. What will you do then?"

"The mill." She did not look at him; her eyes clung to the panorama spread before her.

He flicked the reins and the horse moved on. The faint, trembling sound grew louder. In years to come it would grow to a cacophony. It would obliterate the memory of all the long, slow, peaceful time before: the long years, nearly 200 years, when people in that land lived in time with the seasons, the slow passing of winter sleep to spring planting, summer growth to autumn harvest and so once more to winter. No one, hearing it, would ever be peaceful again. It was the sound of the onrushing future: the new age.

Mrs. Zenobia Clapham, the boardinghouse matron for Number Five, Commonwealth Mill, received Sabra with all the enthusiasm of a mother hen presented with a stray gosling. She was a sharp woman, Mrs. Clapham: sharp eyes, sharp nose, sharp chin, a tall, ungainly frame covered by clothes which hardly concealed the sharp and fleshless bones beneath. Her brain was sharp, too, for Mrs. Clapham was a woman of business, and ever alert to those who would take advantage of her position and so expose her to the calamity of dismissal from her post. She was as much an employee of the Corporation as any spinner or weaver, for the boardinghouses belonged to the mill owners, and Mrs. Clapham, like all the other matrons, was merely hired to run hers on an allowance. She needed to be careful with the account books to see that not too much food was prepared, not too much soap or firewood consumed. And yet, on the other hand, she needed to satisfy her boarders' hungry stomachs and keep them strictly to the Corporation's rules lest all their reputations be soiled by the behavior of one or two flighty ones. It was no wonder that she was so sharp and curious and always on the watch lest something—or someone—slip past her and ruin her for life.

"Well," she said, getting to her feet, unfolding her bony

length, "I'll see where I can put you. Lucky for you I lost a girl three days ago. She had th'lung,[1] poor thing." She led Sabra out into the hall and upstairs, alternately questioning and enlightening as they went. The air grew staler and more fetid with every step. "You have to be healthy to work on the Corporation," she said. "You can't do it otherwise. Girls come in, think they're goin' on a lark, an' they get pretty tired after a week or two and want to go home again, but of course they can't, seein' they've signed the one-year term. You ever worked in a factory?"

"No, ma'am."

"Well, it isn't all bad. The Commonwealth's got pretty fair overseers, and of course they keep their houses decent, paint 'em every year, plenty of food, they see that you're well cared for, that's a fact. Here we are--middle bed, share with Betsey Rudd, she's clean and neat and she doesn't snore, there's a blessing."

Sabra put down her trunk and looked about. It was a small, square room with a fireplace on the inner wall, one window tightly shut, three beds crammed into a space meant for two at the most. Around the walls were rows of pegs at eye level on which hung bonnets, shawls, dresses; trunks and bandboxes were arranged around underneath. Two small chests of drawers stood side by side under the window, a basin and ewer[2] on the top of each. The air in the room was even fouler than in the hallway. Suddenly conscious of her empty stomach, Sabra sat down on the nearest bed and loosened the top buttons of her blouse. Mrs. Clapham, who had been straightening a crooked bedcover, glanced at her with some concern.

"You all right? You sure you ain't sick?"

"No—no, I'm just a bit tired." It seemed an effort to speak; the bad air had made her dizzy. "Do you—could I open the window for a moment?"

Mrs. Clapham's face settled into sharp lines of disapproval. "Windows open on May first, not before," she said. "The girls

---

[1]th'lung: slang term for tuberculosis
[2]ewer: a vase-shaped pitcher

don't like a cold room." She hesitated; then: "Why don't you rest for a minute, then come downstairs to my room. A good hot cup of milk will do you wonders, and then you can get on over to Number Two and see Mr. Weldon, while I see about dinner." And, throwing another sharp glance at Sabra's sodden form, she made her way downstairs.

Sabra sat for a few moments, breathing through her mouth in short, shallow breaths. For an instant she allowed panic to overcome her. She wanted to bolt, to escape—but where? Then she remembered her promise to herself: two years at the most. And at the end of that time she saw herself free, made independent by her saved-up wages. She put her trunk along the wall beside the others and went downstairs.

The huge room was filled with machines that spun out thick white ropes of cotton onto tall bobbins. Perhaps 40 young women tended them.

Standing, waiting for Mr. Weldon, Sabra felt very sick again. The room was hot and humid, the air thick with lint.

After a time, Weldon beckoned her to follow; he led her halfway down the long aisle of whirling bobbins to a girl about her own age. "Stand here! Watch what she does! Those are your frames next to hers!"

70

The girl nodded at Sabra in a friendly way. "Handle here! Just turn it on! Watch the roving[3] doesn't foul! If it breaks, tie it!" Having made sure that her bobbins were filling smoothly, she led Sabra to the next row of frames and turned the handle. At once the machine came to life: whirling, clacking, throbbing, a little iron monster with a pulse stronger than any human's.

Sabra nodded and mouthed a "thank you." She confronted the machine before her. She watched closely the 25 or so strands of thick roving spinning out onto the tall bobbins. Everything seemed to be working properly. Throughout the workroom, women were standing as she was standing, watching their frames. The noise was overwhelming. Her acquaintance at the next frame caught her eye and smiled. Conversation was impossible over the noise, but she ventured to shout a few words: "Better mind that roving, it'll get snarled!"

Sabra nodded her thanks and leaned over to examine the thick white ropes feeding onto the bobbins. She misjudged the distance; the whirling quills buzzed at her dress. She stepped back quickly. To catch one's hair on that—!

The girl left her frame and came to Sabra's side. "Like this!" she shouted, holding herself well away from the bobbins and reaching back into the frame to straighten the roving. "There," she shouted, "you'll be all right now!" With a friendly nod she returned to her station. Sabra observed her frame with new respect. It was a tedious master, but a demanding one.

She stood for what seemed hours but was probably no more than an hour and a half. She fell into a kind of stupor, mesmerized by the movement of the parts, and so she was startled by the sudden cessation of the noise when it occurred. Only her frame continued to run; all the others had stopped, and now, faintly, she heard the sound of the bell. All around her the operatives were rushing from their frames and crowding to the stairway door.

"Come on—we haven't much time. You need your dinner!"

Hastily Sabra turned off her machine as she had been shown and followed after, joining the throng on the stairway. Sabra

---

[3]roving: a slightly twisted roll or strand of textile fibers

was propelled by the crowd, and found herself in Mrs. Clapham's warm and aromatic dining room. Her acquaintance, who sat across from her, finished filling her plate and began to eat rapidly. She spoke to Sabra through her food.

"What's your name? I'm Rosa Cummings. Did you just get here today? Where did she put you to sleep? Better take some of that food, we've only 20 minutes."

Before Sabra had finished her meal the bells began to ring again. Immediately the girls rose and dashed for the door. Sabra followed them as quickly as she could. Outside, as she saw that she was being left behind, she began to run. She arrived back at the spinning room with a painful stitch in her side, her heart beating fast.

The morning had seemed very long; the afternoon was an eternity. Her back ached, her feet ached, her arms and neck ached and then became so stiff that she could hardly move them. Mindful of her earlier mistake, she tended her frame carefully; but even so it demanded only a small part of her thought, and soon her mind was running back and forth like a frantic animal seeking escape from its cage. Whirling and

pounding, whirling and pounding; she became numb, the noise beat in her head, her lungs constricted, she thought that she must sit down or at least walk a few paces back and forth, but she could not leave the frame for fear the roving would tangle again.

At last the bells rang again, signalling the turning off of the machines for the night. The operatives, hungry for their supper, made their way to the stairs, less frantically now, for they would not return until dawn. Sabra followed slowly.

Supper at Mrs. Clapham's was not quite so bountiful as the noon meal, but still far more than Sabra wanted to eat. Relaxed now and looking forward to their few hours of leisure, the girls chatted to each other in a friendly way.

"It's hard, the first day or two," Mrs. Clapham said to her. "Go on up to bed. Take a candle from the sideboard, but be sure to put it out before you go to sleep. I don't want the house burned down around our heads."

Sabra did as she was told with great effort, holding the candle carefully.

The room was empty. She set the candle on one of the bureaus, blew it out and, overcome by weariness, fell onto the bed that had been assigned to her earlier.

Sabra adjusted herself to the pattern of her new life: bells to rise, bells for work and dinner, work and supper, bells again for curfew. Exhaustion dogged her. Every night she thought that her body would collapse before she could return to her bed at Mrs. Clapham's. She lost track of time. She was oblivious to the ripening spring, the first lush weeks of May. Her life had narrowed down to a series of separate moments. Survive this day, she told herself. One more day, one more hour. Keep at it until the dinner bell, and then until supper. She no longer thought of the future; she had forgotten the past. She lived entirely in the present moment, and endured because she was determined to endure.

But then one morning, toward the end of May, when she had been on the Corporation for a little more than a month, she awakened before the rising bell. She moved little, cautiously, so as not to disturb Betsey Rudd. She turned her head and watched the pale rectangle where dawn showed at the window. She found, this morning, that she was able to think of the spinning room calmly, without trepidation. She had become accustomed to it, had come to terms with it. She had passed through and survived her term of initiation; now all that remained was to live on until she could get away.

The next day was payday. Instead of rushing back to their houses at closing bell, the women formed a long line snaking across the mill yard and doubling back on itself. The paymaster stood behind his high desk, checking names in his ledger, calling out the proper amount for each woman as she came through and gave her name; his assistant handed out the pay.

Sabra stood with the others from her workroom. She had not been included in the first pay after she arrived, since new hands had to work two weeks before being added to the payroll. So now she would be paid more than a month's wages: more than eight dollars, as she calculated. Now, she thought, I will buy a length of calico for a work dress and a plain bonnet and a pair of clogs—for her shoes had been ruined by the mud. And perhaps a subscription to the circulating library. And most important I will open an account at the bank . . .

At last it was her turn . . ."Palfrey, eight dollars, twelve cents." She held out her hand; the coins fell into it. She started to say thank you, but she checked herself. None of the other women had said it. Why should they?

Still, now that she had the money hard and heavy in her hand, she felt almost as though she had played a trick on someone. Most women worked from dawn till long past dark, and never had a penny for it: the farm women upcountry, even women in the villages who had worked all their lives for nothing, not a penny to call their own.

She caught up with Betsey Rudd. Together they passed out of the yard, through the gates. The tree-lined street along the canal swarmed with laughing, chattering women. A spirit of celebration seemed alive in the deepening twilight: everyone was happy on payday. Sabra felt a surge of hope; she felt the heavy coins in her fist. I will survive, she thought. I will survive.

74

What Do You Think?

1. The author includes several different moods in the story. Describe two of the moods, and give examples from the story to support your answer.
2. List three examples of sensory information (touch, smell, taste, sight, hearing) provided in the story. How do the examples you chose help to create a mood?
3. How does this story demonstrate the idea that you often have to experience hardships to achieve a goal?

Taking a Closer Look

1. What was the setting when the story opened? Describe the characters and the place.
2. What was the setting when the story ended?
3. List four details about the boardinghouse where Sabra stayed.
4. At what point in the story does Sabra's life change for the better? Explain your answer.

Putting Ideas to Work

Can you remember the first time you earned money for doing a job well, or earned a good grade in a difficult course? Think of some experience you have had in which you felt happy with what you had earned. In one or two paragraphs, describe your feelings about the experience.

Study SKILL

Using an Index

Indexes—in some form—have been around since the Middle Ages. Published book indexes have existed since the sixteenth century. They were shifted and shaped through time by indexers around the world. An English lawyer, Sir Henry Thring, was quoted in 1877 by an admirer of his index instructions:

> The basis of an index to a book of the ordinary kind is a series of titles or catch-words arranged in alphabetical order and indicative of the main topics treated in the book.

The language may be somewhat dated, but the definition holds true more than a century later. The main purpose of an index is to help you find information. The index is arranged alphabetically using "catchy" titles that tell the main topics. An index works as a guide. Throughout its journeys, the index's "reason for being" never changed.

Something in our lives is changing all the time. Transportation, for instance. Can you imagine our country without planes, trains, trucks, and cars—all fast and in constant motion? Journeying here, journeying there. Sometimes too boldly! Well, over the centuries, people and freight movement have changed a lot—especially during the last 100 years. Let's check a reliable item (encyclopedia index) to see how a not-so-steady item (transportation) developed.

The portion of an encyclopedia index shown here was located at the back of the book—Volume T, Transportation. As you skim the index, notice it shows other titles to check for more information about the subject. (Some books place indexes at the end of articles or chapters.)

Listed under the main entry of *Transportation* are subentries in alphabetical order. These subentries, or "catchwords," show the topics related to transportation. Subtopics are given after each topic. These tell the volume and page(s) of the encyclopedia where you can find the information. To take advantage of an index, decide which topics are related to the question you want to answer. Look for key words—both in the question and in the index.

TRANSPORTATION

"Journey" through the following questions. Use the index as your guide. Select and write the key word or phrase for each question. Then write the volume and page(s) where you think the information can be found. Note if pictures are shown.

The first question is done for you. (You may wish to use the same headings for your paper.) "Yak" is the key word. "Y" is the encyclopedia volume where yak information can be found. The number "335" is the page in the *Y* volume to check.

1. Is there such a thing as yak-powered transportation?

2. How has civilization affected transportation?

3. When were snowmobiles invented and for what purpose were they first used?

4. Tell how the postal service transported the mail over the years.

5. Are reindeer reliable traveling companions?

6. What are railroads for horse-drawn vehicles?

7. How does an escalator move?

8. What exactly is a rocket?

9. Discuss how communication is linked to transportation.

10. Is piggyback considered transportation?

key word or phrase	volume(s)	page(s)
yak	Y	335 (picture also)

Roads Go Ever Ever On

J. R. R. Tolkien

Roads go ever ever on,
   Over rock and under tree,
By caves where never sun has shone,
   By streams that never find the sea;
Over snow by winter sown,
   And through the merry flowers of June,
Over grass and over stone,
   And under mountains in the moon.

Skiing without Seeing

Mimi Winer

Skiing down a mountain is a short journey—unless you are blind.
Then it is not the distance you travel but the fear you
overcome that is important.

Reaching the summit of Madonna Mountain, I glided off the lift and brought my skis to a quick stop. The swirling snow was blinding, but that didn't make any difference to me. I was blind anyway.

Three feet behind me, at the edge of the drop-off, stood my 18-year-old son and guide, Matthew. "Ready to go, Mom?" he called.

I paused briefly to adjust my dark glasses. "Ready!" I shouted back.

"Make that first turn to the right!" I heard Matt's voice straining above the rising wind. "Go! Go! Go!"

And down I went. Soon we were racing along the trail, past trees and around moguls, and past other skiers too. All I could see was a world of white. My only connection with reality was that voice behind me calling: "Right turn! Left turn! Go! Go! Go!"

I wasn't always blind, but then I wasn't always able to ski from the top of a mountain either.

I had first tried downhill skiing in the early 1940s, and could see perfectly then. But the giant wooden skis and old-fashioned cable bindings did nothing to help my turns.

Every December, loaded down with skis, poles, and boots, and wearing the baggy black ski pants of the era, I would climb aboard the Boston bus for Stowe, Vermont. Yet no matter how many lessons I took or how hard I tried, I could never advance beyond snowplow turns on the novice Toll Road Trail. Thinking I might someday reach the more glamorous elevations of Mt.

Mansfield, I would return with the first big snowfall each winter, but seemed forever rated as a hopeless nonathlete.

In the years that followed, my family filled my life. By the time I was ready to ski again, my eyesight had started to fade, and I found that even though new techniques and shorter skis made skiing easier for most people, my sight loss had severely impaired what little ability I once had. At last, my sight deteriorated to the point where I had to stop skiing completely.

Then I heard of Jean Eymere, a former member of the French Ski Team, and his downhill blind skiing program called BOLD (Blind Outdoor Leisure Development). After coming to the United States, Eymere had settled in Aspen, Colorado. He was a ski instructor there until 1969, when at the age of 34, he was suddenly stricken with total blindness from diabetes. But blindness did not stop Eymere. He was soon back on the slopes and, in 1970, he started BOLD. Having been involved with skiing all his life, he knew what was needed to teach the blind to ski.

If totally blind people who had never seen snow—never mind skied—could learn to skim the mountains, then so could I. Taking my new short skis, I flew to Aspen, where I was inaugurated into the BOLD program.

In five days I went from beginner slopes to parallel skiing on advanced-intermediate trails. I was skiing the way everyone should ski—in controlled turns but with a freedom of movement I had never experienced before. Beyond the emotional high, learning to conquer a mountain on skis as a visually handicapped person had given me renewed confidence and courage to meet the challenges of living blind.

I wanted to share my experience with other blind people, and soon after returning home, I became the New England Coordinator of BOLD. The following winter, Jean Eymere came to help me open the first BOLD Club in the East. George Spangler, an instructor at Smugglers' Notch Ski School, was very interested. In fact, he couldn't wait to get started. Nothing seemed to bother George—not even having to ski blindfolded. He wanted to know, first-hand, what it was like to zoom down a mountain trail without being able to see it.

George put on his blindfold, a homemade job of ski goggles stuffed with socks. He started down the mountain, and his partner shouted voice commands from behind. Skiing with a blindfold can be upsetting to sighted skiers. They often feel vertigo, and even experts find themselves slowing down to beginner turns. But not George. Finishing his run in graceful short swings, he pulled off his blindfold. "That was some run," he said. "But now I know what it's really like—skiing without seeing."

Anyone who has skied in total darkness will never forget how much the blind skier depends on his or her guide, and the terrible fear that the skier feels when the reassuring sound of the guide's voice is lost. As part of their training, all BOLD guides and instructors are required to ski "blind" for several runs—closely followed by a sighted skier shouting commands as they descend. To teach the blind, they have to rely on sound and touch. Although an experienced BOLD blind skier is guided from behind by voice command alone, Jean advised George to have all beginners hold on to their instructor's waist to get the feel for correct body movement.

A week after the blind ski clinic, my son, Matt, took three other blind people and myself to Vermont ski country. George Spangler had us all in tow as soon as we arrived. George had trained

three other instructors for this pilot program—Fitzie, Linda, and Judy—all in their early twenties and dedicated to this new adventure in blind skiing.

Although I was the oldest, I was the only one of the blind enthusiasts who had skied before and the only one that was not totally blind. Ruthie and Cookie had lost their sight from diabetes. Chuck had been blind from birth and had never seen lifts, skis, or even snow.

"So long, Super-Jock!" I heard them call as they left for the beginner slopes.

I couldn't believe it. For the first time in my life I wasn't going to be the worst skier in the group. At last, I was a hot-shot. I would ski from the top of the mountain. Donning my fluorescent-orange bib, marked boldly with the words "BLIND SKIER" in black, I took my guide Judy's hand, and we seated ourselves on the chairlift.

I was a little smug and a lot scared. "If only Matt was my guide," I thought. I was used to skiing with my son and already feeling the loss of my security blanket. But Judy wanted to practice guiding a blind skier, and I wouldn't get to ski with Matt until the next day.

We reached the top of the mountain and started down the trail. I skied badly. I didn't know my guide yet, and I felt no trust.

Close behind me, Judy shouted her commands. "Right turn! Left turn! Right turn! Traverse! Traverse! Traverse! You're over-turning. More to eleven o'clock—one o'clock! That's it. Go! Go! Go!"

I pointed my skis farther down the hill as Judy wanted. Now I began to catch the rhythm of her voice. My rigid limbs relaxed. Soon I was flying down the mountainside, moving like I had never moved before. The wind whistled in my ears. I felt the terrain with my legs. I was free. Unrestrained. I forgot that I was blind.

Suddenly the joyous flight was halted by the sharp command: "CRASH!" Asking no questions, I dropped immediately to the ground. A sighted skier had spotted us, and realizing I was blind, had frozen on the spot. I had been given the "CRASH" command to avoid plowing into him. Blind skiers must obediently follow all commands if they are to arrive at the bottom of the mountain in one piece.

By the second day, I was not the only blind skier riding the lift. Though Ruthie and Cookie were progressing more slowly—they still had to hold on to their instructors' waists to get down the hill—Chuck no longer needed physical contact with his guide. He was now ready to take the chairlift to more challenging sites.

The pilot program at Smugglers' was a winner.

"It's the most exciting thing that's happened to me since I went blind three years ago," Ruthie stated.

"Me! Skiing? And totally blind!" Cookie exclaimed. "I feel like a *giant*. Nobody will tell me I can't do this and I can't do that—when I get home and tell them I've been skiing down a mountain!"

Chuck didn't say very much. He just wanted to know if there was a steeper trail he could try tomorrow.

As for myself, BOLD has gotten me out of my rocking chair and skiing better than ever. And if I know George Spangler, he'll see to it that we, who ski without seeing, enter into rigorous training so we can hold the first Blind Ski Olympics in the embracing atmosphere of a Vermont winter.

What Do You Think?

1. Why does a blind skier need to trust completely his or her guide?
2. Like sighted people, blind people would have to be physically fit to master skiing. What other qualities would they need to enjoy and succeed at skiing?
3. What things about skiing do you think a blind person would enjoy? What might they feel? Hear? Smell?
4. The author says that her success at skiing gave her confidence and courage to deal with her blindness. How might this be so?

Taking a Closer Look

1. What did the ski instructors for the BOLD program do to learn how it felt to be a blind skier?
2. How do skiers who are blind know where to go when they ski?
3. How did the author's son help his mother ski?

Putting Ideas to Work

Select some activity you enjoy, such as cooking a particular dish, roller skating, working with wood or clay. Can you devise a way to teach a blind person to enjoy that activity? List the steps that you would use in doing this.

The Voting Experience

The people of the United States and Canada elect leaders to run their government. And we, the people, decide major public issues. All this is achieved by the power of each person's vote. Voting power is a right and a responsibility for every citizen. Only in democratic countries can citizens choose who will govern. Preparing to vote is a worthwhile challenge—you and your choice do count!

It's a "bold journey" to the voting booth. If you follow some simple steps, you will be prepared for the trip.

1. Register to vote.
2. Know the issues and offices that are at stake. Local newspapers write about current events from different angles.
3. Find out what the candidates stand for. Really listen to what candidates promise. Ask questions.
4. Decide whom you want elected before you go to vote. Stick to your decision.
5. Go to your local polling place on election day. Make sure you know the hours it will be open.
6. Vote! Double-check that you marked your ballot correctly. The ballot is secret. No one knows who or what you voted for—unless you want to tell.

To be registered, you must be a citizen and at least 18 years old by election day. Before age 18, find out about registration in your country. In Canada enumerators come to each home to register the occupants eligible to vote.

In the United States registration can be done at the local city or town hall during regular business hours. Some communities offer additional registration times and places before elections.

When you register, you will fill in and sign an affidavit, a written statement that you swear to be true. The affidavit will ask questions like: (a) name; (b) present address; (c) residence as of January 1, if different; (d) last previous residence in another city, if any; (e) name used at that residence, if different; (f) date of birth; (g) citizenship (by birth or naturalization); (h) occupation; (i) preferred political party, if any.

Think how you would respond to each item. On a separate sheet of paper, write your answers for *a* through *i*. If there are any questions you cannot answer at present, plan a way to get the information. You must register to be eligible to vote.

When you register, find out where to vote in your neighborhood. On election day, officials at the polling place will check for your name on a master list of eligible voters. Your name must be there for you to vote.

The voter is challenged to decide which candidate is best for each position. Now is a good time to practice. Evaluate officials now serving in elected positions. Read the newspapers and pay attention to other media coverage of government activities. Judge your politicians. Think about their qualifications and experience. Ask yourself: Have they performed well? Do their promises match their actions? Are they clear about important issues? Are they honest? Remember, you have the power of the vote.

Different polling places offer different kinds of balloting. You might be given a paper or a punch-card ballot to carry into a private voting booth.

Or, you might go directly into a booth and record your vote on a voting machine. Believe it or not, many people carelessly mark their ballots or incorrectly operate the machines. Avoid this disaster. Arrange to see a sample ballot or to practice using the voting machine before election day.

Now, citizen, put your voting power to these questions. (Someday soon, you could run for office and get elected!)

1. Where could you get voter information?
2. Describe your local form of government.
3. Name your country's political leader.
4. As a candidate for office, what could you offer the voters?
5. What issues do you think are the most important?
6. How would you improve the voting process in your country if you could?

As in a Foreign Land

By faith
Abraham obeyed when he was called to go out
to a place which he was to receive
as an inheritance;
and he went out,
not knowing where he was to go.

By faith
he sojourned in the land of promise,
as in a foreign land,
living in tents with Isaac and Jacob,
heirs with him of the same promise.

For he looked forward to the city
which has foundations,
whose builder
and maker
is
God.

—Hebrews 11:8-10 RSV

◄ *The Call of Abraham,* by Harry Anderson

One Adventure after Another

Gary Gilbert

A young doctor with training, but little experience, went to Africa. His journey, though not especially dangerous, was a bold one, an adventurous one.

I went to Mwami for adventure, to hike through bush country with no fences, where baboons run between the trees. I wanted to talk with people who live in grass-roofed huts, who have never traveled more than a day's walk from their gardens.

There were questions. How do Adventist missionaries live? What effect do they have on village people's lives? What would it be like to live away from television and football and ice cream?

At the time I finished medical school, I had never cared for a patient without close supervision, never done surgery or been responsible for an emergency. But the doctors at Mwami Hospital knew of my inexperience, and I felt a little better knowing that they expected someone who would need to be taught. My internship in a jungle hospital would be an adventure for all of us.

Mwami was fascinating from the beginning. After flying to Europe and then to Africa, we drove for hours to get to Mwami Hospital. The road was narrow, cars were rare, and bush country stretched far into the horizon. From time to time baboons loped across the pavement, and disappeared into the foliage at the other side.

I saw villages—groups of mud huts with grass roofs. Children, pigs, and goats mingled on the hard ground. If we stopped the car, the children, dressed in tattered shorts, quickly surrounded us.

The hospital at Mwami was a drab building. A corrugated tin roof topped a tan concrete structure with glass windows. It was much like older buildings at home.

Near the hospital were several other buildings. There was the nursing school, a modern building that wasn't quite finished. The other buildings varied. In the leper colony some patients lived in mud huts, but many of the hospital workers lived in houses much like those back home.

Teenage boys and girls swung their hoes in the hospital garden, cultivating cabbage and tomatoes. I met doctors and nurses and maintenance workers.

The adventures came.

It was an adventure to go to church for the first time, to walk into a building where men sat on one side and women on the other. It was surprising to see children with bare feet filling the front half of the church and to hear recognizable hymn tunes sung with African words. I was startled by the chameleon that fell from the rafters to land at the Sabbath School teacher's feet.

It was an adventure to go with the African nursing students to the game park where animals are as wild as they were a hundred years ago. Most of the students had never seen lions, elephants, or zebras before, and they were more scared than I when we drove the Volkswagen within a few feet of a resting lion.

It was an adventure to visit an African party. We walked through the bush toward the sound of throbbing drumbeats one moonlit night. A native dancer with a mask and grass skirt moved rapidly to the drum beat. We joined the crowd of onlookers who backed away cautiously when the leering dancer's mask came too close.

It was a small adventure to walk through the hospital for the first time. Children sat on the concrete floor eating corn mush with their fingers. A child's mother always stays with him in the hospital.

I had bigger adventures too.

Once I paid a social visit in an African village to John Zonzi, a farmer and a part-time hospital worker who invited me to visit his home and see his garden.

On a warm morning I set out for the Zonzi village. The cool

season had passed and the rains had not yet begun. Small gardens often bordered the path, and I had learned enough words to greet the women who worked in them. Their children stared at me from beneath trees near the gardens.

The Zonzi village huts were in excellent repair, roofs were well covered, and most of the windows had glass in them. Between the huts the hard dirt had been swept clean. All of the men were at work in the fields, and I soon found John in his garden where he and his father were cultivating cabbage plants. John's mother was in the shade of a tree bathing a small child. The child splashed water from his bath bucket, and other children played nearby. They watched as I approached. John introduced me to his mother, who timidly nodded, and the children, who giggled.

The garden was large, and a variety of crops appeared to be growing well. Green palmlike trees bent with bunches of upside-down bananas. It seemed wrong for bananas to grow with their ends pointing to the sky. John and his father named the plants as we walked. They explained how the vegetables would

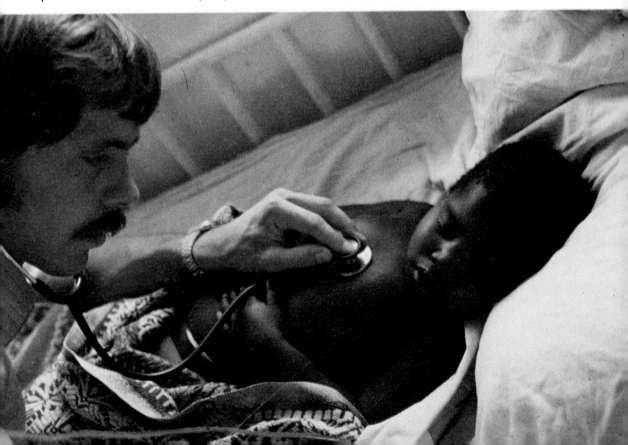

be taken to town and sold. With the money they could buy cement and glass to improve the huts.

We talked of the past. The British governed Zambia before the country gained independence. Mr. Zonzi, John's father, talked of the differences between Africans and Europeans. Europeans, he said, have a different kind of family. The children grow up and leave their parents to live by themselves.

Africans are different. When his daughter or son married, Mr. Zonzi built a new hut and they stayed to live in his village. Everyone worked in the garden, and money from the garden was used to buy necessities for all. What each village member owned could be shared and used by others.

Numerous adventures took place in the hospital. "It's my niece," a hospital worker said. "She has a big infection on her stomach. Will you come to the examining room to see her?"

The girl was five years old and looked very sick. She had a fever and only enough energy to cry softly. The lower half of her abdomen was soft, warm, and swollen as if covered by a giant blister. Pus drained rapidly after I made an incision through her skin.

"The family didn't want me to bring her," Mr. Mabli said. "They thought that she had been cursed and was going to die. 'It is witchcraft,' they said. But I told them, 'No, it is pus.' "

The child would get well soon. She could thank her undaunted uncle for her life. In spite of her parents' protests, he had picked her up and carried her off. Before they could stop him he was on his way to the hospital. They followed at a distance, shaking their heads and crying, but now they would have a healthy daughter who would go home with them instead of a funeral and a loss that they would have blamed on witchcraft.

Another adventure started with a knocking noise. "Thunk, thunk, thunk." I turned over in bed and listened. "Thunk, thunk, thunk." I was on call for hospital emergencies, and there was nobody but me in the house. Someone must be knocking at the door.

I pulled on my trousers and started for the door. Through the window I spotted the guest and stopped abruptly. He was tall, held a spear in his left hand, and wore a stern look on his face. I had seen spears only in museums. The metal tip was at least eighteen inches long.

The man knocked again, looking through the window at me. I saw that he had a note in his hand and decided to open the door. "Thank you," I said as he handed the note to me. He bowed slightly and turned to walk away. The note was from the hospital, and I later discovered that the spear-bearing man was a substitute night watchman.

"Dear Doctor," the note said, "we have a new patient and she is badly burned. Please come quickly."

The hallway in the children's ward was crowded. Adults and children stood at the doorway of the patient's room. The women wailed so loudly I couldn't hear what the nurse said as she motioned for me from the doorway. The group parted to let me pass.

The patient was a girl about twelve years old. Only a few charred pieces of her dress remained, clinging to her body. Big blisters covered her arms and her lips were swollen. Both thighs and the abdomen were black where the skin had been burned off. The girl moaned continuously.

"Get ten milligrams of morphine, a bowl of antiseptic solution, and a large intravenous catheter," I said. The three nurses pushed through the family members and ran for supplies.

The girl cried out when I touched her. One of the women at the door covered her eyes and wailed louder. Blood pressure and pulse were stable. After an injection of morphine the girl felt less pain, but she was still terrified. Two of the nurses held her while I plunged the intravenous catheter through her upper chest wall into a large vein.

She relaxed and slipped off to sleep. The solution running into her veins would replace the body fluid that oozed from the burned tissue on more than half of her body and keep her from dying from that loss.

She awoke immediately when I began cleaning the burned parts. Starting with the feet I peeled away and cut the charred dead skin. If it remained, she would certainly become infected. The milder burns hurt most. Nerve endings were destroyed in the areas of severe burns, so there was no pain there.

One of the nurses recorded the medical history. The family hut had burned, and her father and mother had awakened the children and carried the baby to safety. Only after they were standing outside had they realized that their older daughter was still in the blazing hut. She had slept until her clothes caught fire and then ran out screaming.

The eastern sky was blue when I walked out of the hospital. The night was gone, and there would be no sleep until I finished a long day of work.

Back at the house I spread peanut butter on toast and thought about the burned girl—her wide eyes, and her frightened family. She was still critically ill. If she had lived a few miles farther from the hospital or if the family had called the witch doctor, she would have had no chance.

The muscles in my back and neck ached from hours spent carefully cleaning damaged tissues. I was satisfied, though, and glad that this African adventure included giving a twelve-year-old girl a chance at life.

What Do You Think?

1. How do you think the doctor would have defined *adventure?*
2. Why do you think Dr. Gilbert classified his visit to John Zonzi as a big adventure? What things made it significant?
3. Mr. Zonzi compared the European family with the African family. Which do you think is better? Why?
4. In what way were Dr. Gilbert's adventures a bold journey?
5. Dr. Gilbert noticed differences in how the Africans worship in church. How would you change the way your church worships on Sabbath?

Taking a Closer Look

1. Why did the doctor fear the messenger who came in the middle of the night?
2. Describe in your own words how going to church for the first time in Africa was an adventure for Dr. Gilbert.
3. How did the little girl in the story get burned so badly?
4. What misgivings did Dr. Gilbert have before going to Africa?

Putting Ideas to Work

What would you say are the most important characteristics a prospective missionary needs? How would you prepare yourself if you were going overseas as a missionary? Write a short paragraph to answer each question. Be ready to share your ideas with the class.

FUR AND FEATHERS

Animals are part of the natural world. People are too. In sharing this common space, their paths cross. What do the characters in these stories learn about the world of animals and nature?

A Change of View

Robert Murphy

Do you know the meaning of the expression "You can't see the forest for the trees"? Think how this applies to Andy. What changes his view?

It was a little after dawn when the big otter's broad, whiskered head broke the calm and flawless mirror of the lake. A widening circle of ripples slid away from him, and he reared half length from the water to look about. The near shore was dim and quiet. On the far shore, the spruce and hemlock made a dark band against the paling sky. The otter whistled, cocked his head to the rolling echoes and dropped back into the water again. He was an animal of great and happy vitality. He began diving and rolling, with movements as effortless and fluid as a dance, hardly disturbing the calmness of the water.

Presently, he vanished as silently as he had appeared. A swift line of bubbles followed him toward the bank. He dived deeper for the submerged entrance of the burrow, followed it above water line, and in the dark den found his mate with the one pup beside her, and waked them both. There was a short, good-natured scuffle among the three, and then they pushed the pup before them down the tunnel.

When they all appeared on the lake's surface, they began to hunt the bank. They hunted with great thoroughness, from surface to bottom, exploring every hole and cranny, every root

hollow and crack among the stones, finding a few crawfish and an occasional frog. These were some easy kills. They let the pup make the most of them. His little belly began to bulge, and his mother, growing hungry, left them to catch a pickerel in deeper water and bring it in. They climbed out on the bank and shared it. Then, gleaming and sleek from the water, they rolled and galloped about, hissing at one another with mock ferocity.

Day stole in upon them. Out on the lake, the trailing mists of night thinned and vanished. As the long rays of the sun fell on the otters, they gave over their play, cleaned their fur and went into the water again. They continued up the lake toward one of the streams which fed it. When they reached the stream mouth, the mother and the pup swung away along the shore line. The otter remembered the great brown trout which lived above the bend of the stream and left them. The trout was old and wise, and the otter had missed it so many times that the contest between them had become a fascinating game.

It was characteristic of the otter that he didn't go directly. He zigzagged to and fro across the stream, playing as he went. When he came out of the water to cross the rocks at the first shallows, he heard the distant barking of a dog, up the lake in the direction his mate and the pup had gone. He hesitated for a moment and went on.

He rounded the bend carefully, and began his stalk of the trout. He knew it would be lying like a shadow a little above the sandy bottom in the rushing green gloom of the pocket under the great gray rock. It would be facing upstream, and he would gain an advantage by coming up from the rear. He stretched out full length and, paddling gently and slowly with his forepaws, slid through the water like a stealthy shadow, close to the bank and halfway to the bottom. He came to the corner of the rock and paused, sank until his belly softly scraped the sand, and became one with the bottom's shadows. Then, sinuous as a snake, he began to flow around the rock. He saw the trout several yards away, hanging motionless. He tensed for the spring.

The trout caught a slight movement of the otter's shadowy form. It drifted a little farther out and swung toward him. The otter arched his back swiftly, thrust against the water and darted in. An explosive burst of power sent the trout to the surface. The otter's teeth scored a thin bloody line on its side and the power of its tail stroke rolled him over and over. The trout reached the surface and shattered it by a leap. The otter righted himself and surfaced for air. Although a wild chase upstream and through the rapids was as much a part of the game as the stalk, this time the otter didn't follow. He lay for a moment resting, his sleek head dappled by the sunlight falling through the leaves, and then remembered the barking of the dog.

His game with the trout was over. He started swiftly downstream and came to its mouth. Good fishing water was there, but he didn't hesitate. He turned up the lake. As he rounded the bend, he saw, fifty yards from him, the head of his mate break water a good distance from the shore. The pup was sliding down the bank. As the otter watched, the brown-and-white shape of the dog ran out of the hemlocks toward the pup and snapped at it. The pup was startled and confused. It scrambled between the dog's legs, turned again and leaped from the bank. The dog leaped after it with a great splash. Because the pup had lost time and couldn't get out of the shallows, the dog's long jaw closed on it and it was tossed into the air.

The otter was moving before the dog left the bank, swimming with desperate speed. As the pup curved into the air, a boy ran out on the bank, yelling. Although the otter avoided people above any other creature, he paid no attention to the boy now. He reached the dog a little before his mate, as it leaped for the falling pup. Rising beneath the dog, he fastened upon its throat. The female swirled away from them, getting behind the pup and driving it before her out into the lake.

The dog reared to free its throat, but the otter overbalanced it, fighting with deadly coolness to get it into deeper water. He was all about it, attacking and slipping away with disconcerting swiftness, always maneuvering it a little farther out. The boy on the bank realized this. He grabbed a branch to use as a club, and, jumping from the bank, began to splash toward them. The otter saw the boy coming and pulled the dog into deeper water. The dog tried wildly to free itself, but the otter fastened implacably on its haunches, pulled it down and entangled it in a pile of brush on the bottom. The dog struggled desperately in a world alien to it, but in which the otter was at home. But it was trapped. The air in its lungs fled in silver bubbles to the surface, and the otter struck again.

Standing up to his chest in the water, Andy Gates stared in helpless anguish at the spot where the dog had gone down. He saw the bubbles burst to the surface and, a short time later, a swirl far out where the otter surfaced for air as it followed its mate and the pup. At first he couldn't believe that the dog wouldn't come up again. But time drew out and realization finally came upon him. He dropped the branch he was holding, his fists clenched at his sides and his blue eyes filled with tears. The world about him was suddenly a new and terrible place. He forgot that the dog had been brash and foolishly quarrelsome, that no one had ever been able to teach it anything, and that it had usually been a nuisance. All that he remembered was his brother, standing by the gate before he left for the Peace Corps, saying, "Take care of the pup, Andy. We'll make a bird dog of him when I get back."

He didn't realize that Joe, who knew the dog would never amount to anything, had said that to make them feel closer to each other for a moment and hold off the threatening tears. It made the parting easier for them both. The dog was a trust Joe had placed upon him, his most immediate link with his brother. He had let it be killed. He turned and stumbled out of the water, tears blurring his sight. When his feet found the hard-packed surface of the path, he started along it toward home, stumbling a little now and then. There was an aching emptiness within him, an emptiness which seemed to have swallowed up all his strength. Halfway up the long hill, he had to stop, and stood panting, unconscious of the dry fragrance of sun-warmed hemlock on the morning air.

He stopped crying after a while, and the world slowly came back to him. He grew aware of the birds that moved about him, the leaf shadows on the path and the slow movement of clouds across the sky. But he didn't go on. He sat down beside the path, dry-eyed now, but the emptiness hadn't gone. He saw his surroundings as though from a great distance. Time stopped as his mind tried to rationalize the dog's death and soften the shock of it. The afternoon was growing late when he crossed the top of the hill and saw the farm in the little valley below, and his father walking slowly between the house and the barn.

His father saw him and waited with his hands tucked into the top of his jeans. Gates was a kindly and unhurried man. He looked at the chores that he'd done himself.

"Trouble, Andy?" he asked.

The boy's chin trembled. "Nicky," he said. "There was an otter—" He couldn't go on. He began to cry again, and suddenly went to his father as he hadn't done for years, and leaned against him, crying. "He went after the little one," he said, shaking with sobs, "and the big one drowned him. And Joe—" He couldn't talk about Joe.

"Joe would understand it, boy," his father said, sliding an arm around him. "Joe would know you couldn't help it."

"I was keeping him for Joe," Andy said. "Joe left him with me. He was Joe's and mine." He began to cry violently again. "Joe's and mine," he repeated, remembering Joe at the gate, going away. "I'll kill him!" he burst out, thumping his father's broad chest. "I'll find him and kill him!"

The man started to speak and checked himself, realizing the futility of words. The boy was extraordinarily moved. It was useless to talk against an emotion so deep that he could only guess at it. Time would have to smooth it out—time and what patient understanding he could give. The man was silent for a long time, holding the boy in the crook of his arm.

"Supper, Andy," he said finally. "Get ready for supper, boy."

"I don't want any supper, Dad," Andy said. "I—I couldn't eat any supper."

"All right," Gates said. "Go along up to your room, then. Go up the front stairs. I'll tell Mother you won't be down."

The boy went into the house. After waiting for a few minutes, Gates went around to the back door and into the warm kitchen. Mrs. Gates looked around and smiled. She was small and very neat, and her movements were quick and skillful. Her eyes were blue like the boy's.

"Andy won't be down, Helen," Gates said. "We'd better eat without him."

"Why?" she asked. "What's the matter?"

"Well," Gates said. He took off his hat, hung it behind the door and thought a moment. "That fool dog," he said finally, "got himself killed by an otter. There was a young one, I think, and he went for it. Andy is—I've never seen him so worked up. Joe must have said something about taking care of the dog, and Andy thinks he's let Joe down. He's going to kill the otter, he says."

"But it's not like him," she said. "He doesn't just kill things, Harry."

"No," Gates said. "He's not a cruel boy."

"You'll have to talk to him," she said. "I don't want him to be that way. Vengeful like, I mean."

"It's not revenge," Gates said. "It's—he's—" He shook his

head, irritated that he couldn't put words to it. "This is a deep thing, Helen. He'll have to work it out himself. Maybe he'll kill that otter, but I hope not. If he kills it, I'll have to talk to him."

She looked at him, puzzled. "What do you mean, Harry?"

"That's just it," he said, exasperated. "I don't know what I mean. I can't say it, I just feel it. Let's eat, shall we?"

"All right," she said, and began to fill their plates.

Upstairs, the boy lay on his bed. The picture of Joe smiled at him from the bureau, but he had stopped looking at it. He felt that he couldn't look at it again until he'd found the otter. As his father had said, he wasn't a cruel boy. But all his emotions confirmed the decision, made so suddenly, that the otter must pay with its life for the life of the dog. The justice of the matter, the fact that the otter had been defending the pup, never occurred to him. Many plans went through his mind, but there was no pleasure, no anticipation of exciting sport connected with any of them.

He went about his hunting with a singleness of purpose unusual for his age, with a definite and unvarying schedule. First he'd do the chores, carefully and thoroughly, then get his rifle and go out. At first, he spent a lot of time at the lake, hiding near the place where the dog had been drowned. He knew, from remembered bits of Gates' talk, that otters didn't stay in one place, but made a wide, regular circle about the ponds and streams of the countryside. Sooner or later, he thought, they'd come past him again. He spent days hidden among the hemlocks, and, although he learned a great deal about other animals and birds, he never saw the otters.

The thought came to him finally that they might have passed near dawn, before he got there, or after dusk, when he couldn't see them or had left for home. For several days, disappointment took all the energy out of him. He stayed at home, and his mother thought, with relief, that he'd given up.

"I'm glad it's over, Harry," she said to Gates. "It wasn't like the boy to act like that, going so regular wherever he went."

But Gates had been quietly watching the boy, and he shook his head. "No," he said. "He's not through yet. He's just trying to get away from the place."

Gates was right. The boy was deciding that he would have to move about, to find the otters' route and intercept them somewhere. The place where the dog had died had held him through a wistful hope that somehow it might come back again. But the bond weakened. Reality came closer to him than it had ever come before. As hope died, some of his childhood died with it. He finally broke away from the place and made his first circuit of the lake.

He went too fast at first and found nothing. The otters left very little indication of their passing along the shore line—a few fish scales and bones in widely separated places, a single rare pad mark in damp ground not covered by leaves or vines. On his first trip up the shore he found nothing. Slowing down and going very carefully, he found a faint sign at last, and knew how painstakingly he would have to search from then on. He found the place where they left the lake, the stream they used, and how far they followed before leaving it.

In time he knew the otters' entire twenty-five-mile circuit of the country. It was an achievement in woodcraft which few people could have accomplished. Few people would have had the patience or the time. He had covered a tremendous amount of country. He was well scratched by briers, but he was tanned and strong, and had filled out surprisingly.

He changed, little by little, during those weeks. The boyish heedlessness with which he had formerly moved through the woods was gone. He took no more account of hours than a squirrel. He learned the causes of sounds and the little chains of circumstance which stem from them—the techniques of the hunters and the defenses of the hunted. He saw young grouse[1] freeze and blend with the leaves when the shadow of a hawk swung over them. He watched the steps by which the litter of young foxes learned to catch mice. The play of life about him increased with his skill in seeing it, but his understanding of it and his growing sympathy with it were both completely subconscious until his adventure with the lynx.[2]

He had found its tracks several times. They seemed to be near the places where he had walked or hidden, and he grew curious. He gave over the otters for a time and hunted it, and found that it was stalking him. He spent a good deal of time in the thick hemlocks it liked best. Finally, he went through this woods noisily, backtracked with great care, and hid in a very thick place.

A long time went by before he saw a movement, an indistinct blur as the pale fawn-colored fur slipped across a patch of sunlight. It came closer, silently, never distinct in the thicket. And then it was standing in a little opening not thirty feet away, the yellow eyes staring at him, the big, soft paws tense and the tufted ears cocked. There was a good deal of wild power in it, but he never thought of being afraid. It stood regarding him, poised, unblinking, framed against the wild tangle of the thicket, but without menace. He smiled, and there suddenly seemed to come upon it a look, an expression, of shame that it had been outmaneuvered and taken in. It made a little sound, turned, and, with great care for its dignity, moved off and vanished.

---

[1]grouse: a brown game bird
[2]lynx (lingks): a type of wildcat

108

This dignity was such that it brought to life in his mind all the animals he had watched as rather mechanical figures clothed in fur which had moved about him. For the first time, he realized how much a part of his life they had become and how much he liked them. He realized, too, how clear and simple their reasons for action were, even when they killed.

His thought naturally came to the otters, and swung quickly away. But the fact that he had almost looked upon them sympathetically confused him. He got up, puzzled and a little ashamed, and went home. The disturbing questions which came to him refused to be dismissed. His father was alone in the kitchen; he looked up and saw that the boy was troubled.

"Yes, son?" he asked.

"Dad," he began, knowing that his father would help him, "the otters—"

Just then, his mother came in. "There's a letter from Joe for you, Andrew," she said. "I put it in your room."

His father watched the swift change of his expression, the closing of his mind against the question, with regret.

"I wish you hadn't mentioned that letter, Mother," he said after the boy left. "I wish you'd hidden it. I think he's seen something he liked about those otters, and it was about to change his mind."

"Oh, no," she said. "Oh, no, Harry. Do you think—"

"I think it's too late," Gates said. "He's right back now where he was before."

The uneasiness which at first had been like a formless shadow in the old otter's brain was sharper now. He encountered the human smell which evoked it more frequently. To be followed was a new experience to him, and he didn't know what to make of it. It had not been difficult to avoid the infrequent and casual encounters all animals have with people sooner or later. His senses were superior to theirs, and watchfulness and care were all that was necessary. He saw or heard or scented them and got out of the way. They passed and were gone, and places which held evidence of their presence were better left alone. But this was different. The smell waited in many places for him, clinging to the under-brush or the banks. His temper grew short with constant watchfulness, and he began to avoid the daylight hours.

The female didn't take well to the curtailed activity either. She was of a more casual temperament than her mate. She had never, as he had long ago, been caught in a trap and nearly drowned. She had not felt the blind terror of it nor lost two toes. Her brain wasn't marked by an experience impossible to forget. She chafed at being quiet in the dank blackness of a bankside den when she knew that the world was filled with sunshine and freedom and sport a few feet away.

They all grew morose. Their rollicking vitality, with its urge toward ceaseless activity and play, was frustrated and turned against them. They bickered and snarled at one another.

But this retreat, which would eventually have discouraged the ordinary hunter, was doomed to failure with the boy. All his determination and effort were concentrated solely upon them. Because they could not exist by moving about altogether in the dark, it was inevitable that he find them. The impulse to change his range came to the old otter many times, but he resisted it. The old range was home, familiar and somehow comforting. The memories of his life along its banks and streams were deeply etched into his brain, and they held him there.

Clouds were beginning to cover the late afternoon sun when the boy found the pad mark on the little sandy margin of the stream. It was very fresh. Water was still oozing slowly into it, and he began to tremble. The fact that he had always got home before dark, to avoid worrying his parents, and that he wouldn't be able to do it this time if he didn't start at once were forgotten. A strange sort of surety came upon him, and, after a moment the trembling stopped and he grew calm. He knew that the stream didn't go much farther. Within a quarter of a mile the otters would leave it and go across country, through a hemlock swamp and over a low ridge, to reach the stream on the other side which flowed finally into the lake.

He knew the thicket so well that he could predict where they would pass through it—a marshy little path which had once been a lumber road, cut through a high and tangled bank. He knew he could intercept them there by going through the woods. He knew he had them.

He had so often imagined the feeling of triumph that would be his when he found them that he was confused by the lack of it, by a sort of unwillingness that had suddenly come into his heart. This emotion was unexplainable to him, and seemed like a betrayal of his brother. He thought of his parents, who did not approve of the thing he was doing, but who had been patient and kind and had said nothing against it. Suddenly he felt lost and alone. He stood indecisively for a moment in the darkening woods. The thoughts of his parents changed to thoughts of Joe, and his back stiffened.

He started to walk. A deeper gloom fell upon him as he went into the hemlock, and a deeper silence. He moved like a cat, for his feet made no sound in the fallen needles. When he came to the place, the bank above the lumber road, the setting sun came out more brightly and the thicket was filled with a coppery light. The low branches were so thick that he had to crawl to the top on his hands and knees. He reached the top and lay down, stretching out with the rifle cocked in his hands. It was very quiet. The swampy little path lay before him for a few yards.

The coppery light faded again. After a long time the silence was suddenly broken by a spitting snarl. The boy raised himself on his elbows quickly. There was a rapid, slurred pattering of feet, and the three otters were bunched below him. The old male's back was claw-raked and bleeding. He snarled at his mate and moved toward her as though to drive her along the path, then turned and galloped the other way. A lynx materialized in front of him, crouched and spitting. Its ears lay flat and its teeth gleamed. He went at it hissing, and it gave ground. Another bounded off the bank toward the pup, but he whirled and drove it off. Short-legged and awkward on land, he was at a great disadvantage before the pair of lynxes. But somehow he managed to be everywhere at once.

The snarling lynxes, trying to draw both otters away from the pup, were very quick. But the old otter moved like a dark flame. He closed with one of them, took his raking and punished it. He broke away in time to fasten on the throat of the other, which was batting with a hooked claw at his mate. He shook its big body, threw it aside and whirled again toward the first. Quiet suddenly fell. The lynxes drew off a little, and they all stood panting, glaring at one another.

The path had been so quiet and empty one moment and so full of violent action the next that the boy was held motionless and staring. The sudden quiet freed him. He got up on his

knees, his eyes on the otter. He was so filled with a sudden overwhelming admiration for its courage that he nearly shouted encouragement as it stood, black and bloody, and so obviously ready to carry the fight on. One of the lynxes moved. It drew off a little farther, as though deciding to abandon the fight. The boy didn't think. He raised the rifle and fired a quick shot into the air. The lynx turned tail with a snarl and bounded off through the hemlocks. The other went after it, and the old otter turned its head and looked at him for a moment with curiosity, but no fear. Then it shook itself and drove the female and the pup before it down the path and out of sight.

It was well after dark when the boy heard his father shouting in the distance and answered him. Presently, he saw the lantern moving off among the dark trees, and hurried toward it.

"Are you all right, Andy?" Gates called. "Are you all right, boy?"

"We were a little worried," Gates said gently.

"I'm sorry," he said; and then, "I found them, Dad."

Gates didn't say anything. He just stood there holding the lantern. The boy could see a star or two among the scattering clouds and branches high above his head. "I found them," he said again. "There were two lynxes after them, and he—the old one, the otter—fought them off. He was wonderful, Dad. He licked them both."

"Rabbits must be scarce," Gates said, "to make them tackle him."

"It was the little one," Andy said. "They were after him. But the old one—I—shot to scare off the lynxes, Dad."

There was silence for a long moment, then Gates said, "You're not sorry?"

"No," the boy said. "No. He's not mean, Dad. It was the little one all the time. He was watching out for it—even the day he took Nicky. But I didn't know it then. Do you think Joe will understand that, Dad?"

"Sure," Gates said. "He'll understand it. He'll be glad you understand it too." His long arm went around the boy's shoulders. "Come on," he said. "Let's get on home."

What Do You Think?

1. How did Andy think he would feel when he finally found the otters? What feelings did he have?
2. How did Andy's understanding of animals grow from his experience with the otter?
3. Why did Andy take the otter's side in its confrontation with the lynxes?
4. What lesson did Andy learn from the otter's brave fight against the lynxes?
5. What did Andy learn from the way his parents acted?
6. How do you think Andy will explain the death of the dog to Joe? Do you agree that Joe would be glad that Andy hadn't killed the otter? Why or why not?

Taking a Closer Look

1. What happened to Andy's dog? Why?
2. What had Andy's brother, Joe, told him before he left?
3. What did Andy plan to do to the old otter?
4. How did Andy's parents feel about the plan? Did they try to stop him?
5. What signs of the otters' passing did Andy learn to recognize?
6. After weeks of searching, what clue told Andy that he could finally corner the otters?

Putting Ideas to Work

Write a letter like one you think Andy might send to his brother Joe, explaining the death of the dog. Tell Joe how the event happened, how you (as Andy) felt about the otter at first, and why you changed your mind about killing it.

The Urge to Follow

Russell Freedman and James E. Morriss

An Austrian scientist once discovered, to his surprise, that he had become a "Mother Goose."

Graylag geese following Dr. Konrad Lorenz

Years ago, Dr. Konrad Lorenz placed some graylag goose eggs in an incubator. He was standing by to watch as the goslings struggled out of their shells, dried off, and started to walk. After a while, he took them to an old goose who had raised many young of her own.

He put the goslings beside her nest and walked away. But the little birds ran after him. He picked them up, put them back by the nest, and walked away again. They still ran after him, refusing to stay with their foster mother.

115

From then on, the goslings tried to follow the scientist wherever he went. If he walked across the meadow, they ran along close behind. If he sat down under a tree they clustered around him. If he swam in a nearby lake, they splashed into the water and swam after him. And if he disappeared into the house, they called for him with loud, insistent honks.

As far as these goslings were concerned, Konrad Lorenz *was* their mother.

Dr. Lorenz is recognized as one of the founders of ethology—the modern science of animal behavior. He has been living with animals and studying their habits ever since his student days in Vienna, when he shared his room with a monkey named Gloria.

At one time he directed the Max Planck Institute, a large animal research center in Germany. For many years, however, he carried on his work at his country home in the village of Altenberg, overlooking the Danube River in Austria. It was there that he accidentally mothered his first gaggle of geese.

Dr. Lorenz wasn't the first man to become "mother" to a goose. Farmers had told about similar experiences with newly hatched geese, ducks, chickens, and other ground birds. A few scientists had also observed this strange following behavior, but no one could offer much of an explanation.

One farmer had taken a baby chick from its mother right after it hatched. Later, he tried to return the chick to its mother, but it wouldn't stay with her. Instead it ran after any person who happened to walk by. It became such a pest that the farmer shouted at it, threw rocks at it, and even tried to beat it back with a stick. Yet the stubborn bird continued to run after people.

Why was this chick unable to accept its mother after being separated from her for such a brief time? Why did Dr. Lorenz's goslings reject a real mother goose and try to follow him?

Dr. Lorenz decided to investigate. He placed another batch of graylag goose eggs in his incubator and waited for the goslings to hatch. Then he immediately put one of the birds into a small box. He carried the box to a quiet room, opened the lid, and sat in a corner.

Before long, the little gosling poked its head out of the box and looked upon the world for the first time. It climbed down to the floor but did not attempt to approach the scientist, who was sitting motionless in his corner. Instead, it stood in the center of the room and called frantically.

Dr. Lorenz had left a cushion, attached to a string, lying on the floor. When he pulled the string, the gosling stopped calling and started to run after the cushion. Wherever Dr. Lorenz pulled the cushion, the gosling followed it.

By conducting many similar experiments, Dr. Lorenz found that a newly hatched gosling will run after the first moving object it sees. Normally, it sees its own mother and follows her. But if for some reason the mother bird is not there, the gosling will try to follow a man, a dog, a moving cushion, a rolling ball, a toy car, or almost anything else it sees moving away from it. And after following something for just a brief time, it will refuse to follow anything else.

Dr. Lorenz also found that this following response is strongest during the first few hours of a gosling's life. If a newly hatched bird is kept in a room by itself, and isn't given a chance to follow, it gradually loses the urge to follow. At the end of only one day, it hesitates and even seems fearful of anything that moves. At the end of two days, it won't follow at all.

Apparently, there is a time when goslings are ready to learn what to follow. If they miss this time, it is too late for them to learn.

Many scientists have now joined Dr. Lorenz in studying this kind of learning among ducks, chickens, turkeys, and other birds that walk around soon after they hatch. Like geese, these birds are born with an instinctive urge to follow. However, they must learn *what* to follow. Once they do, the lesson is not easily reversed or undone.

Some birds learn to follow more quickly than others, and some are more permanently affected by this experience than others. But in all cases, the learning must take place during the first few hours or days of a bird's life if it is to take place at all.

Konrad Lorenz called this kind of learning *imprinting,* because an infant bird's first impressions seem to become so deeply imprinted upon its mind.

By following its mother, a newly hatched gosling learns to recognize her and to associate with others of its kind. But if it follows a man and accepts him as its mother, it may then want to associate with humans for the rest of its life. Such a bird has become imprinted to humans.

Scientists have described many strange examples of imprinting. At an animal training farm in Arkansas, a newly hatched duckling was raised with a group of baby chicks. When the duckling was nearly grown, he was moved to the duck pond so he could swim with the other ducks. But by this time, he wasn't interested in other ducks. He spent all his time running back and forth along a wire fence, trying to get back into the chicken yard. When he was finally put back, he seemed perfectly content. Apparently, he considered himself a chicken instead of a duck.

At the Vienna zoo, a beautiful white peacock was hatched during a bitter cold spell. The peacock was the only survivor of his brood, and the zoo keeper, hoping to keep the bird alive, took him to the warmest room in the zoo. This room was in the reptile house and was occupied at the time by some giant tortoises.

The tortoises paid no attention to the baby peacock. But the little bird became imprinted to the sluggish, slow-moving creatures whose home he shared, and he followed them everywhere. When he was old enough to pick a mate, he began to spread his magnificent tail feathers—as all male peacocks do when they court a female. This peacock, however, spread his feathers in a futile attempt to woo one of the giant tortoises.

Most birds are completely helpless when they hatch. Instead of running after their mothers, they remain in the nest for days or weeks while their parents feed and protect them. If one of these birds is taken from its nest and is raised by hand, it may become imprinted to the person who feeds it, just as a ground bird becomes imprinted to the person it follows.

What Do You Think?

1. Why do you think God created the imprinting instinct in these kinds of birds?
2. How useful do you think the discovery of imprinting is to mankind? Explain your answer.
3. Can you think of any reasons why the instinct to follow would be necessary to a bird in the wild?
4. Of the instances of imprinting mentioned in this article which did you find most interesting? Which showed the greatest contrast between the imprinted animal and what it followed? Explain your answers.
5. Can you think of any way the human mind may be affected by a kind of imprinting? Explain.

Taking a Closer Look

1. Explain how Dr. Lorenz found that a newly hatched gosling will run after the first moving object it sees.
2. During what time period must a bird learn what to follow?
3. Describe in your own words the meaning of *imprinting*.
4. What is ethology?

Putting Ideas to Work

Describe some other examples of instinct in animals.

Study
SKILL

Adjusting Your Reading Rate

There are almost as many ways to read as there are types of reading matter. How do you handle the diversity? Should you read every word of an advertisement? Should you just glance at an invitation from Buckingham Palace?

It all depends on your reason for reading. If your purpose for analyzing the ad is to write about advertising methods, then careful reading is a good approach. If you are unable to get to England, then a superficial look at the invitation will do.

Most of the time, however, using both approaches is useful. Skimming—looking over the material quickly—is the first step. This first glance gives you an idea of what the reading matter is about. If the topic is of interest to you, then you want to do a careful reading to gather detailed information.

Now follow the steps of some furred and feathered friends. First, you will trail them just for the basic facts (skimming). Then, you will track their every movement (careful reading). Take this route to skim the story that follows:

First, look at the heading and subheadings. They should tell you something about the subject.

Second, glance at the first paragraph for key words and a summary of the report.

Third, quickly move your eyes through the whole article. Check for familiar ideas.

Survival on the Steppe

Twilight deepens over a rocky plain that was once volcanic. The broiling sun and dry winds are temporarily at rest. With the dusk, activity begins to rustle the shrubs and pines that carpet the steppe. Animals venture into the cool night, seeking food and water.

Hoofprints, Scratchmarks, and Whirring Wings
A mule-deer doe begins her trek to the mouth of the creek. There the thirsty doe will drink the creek's plentiful waters. The doe follows the uphill path while alert for enemies.

The doe's path crosses the paths of smaller creatures. A soft-furred wood rat retreats to the safety of its home, a pile of pinecones and sticks, until the doe passes by. Only then does the wood rat go back to eating juicy plant stems.

Farther along the trail, a short-tail

weasel chases a tiny pocket mouse among the rocks. Using its long hind legs to advantage, the pocket mouse darts into a hole, escaping the agile weasel. Later, the pocket mouse continues its search for dry seeds.

Overhead, fluttering wings drive a lone bat, pursuing insects in the air. A feathery whippoorwill is also scooping up flying insects. But bird rarely meets bat, because the whippoorwill feeds closer to the ground. Gently winging among its pine-tree haunts, a great horned owl picks up the sound of a deer mouse. Having climbed a shrub to search for food, the small mouse is now devouring a large insect. Caught unaware, it detects too late the soft swoop of wing as the owl descends.

Quenching Brings Calm
The mule-deer doe reaches the creek safely. She is joined by other creatures that have journeyed there. They all drink deeply at the creek. With water to carry them through another day's heat, the animals retrace their paths across the steppe, pausing only to nibble on leaves of the bitterbrush.

Congratulations! You have just skimmed the whole story. At this point you have some insight about the subject. Now do a careful reading of *Survival on the Steppe.*

To answer questions about the story after a careful reading, you need not reread it. You can skim for key words to find the answers. Look at this question: *Where does the mule-deer doe search for water?* The key words are *mule-deer doe* and *water.* By skimming, locate paragraphs that contain those key words. Then skim those paragraphs. Notice that they

mention both the doe and the water source, the creek.

Use the same procedure to answer the following questions.
1. As the mule-deer doe treks to the creek, what is she alert for?
2. Where does the soft-furred wood rat retreat to?
3. What is the pocket mouse's favorite food?
4. Do the bat and the whippoorwill have anything in common?
5. After drinking at the creek, some animals stop for one last nibble. What is the food?

A Minor Bird

Robert Frost

I have wished a bird would fly away,
And not sing by my house all day;

Have clapped my hands at him from the door
When it seemed as if I could bear no more.

The fault must partly have been in me.
The bird was not to blame for his key.

And of course there must be something wrong
In wanting to silence any song.

Kay McKeever and a Parliament of Owls

Margery Facklam

When the habits of a wild animal are changed by people, the animal becomes defenseless. How does Kay McKeever help owls to return to their natural environment?

Tiglet is a screech owl not much bigger than a fat robin. His favorite perch is the top shelf of a bookcase in Kay McKeever's living room. There he waits until Morag, an enormous Irish wolfhound, has settled in to sleep on the rug. Then, without a sound, Tiglet swoops from the top shelf with his talons ready. Barely hesitating in flight, he rakes Morag's curly backside with his long claws. Before the gangly dog can scramble to his feet, Tiglet has swooped back again and is peacefully perched on the shelf as though nothing had happened.

Tiglet spends the daylight hours confined to a large bathroom. After the McKeevers' dinner, Tiglet is allowed the freedom of the house, flying wherever he pleases. At bedtime, Kay calls him with a screech owl call. Tiglet flies to her

123

head, and she carries him back to his bathroom where his dinner—a freshly thawed dead mouse—lies neatly on a paper towel next to the sink.

As the moon rises over the tall pines that surround the McKeevers' house in Vineland, Ontario, you can hear the chorus of soft, haunting hoots mixed with a dozen other screeches, sighs, and cries as one hundred owls settle in for the night.

The owls live in large, outdoor flight cages at the Owl Research and Rehabilitation Center—the only one of its kind in North America. Tiglet, and a great horned owl named Wheeper, are the only ones who don't seem to know they are owls.

Tiglet and Wheeper have been imprinted with humans. Imprinting is nature's method of making sure a baby animal will know its mother. When a baby duck or goose hatches from the egg, the first moving, living thing it sees becomes imprinted on it as the parent, the source of food. A baby goose will follow the farmer if that is who it has seen first. Konrad Lorenz had geese following him everywhere when he was studying imprinting.

Tiglet was only a bit of fluff the size of a Ping-Pong ball when he set eyes on Kay McKeever, and he has been totally attached to her ever since. Tiglet barely tolerates the strange feathered creatures that hoot and call from the outdoor cages.

Because of the imprinting, animals like Tiglet and Wheeper cannot return to the woods. They are totally dependent. The aim of the rehabilitation center is to return the birds to their natural habitat.

Kay and her husband, Larry, live in a country house in the fruit orchards of the Niagara Peninsula, a region between Lake Erie and Lake Ontario. One day a friend called and asked, "Would you like to have a screech owl?"

"I knew nothing about them, but I said yes," Kay said later.

After weeks of ardent care, the tiny owl died in convulsions. Kay was upset, but she had the good sense to have the bird autopsied. The report showed death from pesticides. She had been feeding it juicy worms from the fertile soil around the fruit trees. It had not occurred to anyone at the time that the insect spray lavished on the fruit trees had washed into the soil and then into the earthworms.

Kay was determined that such a thing would never happen again. Shortly afterward, she became the caretaker for three more owls. And she began to study everything she could find about these birds of prey.

Much of what Kay learned about owls came from books, but most of it came from trial and error.

As people heard of Kay's success with owls, they brought birds to

her. Without intending to, she found herself becoming more and more involved.

What began as a hobby has become a full-time job, and much of it is hard, grubby work. Every day cages must be cleaned, rats defrosted, owls fed with freshly killed mice, mouse cages cleaned, mice fed, injured birds exercised, wounds dressed and treated. There are no days off when you care for animals.

Even without a calendar, Kay knows the first day of hunting season. On that day, injured owls begin to arrive at their hospital. Conservation officers, police, game wardens, and bird watchers bring in owls that have been shot. Nine-

ty percent of the owls at the center are injured by guns. Others may have flown into a moving car at night when the lights confused them. Some have flown into television towers or picture windows. All the owls they help have been, in Kay's words, "interfered with"—that is, injured by humans.

Each new arrival is carefully examined in a room in Kay's basement that was originally a laundry room but was gradually converted to a hospital treatment room. There is a lighted wall box for reading X rays and a special cage with a heat lamp to warm birds in shock.

First aid, warmth, and some food usually get an owl through

125

the first shock of injury and capture. Birds requiring surgery are taken to a veterinarian, who can administer an anesthetic and treat them in a fully equipped operating room.

Early in her work with owls, Kay decided that her center would never become just a series of cages where crippled birds lived out useless lives. Even after she has made the birds comfortable, she tries to give them more. She feels that quality of life is the most important consideration.

She would like to return all the owls to the wild, of course. But some of them, in spite of care and intense treatment, can never fly well enough to defend themselves or hunt. The injured owls that recover enough to care for themselves in the protection of captivity but cannot care for themselves in the wild become the breeding pairs. From one pair of barn owls, thirty healthy offspring were released from the center in two and a half years.

Owls are nature's rat traps. They fill an important niche in the food chain, and farmers depend upon them whether they know it or not. A farm without owls and hawks around it is going to have a big population of rats and mice to nibble on grain and corn.

Kay is doing what she can to see to it that these rat traps have a farm to hunt around.

The young birds born to the captive owls are always treated as wild birds. They are not tamed or handled, so they will not become dependent on humans. She provides the young ones with "hunting therapy"—her substitute for the skills an owl usually learns from its parents.

Release training begins in early spring, when the birds are moved from their usual cages to special ones. The training cages are built with wide fiberglass panels around the bottom to make them mouseproof—there are no holes through which a mouse can scoot. Until this time, the owls have been waited on like visitors in a plush hotel. Each day at the same time, freshly killed mice have appeared in the clean feeding boxes in their regular flight cages. Suddenly, no food arrives.

Now the mice are alive. They are put into the cage and left to scurry through the rustling dead leaves just as they would in the woods. But the mice are laboratory-born and raised, and they don't even know they are supposed to be afraid of these feathered monsters. So the mice run along the perches looking at the owls, and the owls are puzzled at these furry things that are sharing their quarters.

On the first day of this new feeding schedule, the owls act annoyed, sort of asking, "Where's the food?" On the second day, when they are really hungry, the owls begin to make a racket when

Kay passes the cage on her way to feed the others. But still there is no food lying neat and dead in the food box. Only those running furry things. Finally, on the third or fourth day, the hunger seems to trigger some deep, unused instinct, and one of the owls pounces clumsily at a startled mouse. By the second pounce, the open talons making a quick, clean kill, everything seems to click into place, and the owl has become the hunter, the mouse trap nature intended it to be. The mice, too, suddenly become educated, and the word goes around among the mice to stay hidden. There is no more scrambling of mice across the perches.

After the owl has learned its part, the McKeevers have to find a place to release it. They drive around the countryside looking for likely territories. The best place for a barn owl is, of course, around a barn, preferably filled with animals, and corn fields or a corn crib where mice and rats raise their families. They look for a farm away from highways, and they like to find one with old buildings so the owls can fly in and out of cracks and broken boards. Kay once persuaded a farmer to cut holes in a brand-new barn just for the owls.

When they spot a likely-looking barn, Kay gets out of the car to imitate her barn owl call, a talent she has developed well. If she gets no answer, she can safely assume there are no owls using that territory.

When she releases an owl, she has a great sense of accomplishment. But she also feels a sadness. It is difficult not to feel an attachment for an animal you have raised.

When the McKeevers began their owl project, the neighbors probably thought they were crazy. Who else would buy meat at a butcher shop for owls? But stranger still, what kind of person would hire someone to build a nest?

The McKeevers had watched a pair of great horned owls courting in nearby trees. They had heard the calls and watched the male trying to court the female with no success.

"How terrible," said Kay, "those poor young things don't have a nest."

Owls seldom build their own nests. They prefer to occupy an abandoned nest, sometimes a hawk's nest. Kay and Larry searched the area but could not find an empty nest.

"So I called the tree-pruning people," said Kay, "and explained that I wanted a nest built in a fifty-foot oak tree."

"You want a *what*, lady?" asked the man on the phone.

Two men arrived and listened while Kay described how to build an owl's nest. But they kept exchanging glances of disbelief.

Following directions, they built a platform fifty feet up the tree. They put drainage holes in the wood bottom and attached small sides to keep nesting material from falling out. They hoisted bundles of sticks, twigs, and pine needles up the tree.

"How do you want 'em put in here, lady?" called the man in the tree.

Kay told him to put the large sticks down first, then smaller ones, until finally the top layer was soft pine needles.

"Now make a depression in the middle. You know, shape it like a nest."

"How do I do that?" hollered the man.

"Just sit in it and move your backside around a little, Harry," called the helper on the ground.

Although Kay speaks lightly of the owls and the things she has done with them, she takes the work seriously. She does not allow the public in to see the owls because visitors disturb the birds. It is not a zoo. But she does show groups of college students and other ornithologists around.

The most recent triumph at the center, and cause for great rejoicing, was the birth of the first baby screech owls ever hatched in captivity by disabled wild parents. "And they are releasable," Kay wrote, underlining, "It's working, it's working!"

"Perhaps someday," Kay McKeever says with longing, "people will appreciate the owl. And this place won't be necessary."

What Do You Think?

1. How is the Owl Research and Rehabilitation Center different from a veterinary hospital?
2. How do you know that Kay McKeever really believes that owls should live in nature?
3. Do you think Kay McKeever's work might contribute to the scientific knowledge about owls? Explain your answer.
4. How did Kay McKeever learn about owls? Give examples of some things that were learned from trial and error.
5. Do you think common sense is important in Kay's care of the owls? Explain your opinion.

Taking a Closer Look

1. What is imprinting? How does a duck or goose become imprinted?
2. What is the aim of the Owl Research and Rehabilitation Center?
3. List some of the causes of injuries to the owls that Kay McKeever treats.
4. How are owls useful to farmers?
5. What is release training? Explain the steps involved in this training.

Putting Ideas to Work

Imagine that you have an opportunity to visit with and interview Kay McKeever at the Owl Research and Rehabilitation Center. What aspects of Kay's work would you like to know more about? Prepare a list of questions that would examine these aspects.

Shoeing the Geese

Murray T. Pringle
Everyone has heard of shoeing horses. But horses aren't the only animals that need clothing now and again.

Suppose you saw geese wearing shoes, cows with sunglasses, or a donkey dressed up in two pairs of trousers. Would you believe it? If you could travel all over the world, you would see such sights and many others. What's more, though they might look funny, there is a good, sensible reason for the animals' strange dress.

One place where you would see an odd sight is in Poland, as well as some other parts of Europe. Many farmers in Poland cannot afford to own trucks, but even if they did, gasoline would be too expensive to buy. When it is time there for geese to go to market, they must walk all the way! Because there is often a considerable distance over rough roads between the farm and the marketplace, the farmer prepares his flock for the journey by shoeing them first. Putting shoes on geese is simple and costs almost nothing. The birds are driven back and forth over patches of warm tar and then through a stretch of sand. The sandy tar sticks to their webbed feet, forming a hard crust. This enables the fowl to travel the long distances from farm to market without getting sore feet!

130

Why would a cow need to wear sunglasses? Most of them don't, but some of the cows that live in the steppes region of Russia do. Snow covers the ground there for six months out of the year, and cattle have a hard time finding tufts of grass to munch on since they are scarce and mostly hidden by the snowy blanket. If that weren't difficult enough, brilliant sunlight reflecting from the snow makes it difficult for the animals to see. They had to rely on their noses until someone became concerned about their plight and decided that something should be done to help the poor creatures.

The answer, of course, was dark glasses. But how do you fit a cow with spectacles that will stay on and be comfortable without the animal trying to tear them off? It took quite a while to solve this problem, but a solution was finally found. Now, many cows in the steppes wear sunglasses, and snow blindness is no longer a problem.

Finally, did you ever see a donkey wearing trousers? You would if you visited the Isle of Re off the west coast of France. These animals that toil in the vegetable fields and vineyards there have been wearing pants for many years. And because a donkey has four legs, of course, he needs two pairs of trousers! This unusual costume is worn for a very practical reason. Swarms of insects infest the island's beaches, but they can't bite through a pair of pants!

Farmers' wives sew each pair of donkey trousers with separate legs, and suspender straps hold the legs onto the animal's body. These "donkey duds" are made out of any available material and are sometimes very colorful. Imagine seeing a striped pair of pants as well as a checkered pair being worn at the same time!

So the next time you hear or read about geese wearing shoes or cows wearing spectacles or donkeys dressed up in fancy pants, you'll know it's true. And you'll also know that someone was thoughtful and kind enough to try to make things a little more comfortable for our animal friends.

What Do You Think?

1. Why does it seem humorous for animals to wear human clothing?
2. Can you think of any other animals that might benefit from clothes? Describe the clothes you would design for them.
3. Think of another good title for this article.

Taking a Closer Look

1. What makes clothing necessary for the animals mentioned in this article?
2. Explain in your own words how and why geese in Europe are "shoed."
3. List the three countries mentioned in this article. Locate them on a world map or a globe.

Putting Ideas to Work

Find out more about the Russian steppes. Be ready to tell the meaning of the term *steppes* and in what part of Russia the steppes are located. Also try to find out what other animals are common in that part of Russia.

Using Map Coordinates

Finding a particular place on a map can be difficult. Most maps show hundreds of cities, towns, lakes, rivers, and other places. It would take a lot of time to read every name, and there is always the chance that you will overlook the name of the place in your search.

Look at the map on the next page. It shows a section of Alaska. On the edge of the map, you will notice that the letters I, J, and K are evenly spaced along the side. On the top edge are the numbers 7, 8, 9, and 10. These letters and numbers are called coordinates. They divide the map into square sections to help you locate places more quickly.

If you know the coordinates of a place, then you know where to look on the map. For example, the town of Denali is located in the I-9 section of the map. To locate this section, place one index finger on the letter I on the side of the map. Place the other index finger on the number 9. Now move the finger on the letter I straight across. At the same time, move the finger on the number 9 straight down. The place where both fingers touch is the I-9

section. You now have a smaller area to search for Denali. It will be close to where your fingers met.

Now find the section K-7. What National Park is in this section? Follow the same steps to locate the K-7 section. Did you find Kenai National Park?

In sections I-7 and I-8, seven mountains are listed. Next to each mountain, its elevation, or height, is given in feet. Which is the highest mountain? A careful comparison will show you that Mt. McKinley is almost 3,000 feet higher than the other mountains. In fact, it is the highest mountain in North America.

Many maps will provide a list of important places and the coordinates for these places. Look at this list if you want to locate a particular place. Note the coordinates and locate the appropriate section on the map to begin your search.

Look at the map on page 136, showing Nevada and part of California. Below is a partial list of the many cities and towns in Nevada and California. Next to each name are the coordinates for that city or town.

ALASKA

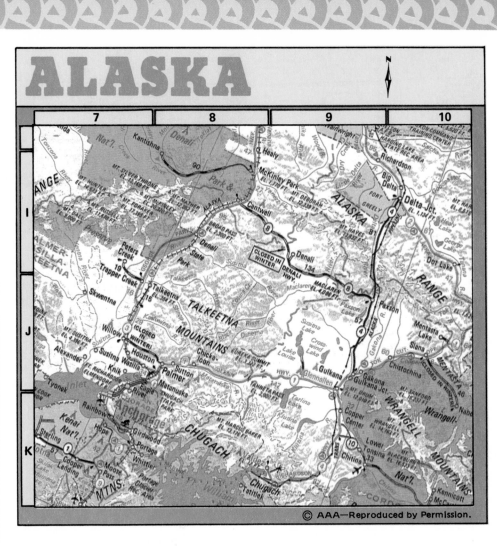

© AAA—Reproduced by Permission.

Read statements 1 through 8 referring to the map of Nevada and part of California. If the statement is correct, write *true* on your paper. If the statement is not correct, write *false*.

1. Sequoia National Park is in the same section as Independence.

2. Indian Springs is south of Las Vegas.

3. If you were visiting Yosemite National Park, a close town to stay in would be El Portal.

4. Goldfield is in the same section as Nivloc and Gold Point.

5. Reno is near a large lake.

6. Carson City is north of Lake Tahoe.

7. Death Valley is very near Yosemite National Park.

8. Independence is west of Death Valley National Monument.

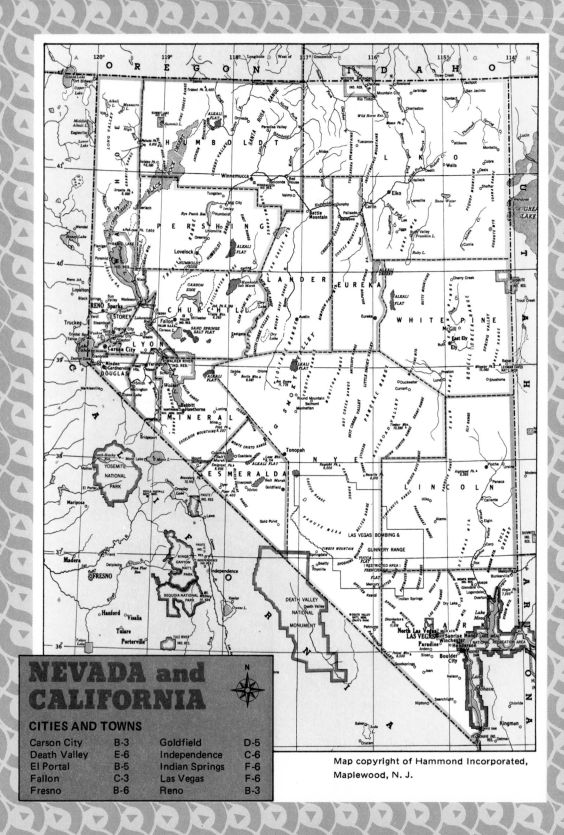

NEVADA and CALIFORNIA

CITIES AND TOWNS

The Power of the Dog

Rudyard Kipling

There is sorrow enough in the natural way
From men and women to fill our day;
And when we are certain of sorrow in store,
Why do we always arrange for more?
Brothers and Sisters, I bid you beware
Of giving your heart to a dog to tear.

Buy a pup and your money will buy
Love unflinching that cannot lie—
Perfect passion and worship fed
By a kick in the ribs or a pat on the head.
Nevertheless it is hardly fair
To risk your heart for a dog to tear.

When the fourteen years which Nature permits
Are closing in asthma, or tumor, or fits,
And the vet's unspoken prescription runs
To lethal chambers or loaded guns,
Then you will find—it's your own affair—
But . . . you've given your heart to a dog to tear.

When the body that lived at your single will,
With its whimper of welcome, is stilled (how still!);
When the spirit that answered your every mood
Is gone—wherever it goes—for good,
You will discover how much you care,
And will give your heart to a dog to tear.

The Silver Fox

Anne LaBastille

Anne LaBastille lives in a log cabin in the
Adirondack wilderness. In 1974, she
received an award for her work in ecology.
She describes here a part of her work that
often goes unrecognized.

I spent two winters in residence at a university working on
my doctor's degree in wildlife ecology. Our wildlife diseases
class met at the veterinary college. Here they were conducting
an experimental rabies program, using wild foxes as the control
animals. One day I happened to pass the pens and saw a
young male silver fox staked out in the snow. His coat was full
and shiny, and his tail brilliant and bushy. We stood gazing at
each other—he with slanted yellow eyes as wild as the day he
was born—mine full of an immediate affection and admiration.
By changing my usual route to classes, I was able to see this fox
several times a week. A name came to mind, recalled from a
course on South American native peoples. It was "Mapuche,"[1]
name of an invincible tribe of Indians in southern Chile, as
invincible as this fox's eyes.

One day I heard that many of the control foxes were no
longer needed in the program. I checked with one of the vet
professors to learn if my fox friend was one of these. Already I
was thinking what a magnificent pet Mapuche would make
and how free he would feel at the cabin. Before the week was
out, I had acquired the silver fox, but no place to keep it.

---

[1]Mapuche (muh pü'chē)

Since I spent most weekends at the cabin, I had only rented a small room in a graduate student dormitory. No pets were allowed. Most of my friends lived in rental rooms or apartments where similar rules applied. My professors had homes full of children, cats, dogs, parakeets, and other pets. After a frantic search, I finally found a very large empty wire cage outside an ornithology laboratory. On one side a group of wild turkeys gobbled, on the other a rare pair of Japanese cranes preened. It would be a tantalizing, if not appetizing, home for Mapuche. And, it was only temporary.

I moved my silver fox there in February. Now began the most discouraging days I have ever spent with an animal. Mapuche refused to let me near him. As soon as he heard my truck approach, he cowered in a corner. The minute I came through the tiny door, he curled his lips and bared his teeth. When I offered him fresh water, meat, or bones, he hissed and snarled. The pen reeked of the smell of fear. My clothes and boots smelled so badly that I had to keep a separate set just to wear when I came to his pen. Otherwise my roommates would not tolerate me around the dorm.

This awful behavior continued all through a cold and snowy March. I would stay shivering as long as I could in the pen, hands turning stiff with cold inside my heavy gloves, hoping that the fox would relent and make his first gesture of friendship. Yet day after day, he only glared, snarled, and cowered in the corner.

April came and with it warmer weather. One afternoon I was able to visit Mapuche without gloves or heavy jacket. The sun felt so warm that I lay down for a few minutes on a big log in the pen and closed my eyes. Suddenly something pulled my ponytail. I moved my head slightly and opened one eye cautiously. Mapuche was standing behind me, one paw lifted, poised for retreat. His jaws were closed and his ears erect. His white-tipped tail stood out straight as a pointer. This was not the posture of a vicious or frightened animal. I lay very still. Minutes later, I felt another tug on my hair. I opened both eyes and gazed into the fox's. His met mine unflinchingly, yet with a new expression—mischievousness. Astonished, I watched Mapuche edge forward, take the tip of my ponytail between his front teeth, and gently tug. Mapuche was trying to play!

Ever so slowly, I reached out my bare hand to him. After what seemed hours, my finger tips finally touched the fox. Instinctively, I touched him under the chin, palm up, as one does with a strange dog. But this left my wrist completely unprotected. Would Mapuche slash at my veins with those razor-sharp teeth?

He trembled. I began rubbing his chin, then his throat, and around back toward his ears and neck. The fox's trembling stopped, and those wild yellow eyes gentled and half closed. His ears ceased wiggling back and forth like nervous antennae. His fur smoothed down. Mapuche stood as still as a house dog

while I gave him the first human affection and attention he had probably ever known. Certainly it was the first physical contact he and I had shared in six weeks.

Mapuche's overall behavior changed dramatically. Now when the truck drove up, he leaped against the wire walls eagerly, paws clinging like a cat, tail wagging like a dog. Instead of snarling, he was grinning when I came through the door. He accepted meat and bones from my hand. He used his teeth only to tug at my jacket, trouser legs, or hair in play. The fox showed off by bouncing on and off the cage sides. Best of all, the pen no longer had that scent born of fear and anxiety. We spent enchanting hours together.

That spring I learned an amazing bit of information at the vet college. Mapuche had been dragged from his den as a tiny kit by someone wearing heavy gloves and had been handled in the laboratory by students and scientists also wearing gloves. That had been my first mistake—to wear gloves when visiting the fox. My second mistake had been to spend too little time with him. But the bitter winter weather had dictated both actions.

Now Mapuche's whole being was directed toward me, and his day consisted of waiting for my visit. The fox was a curious combination of feline and canine traits. He was fast as quicksilver[2] and smarter than any dog I'd ever known. By mid-May, Mapuche was going for walks with me on a leash! By the end of May and the close of classes, I felt sure he was ready to go to the cabin.

I packed up my books and belongings, borrowed a small cage, and drove back to Black Bear Lake. It was a clear, warm day when we arrived. I piled gear in the boat, trying to handle Mapuche's cage as gently and quietly as possible. His eyes glazed in fear when he heard the outboard engine start and water splash on the bow of the boat.

At the cabin, I immediately tied him to my huge curved spruce tree. Mapuche sniffed at the pine-scented air, dug briefly in the damp earth. Here was no smell of turkeys, cranes, or car exhaust. This was the natural world he had been born into. A beautiful transformation took place. I watched his silvery coat flatten and blend into the dappled shadows under the firs. His motions grew calmer, surer. He scratched a little hollow to lie down in. Only his two points of clear amber remained alert, questioning, cautious.

Mapuche discovered red squirrels, new birds, black bears, wild foxes, beavers, chipmunks, and deer. All day his ears, eyes, and nose scanned the air for information like radar screens. I kept the fox on a chain, moving him around the cabin from tree to tree. At night he slept under a little A-frame shelter. My plan was to let him become accustomed to the Adirondack environment, take him walking, and then free him each evening so he could learn to hunt. My hope was that he would still return to me for companionship, yet build up sufficient independence to fend for himself in the wild. By September the fox was running free each evening for several hours, yet coming back to the cabin before morning.

---

[2]quicksilver: mercury

One day Mapuche did not return. I waited for three days. Had he succumbed to the "call of the wild" or was he in trouble? It was pointless to roam the woods blowing a whistle or calling his name. The answer came in the form of his luxurious pelt in the hands of a state trooper.

"I knew you had a silver fox," he began, embarrassed. "And I think this may be yours."

A sudden rush of tears blurred my eyes, and my hands felt cold.

"Some people over in Hawk Hill shot it two nights ago," he continued. "They said the fox was bothering a pen of rabbits they kept for the kids. They said he acted funny, as if he wasn't afraid of people. They were afraid he might be rabid, so they called me."

"No, he wasn't afraid of people," I whispered, remembering how his thick, silky fur felt in my fingers.

"He wasn't rabid," I added, as an afterthought, thinking that this was the ultimate irony. From babyhood to death, Mapuche's life had revolved around rabies. He had never had it; yet the disease had meant his original capture and his ultimate demise.

The trooper stood quietly, noting the tears in my eyes. "Look," he said, "I had to have an examination made for rabies. That is why I couldn't bring his body; only the pelt."

He stopped for a moment, then painfully went on, "The fox was so beautiful."

My brain whirled. I was both revulsed and grateful. Part of me wanted the fox gone forever so that my grief would be short-lived. And part of me now understood how some people can keep the furs of departed animals. It is an attempt to keep and cherish certain characteristics of the animal which they once loved or admired. I wanted part of Mapuche at the cabin with me. Blinded by tears, I accepted the skin.

Mapuche's pelt now hangs beside my desk. His tail trails over the arm of my chair. From time to time I reach up and run my fingers through the silvery, glossy fur. It's almost as if he's still there, except his faintly pungent fox smell and those wild amber eyes no longer greet my senses.

What Do You Think?

1. The author mentions Mapuche's "invincible eyes." What does "invincible" mean? What do the words "invincible eyes" tell you about Mapuche?
2. Why did Mapuche behave differently after the author stopped wearing gloves?
3. Why did the author try to free Mapuche gradually, rather than just letting him loose as soon as he was in the woods?
4. Why wasn't Mapuche afraid of people? Was this fearlessness good or bad for him?
5. How did the state trooper feel about Mapuche's death?
6. When the trooper gave her Mapuche's pelt, the author felt both "revulsed and grateful" at the same time. Why did she feel these two different ways?

Taking a Closer Look

1. How did the author describe the fox's appearance when she first saw him?
2. Where did the name Mapuche come from?
3. What had happened to Mapuche when he was tiny?
4. How did the author try to train Mapuche to fend for himself?
5. Why did the people shoot Mapuche?
6. What happened to Mapuche's pelt?

Putting Ideas to Work

Did the author do a good thing when she made a pet of Mapuche? Decide how you feel about this, and give your reasons for feeling as you do.

TRAINING FOR THE WILDLIFE

Charles A. Eastman

Courses in grizzly, moose, and wildcat were the curriculum for Charles Eastman (Hakadah), a member of the Sioux tribe.

It seems to be a popular idea that all the characteristic skill of the American Indian is instinctive and hereditary. This is a mistake. All the stoicism and patience of the Indian are acquired traits. Continual practice alone makes the Indian master of the art of woodcraft. Physical training and dieting were not neglected. I remember that I was not allowed to have soup or warm drink. The soup was for the old ones. General rules for the young were never to take their food very hot, nor to drink much water.

My uncle educated me up to the age of fifteen years. He was a strict disciplinarian and a good teacher. When I left the teepee in the morning, he would say: "Hakadah, look closely to everything you see." At evening, on my return, he used often to catechize me for an hour.

"On which side of the trees is the lighter-colored bark? On which side do they have the most regular branches?"

It was his custom to let me name all the new birds that I had seen during the day. I would name them according to the color or the shape of the bill or their song or the appearance and locality of the nest—in fact, anything about the bird that impressed me as characteristic. I made many ridiculous errors I must admit. He then usually informed me of the correct name. Occasionally I made a hit and this he would warmly commend.

He went much deeper into this science when I was a little older, that is, about the age of eight or nine years. He would say, for instance:

"How do you know that there are fish in yonder lake?"

"Because they jump out of the water for flies at mid-day."

He would smile at my prompt but superficial reply.

"What do you think of the little pebbles grouped together under the shallow water? And what made the pretty curved marks in the sandy bottom and the little sandbanks? Where do you find the fish-eating birds? Have the inlet and the outlet of a lake anything to do with the question?"

He did not expect a correct reply at once to all his voluminous questions. He meant to make me observant and a good student of nature.

"Hakadah," he would say to me, "you ought to follow the example of the wolf. Even when the wolf is surprised and runs for its life, it will pause to take one more look at you before it enters its final retreat. So you must take a second look at everything you see.

"It is better to view animals unobserved. I have been a witness to their courtships and their quarrels. I have learned many of their secrets in this way. I was once the unseen spectator of a thrilling battle between a pair of grizzly bears and three buffaloes. It was a rash act for the bears, for it was in the moon of strawberries, when the buffaloes sharpen and polish their horns for bloody contests among themselves.

"I advise you, my boy, never to approach a grizzly's den from the front. Steal up behind and throw your blanket or a stone in front of the hole. The grizzly does not usually rush for it, but first puts its head out and listens. Then it comes out very indifferently and sits on its haunches on the mound in front of the hole before it makes any attack. While the grizzly is exposed in this fashion, aim at its heart. Always be

as cool as the animal." Thus he armed me against the cunning of savage beasts by teaching me how to outwit them.

"In hunting," he would resume, "you will be guided by the habits of the animal you seek. Remember that a moose stays in swampy or low land or between high mountains near a spring or lake, for thirty to sixty days at a time. Most large game moves about continually, except the doe in the spring. It is then a very easy matter to find her with the fawn. Conceal yourself in a convenient place as soon as you observe any signs of the presence of either. Then call with your birch doe-caller.

"Whichever one hears you first will soon appear in your neighborhood. But you must be very watchful, or you may be made a fawn of by a large wildcat. They understand the characteristic call of the doe perfectly well.

"When you have any difficulty with a bear or a wildcat—that is, if the creature shows signs of attacking you—you must make it fully understand that you have seen it and are aware of its intentions. If you are not well equipped for a pitched battle, the only way to make the animal retreat is to take a long sharp-pointed pole for a spear and rush toward it. No wild beast will face this unless it is cornered and already wounded. These fierce beasts are generally afraid of the common weapon of the larger

146

animals—the horns. If these are very long and sharp, they dare not risk an open fight.

"There is one exception to this rule—the grey wolf will attack fiercely when very hungry. But their courage depends upon their numbers. One wolf or two will never attack a person. They will stampede a herd of buffaloes in order to get at the calves. They will rush upon a herd of antelopes, for these are helpless. But they are always careful about attacking people."

Of this nature were the instructions of my uncle. He was widely known at that time as among the greatest of hunters of his tribe.

All boys were expected to endure hardship without complaint. In warfare, a young man must, of course, be an athlete and used to undergoing all sorts of privations. He must be able to go without food and water for two or three days without displaying any weakness. He must be able to run for a day and a night without any rest. He must be able to traverse a pathless and wild country without losing his way either in the day or nighttime. He cannot refuse to do any of these things if he aspires to be a warrior.

Sometimes my uncle would waken me very early in the morning and challenge me to fast with him all day. I had to accept the challenge. We blackened our faces with charcoal, so that every child in the village would know that I was fasting for the day. Then the little children would make my life a misery until the merciful sun hid behind the western hills.

I can scarcely recall the time when my stern teacher began to give sudden war whoops over my head in the morning while I was sound asleep. He expected me to leap up with perfect presence of mind, always ready to grasp a weapon of some sort and to give a shrill whoop in reply. If I was sleepy or startled and hardly knew what I was about, he would ridicule me and say that I need never expect to sell my life dear. Often he would vary these tactics by shooting off his gun just outside of the lodge while I was yet asleep. At the same time, he would give bloodcurdling yells. After a time I became used to this.

When the Sioux went upon the warpath, it was their custom to try the new warriors thoroughly before coming to an engagement. For instance, when they were near a hostile camp, they would select the novices to go after the water and make them do all sorts of things to prove their courage. In accordance with this idea, my uncle used to send me after water when we camped after dark in a strange place. Perhaps the country was full of wild beasts, and, for all I knew, there might be scouts from hostile tribes lurking in the neighborhood.

Yet I never objected, for that would show cowardice. I picked my way through the woods, dipped my pail in the water, and hurried back, always careful to make as little noise as a cat. Because I was only a boy, my heart would leap at every crackling of a dry twig or distant hooting of an owl, until, at last, I reached our teepee. Then my uncle would perhaps say: "Ah, Hakadah, you are a thorough warrior," empty out the precious contents of the pail, and order me to go a second time.

Imagine how I felt! But I wished to be brave. Silently I would take the pail and endeavor to retrace my footsteps in the dark.

With all this, our manners and morals were not neglected. I was made to respect the adults and especially the aged. I was not allowed to join in their discussions, nor even to speak in their presence, unless requested to do so. Sioux etiquette was very strict. Among the requirements was that of avoiding the direct address. A term of relationship or some title of courtesy was commonly used instead of the personal name by those who wished to show respect. We were taught generosity to the poor and reverence for the "Great Mystery." Religion was the basis of all Sioux training.

I recall to the present day some of the kind warnings and reproofs that my good grandmother was wont to give me. "Be strong of heart—be patient!" she used to say.

In the old days, if a youth should seek a wife before he had reached the age of twenty-two or twenty-three, and been recognized as a brave man, he was sneered at and considered an ill-bred Sioux. He must also be a skillful hunter. He cannot be a good husband unless he brings home plenty of game.

These precepts were in the line of our training for the wildlife.

What Do You Think?

1. How did Hakadah's uncle teach him to be a good observer?
2. Why must a hunter know how animals behave? Use an example from this selection to support your explanation.
3. Why are bears and wildcats frightened of sharp-pointed poles?
4. When his uncle dumped the water that Hakadah had found, how did Hakadah feel?
5. The author says that his uncle was a good teacher. Do you agree? Why or why not?
6. What kind of people did the Sioux expect their children to grow up to become?

Taking a Closer Look

1. What things was young Hakadah trained to notice about birds?
2. What is the best way for a hunter to approach a grizzly bear's den?
3. Under what conditions will wolves attack humans?
4. How did Hakadah learn to go without food for a long time?
5. How did the Sioux test the courage of young warriors?
6. How were Sioux children expected to behave toward older people?

Putting Ideas to Work

Imagine that Hakadah will be spending time with you at your home and school. Write an explanation to him about how your education prepares you for your adulthood.

Reading Clothing Tags

Fur or feathers are the complete, lifetime wardrobe for some creatures. People, however, have to buy clothes, and clothing can be expensive. If you understand the clothing-tag information before you buy, you can get the value.

Before buying clothing, check the garment-care instructions. These are usually found on a cloth tag sewn into a seam. Knowing how to care for clothing is essential, and the care can be very costly. Don't buy a garment that does not give you clear cleaning information.

You're "Tagged" to Make the Decision

Your family is planning to vacation in a wintry climate. Everyone needs a quilted vest to wear. The local sports shop offers two kinds. Compare the two garment-care tags shown here. Each tag gives the vest's fabric content and cleaning instructions. Each also tells where the vest was made.

Consider all of the following circumstances before buying. Then, in each case, which vest product would you choose—*Cold-Snapper Chillywear* or *Feather Fancy*?

1. Your father is allergic to feather products.

2. The family will be camping in the Great Smoky Mountains National Park where the temperature rarely goes below freezing (32°F, 0°C).

3. Your sister Beth is going backpacking in Alaska next winter. She plans to use the vest in that colder climate. Beth has no allergies.

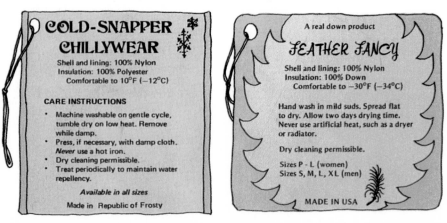

COLD-SNAPPER CHILLYWEAR

Shell and lining: 100% Nylon
Insulation: 100% Polyester
Comfortable to 10°F (−12°C)

CARE INSTRUCTIONS

- Machine washable on gentle cycle, tumble dry on low heat. Remove while damp.
- Press, if necessary, with damp cloth. *Never* use a hot iron.
- Dry cleaning permissible.
- Treat periodically to maintain water repellency.

Available in all sizes

Made in Republic of Frosty

A real down product

FEATHER FANCY

Shell and lining: 100% Nylon
Insulation: 100% Down
Comfortable to −30°F (−34°C)

Hand wash in mild suds. Spread flat to dry. Allow two days drying time. Never use artificial heat, such as a dryer or radiator.

Dry cleaning permissible.

Sizes P - L (women)
Sizes S, M, L, XL (men)

MADE IN USA

4. Dry cleaning is expensive. Also, if needed, neither a laundromat nor a dry cleaner will be within easy reach during the vacation.

5. The only time laundry will be done during your vacation is at Cousin Eldon's home. The family will make a four-day stopover.

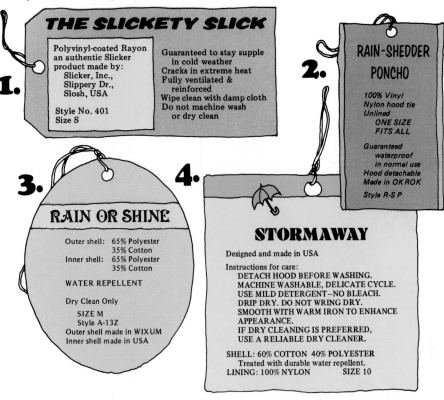

1. THE SLICKETY SLICK

Polyvinyl-coated Rayon
an authentic Slicker
product made by:
Slicker, Inc.,
Slippery Dr.,
Slosh, USA

Style No. 401
Size S

Guaranteed to stay supple
in cold weather
Cracks in extreme heat
Fully ventilated &
reinforced
Wipe clean with damp cloth
Do not machine wash
or dry clean

2. RAIN-SHEDDER PONCHO

100% Vinyl
Nylon hood tie
Unlined
ONE SIZE
FITS ALL

Guaranteed
waterproof
in normal use
Hood detachable
Made in OK ROK

Style R-S P

3. RAIN OR SHINE

Outer shell: 65% Polyester
35% Cotton
Inner shell: 65% Polyester
35% Cotton

WATER REPELLENT

Dry Clean Only

SIZE M
Style A-13Z
Outer shell made in WIXUM
Inner shell made in USA

4. STORMAWAY

Designed and made in USA

Instructions for care:
DETACH HOOD BEFORE WASHING.
MACHINE WASHABLE, DELICATE CYCLE.
USE MILD DETERGENT—NO BLEACH.
DRIP DRY. DO NOT WRING DRY.
SMOOTH WITH WARM IRON TO ENHANCE
APPEARANCE.
IF DRY CLEANING IS PREFERRED,
USE A RELIABLE DRY CLEANER.

SHELL: 60% COTTON 40% POLYESTER
Treated with durable water repellent.
LINING: 100% NYLON   SIZE 10

The Sky Is Crying, but the Family Is Dry and Smiling

Now the family needs new rainwear. So, here you are looking at tags again. The four styles shown here interest you.

6. If you prefer cotton-blend fabrics, which two will you choose?

7. Which one sounds the easiest and least expensive to keep clean?

8. When hiking, your sister Beth needs a way to protect both herself and her backpack from rain. Which garment would you choose for these reasons?

9. The Slickety Slick tag mentions being "fully ventilated." What problem might there be with such a garment?

10. What other unusual features are mentioned on the Slickety Slick tag?

FRIENDS AND ENEMIES

To leave an elephant to babysit a human child may not seem like a good idea. But Karim had no choice.

Circle in the Dust

Norah Burke

To his keeper, Karim,[1] Gajpati[2] was the biggest, best and most intelligent elephant in all Asia. He belonged to India's Forest Department and was employed in the Himalayan[3] foothills as a shikar[4] (hunting) elephant; he could penetrate the jungle like no other animal.

[1] Karim (kə rēm′)
[2] Gajpati (gäzh pä′ tē)
[3] Himalayan (him′ ə lā′ ən)
[4] shikar (shē kär′)

Gajpati stood ten feet tall and weighed more than four tons. His legs were like trees—his tracks 20 inches across—and he had more than once stamped a bear to a pulp. Yet Gajpati was a gentle animal. He was especially so with Karim, whom Gajpati loved with unselfish devotion, and with Karim's infant son. If the elephant was doing nothing when Karim's wife had water to fetch, or dinner to cook, either she or Karim would draw a circle in the dust in front of the tethered animal, and put the baby into it.

"Keep him inside there, O Prince of Elephants," they would order the big tusker, who gently restrained the child if he tried to crawl away.

One afternoon when they were camped near the Rapti River, Karim's wife took a big earthen jar and went off toward the river to fill it. After a while, when she failed to return, Karim shouted in the direction she had taken. But there was no reply. At his yell, every jungle sound had stopped except the roar of the river.

Quite suddenly Karim, with his heel, marked a circle in front of the elephant and put the baby into it.

"Look after him, Gajpati!"

He ran full speed to see what had happened to his wife.

Under Gajpati's trunk, next to his immense toenails, the baby lay and laughed up at the elephant. The infant could do as he liked, but each time he tried to crawl out of the circle he was picked up and put back in again. Gajpati scooped up some dust with his trunk and blew it over himself. Sometimes he flicked a little dirt over the baby, to discourage flies. And sometimes drops of green spit fell from Gajpati's pointed underlip onto the baby's tummy and tickled him. They were perfectly content together, these two. Here, inside the cool shade of the huge wild-mango tree to which Gajpati was tethered, time meant nothing.

Suddenly the sun was gone, drawing over it a sky of velvet and diamonds. Immediately, the air was colder, and the baby began to cry. Jackals howled in the dusk, and there came the whoop of an eagle owl.

Not far away, in the rough grassland, a male hyena

emerged from his burrow and stood silently sniffing the night air for news of food. He was a scavenger of carrion and an eater of skeletons. He would pick up any small, helpless creature he might find. In India, hyenas take human children every year.

His mate and an almost full-grown young hyena came out of the den too. When they heard the baby crying, these bold and loathsome beasts, with their powerful crushing teeth, trotted off in that direction.

In camp, Gajpati was beginning to be agitated about the child. He realized that something was the matter, but what? He offered the baby a mouthful of leaves, and fanned him. It was no good. He put up his trunk and trumpeted for the owners of this baby to come back and do something.

They did not appear.

Gajpati scented the hyenas. He froze, and felt the breeze with his trunk to find out more.

There were three of them, out of sight, but quite close. Gajpati gathered the baby closer to his feet and squealed a threat.

An elephant's sense of smell is acute, but his vision poor. It was not till the hyenas were in the camp that Gajpati saw them and the sight made him range angrily, straining the chain that bound him. The elephant grumbled and blew.

The hyenas were nonplused. One sat down out of reach and fixed its nocturnal eyes on the child, while the others began to circle around behind.

In sudden exasperation, the elephant put his forehead against the mango tree and braced the whole of his giant strength against it to break it down. He did not succeed, but the tree groaned at the roots.

Gajpati swung back and made for the sitting hyena, which sprang smartly away.

The hyenas behind him darted at the baby, so he wheeled toward them instead. They jumped out of reach.

He attacked the tree again and it shrieked as he strove against it. Now the baby was yelling at the top of his lungs, and blindly trying to crawl away; so Gajpati gave up. He

backed up, shook his head, and gathered the baby to him.

Changing his tactics, he stood perfectly still, close to the now leaning tree, and watched.

The hyenas were hungry, bold, and began to close in.

They were watching the elephant with respect, but they did not allow for the slack of the chain.

Gajpati struck like lightning and in a moment got one hyena under his forefeet. Almost at once the struggle was over, the body stamped to a pulp. With a squeal of triumph and rage, Gajpati threw the carcass aside.

It scattered the others, who made off, leaving elephant and baby in peace for an hour or two.

Pillowed in dust and exhausted by hunger, the baby lay half sleeping, half sobbing, and sucked at the stub of sugar cane that Gajpati offered him. Then, warmed by the elephant's sweet breath, he slept. A little after midnight, Gajpati dozed too.

Presently, the baby stirred, sat up, and began to crawl away.

He was already out of reach when the elephant woke.

In the gray of early morning, Gajpati saw the hyenas coming back, and the baby several yards away.

He forged out to the full length of his range. Iron links bit into his flesh and blood poured down.

The hyenas saw their chance and darted in.

At the same moment, the great tree gave and smashed down upon elephant and baby together. Breaking branches and rushing leaves covered them both.

The violence sent the hyenas off in a flash, and they did not return.

When Karim and his wife ran gasping into camp, they saw only the fallen tree and Gajpati under it.

Their baby?

They tore their way into the leaves and branches, where beneath it all, the child lay sleeping in the curl of the elephant's trunk. His mother, in tears, snatched him up. He was very dirty and scratched, but whole.

And Gajpati?

"Fool! Traitor!" raged Karim. "So! Was the baby nothing to thee, that thou wouldst break loose and leave him?"

He took his ax and began to free the elephant, watched by his wife, who stood with her son in her arms and trembled still after her night's adventures.

To have dropped her water jar into deep rapids had been bad enough. Then, as she tried to recover it, to be swept downstream had been a nightmare. Karim had raced off downriver to look for her, but was overtaken by night and lost in the jungle. At dawn they had found each other as both rushed home to the child.

Now, panting and grunting, Karim cleared away the branches and undid Gajpati's chain.

"He will die of his injuries," choked the woman.

But the elephant got his front feet onto the ground and heaved free of the last branches. He was up, bruised, bleeding, and shaking.

"Thou worthless traitor!" Karim told the animal bitterly.

The big elephant stood and sucked his trunk in shame and remorse for wrongdoing.

"Look!" gasped the woman.

Where Gajpati had heaved himself free of branches, these had parted to disclose the body of the hyena, and hyena tracks were everywhere. Karim and his wife read the story: Gajpati was no traitor.

During the months of night, fifty degrees below zero, her cubs would be born. The great task of motherhood was already begun, the time soon coming when she would bury herself deep down under the snow to give birth. From then until the day when she and the cubs burrowed up into daylight again, she would not eat. She and they must live on what she had stored in her body during the summer, and on what she could catch and eat now. She must finish fattening herself up for the event, and there was not much time left.

At the moment she was hunting along the edge of the ice, because where there was water there were seals, also fish, and the chance of a porpoise or walrus. As winter encased the roots and berries and lichen and seaweed of the polar islands in glass, the bears moved to the ice-edge for their food.

This was the arctic region, the area north of the limit of tree growth. The shores of Greenland, Siberia, Alaska, Canada bordered upon this spectral sea. It was a landscape of snow and old ice and new ice, of drifting pack ice, and berg ice from glaciers, all in constant motion, lanes and pools of pure cobalt looking-glass, opening and closing all the time in the pack. Where the old ice had been pushed up together in terraces, ice-eaves burned green and lilac underneath. In summer the skuas and ivory gulls and other birds made the air raucous with quarrels, but now all that

Polar Night

Norah Burke

As the hot arctic summer drew to a close, till the magenta sun only slid along the horizon to sink again at once, the polar bear knew that a hard time lay ahead for her.

the bear could hear was the wash of blue water against grinding ice.

Under the dark sky, on the white land, in the desolation of the arctic landscape, she was part of its white power, moving with a long swinging walk and huge flat yellow hairy snowman footfalls. Strong and dangerous, the largest of bears, able to swim forty miles out to sea if need be, she stalked her kingdom in which no natural enemy challenged her reign. Her feet, bristled underneath to give grip on the ice, carried her huge weight with a light and silent tread; while the low swinging head searched the ice all the time for food.

She was not clearly aware of what was happening in her body, but the instinct was there to love the unborn cubs, to prepare for them and protect them; she did not risk her body in careless adventures as she would at other times.

But food? Food—

Already the iron of winter was in the clean cold air, though she felt the cold only with her eyes and black nose and black lips, where the air stung her, and on the long pinkish gray tongue, moving all the time to prevent freezing, that slung in and out of her mouth among the large cruel teeth.

Suddenly, away down the ice-field, where a dark blue lead showed in the pack, she saw a blackish slug on the ice—a seal. It was essential to catch him. In a moment she had decided on her approach, and slipped silently into the water to cut off his line of retreat. The ice rocked as her great weight left it.

The bear was as much at home in the water as on land—buoyant, swimming like a dog, but on top or submerged—and the water much warmer than the air on her face. Not wet, either. Inside the layer of fat and the shaggy oily watertight coat, she felt as dry as on land.

By a series of cunning dives and approaches, and keeping under the shoulder of ice, she got near to the seal. Breathing carefully, every nerve keyed to the task of silent approach, ready to spring—to dive—to slaughter, she slid nearer—nearer—

Suddenly the seal saw her. Terror convulsed his face. A moment of awful indecision—whether to plunge into the sea, his natural line of escape, and perhaps fall straight into her jaws, or to struggle across the ice to that other hole—

He swung away from her, lumbering madly along. The bear lunged up out of the water, on to the ice, on to the terrified seal.

The water slushed off her everywhere like a tidal wave. There was a flurry of snow and water and fighting seal. His quick struggling body flapped under her as she slew him. Blood spurted on to the snow.

When the seal was dead, the bear attended first to herself, getting rid of the wet from her coat before it could freeze, although oil had kept off the frost so far. She shook, and the drops flew off in rainbows in all directions. She rolled and nosed along in the snow, wiping her flanks, her chin, and soon all was dry. A few hairs crisped up and stuck to each other with frost.

Now for the seal. She ripped up the body, turning back the skin and blubber, letting out a cloud of steam, and ate greedily of hot crimson meat. Seal meat was her favorite, full of flavor, a hot meal, not like the white icy flakes of cod.

Then, although the bear had no natural enemies, she stopped suddenly as she ate, lifted her head, looked, listened, scented. Blood dripped from her chin on to the snow.

There was nothing.

All the same she trusted her instinct and, leaving the rest of the meal, slipped into the water, where she could keep her unborn cubs safe, where it was warmer, and easier to move.

Presently she saw upright seals coming along the shore. They were rather rare creatures, these, and dangerous for all they were so weak. The places where they lived had light and noise, and smelled full of good food. The she-bear often drew near the places, attracted by those smells. These land-seals were not like the sea-seals. They wore seal fur, and their skins were rubbed with seal blubber, but there was a different taste inside.

They in their turn hunted bear, as

the she-bear knew well. She had sometimes found the place of the kill, and seen the white empty skins hanging up by the camps, smelled the dark red gamy flesh cooking.

Now as she watched the approaching men, she considered whether to kill them, but the unborn life in her said get away. So she dived and swam and melted out of their radius.

In the next few days the bear gorged on fish and seal. No longer the hot rocks and scree of summer gave forth good-tasting moss and lichens or the sharp-fleshed berries and sweet roots. She dived into the cold blue ocean for her food.

But now the arctic day was over. In the pink twilight a snowy owl was flitting silently across the waste, moving south and south as life was squeezed out of the arctic desert by the polar night.

Then came the freezing of the sea. Crystals formed below the surface and rose, and needles of ice shot across from one to another, joining them together, thickening, hardening, adding more ice to the floes already many years old. The ice talked, grinding its teeth, sending out every now and then a singing crack. Curtains of colored flame rippled in the sky. The polar night began.

Now the real cold came. Now the food disappeared, and old male bears grew lean and savage.

The she-bear chose her den.

There was a great raw range of decayed ice that had been pushed up into mountains whose hollows were packed with snow. Icicles yards long hung on the south side from the summer, and behind this curtain of ice she found a great purple cave, carved in diamond and full of snow.

This was the place.

Her body was ready now for the ordeal. Thick fat, gathered from seal and halibut, lined her skin.

She burrowed down into the violet snow on the floor of the cave. It was so light that the wind blew it about like feathers, and she could breathe in it. She burrowed deeper and deeper, while the snow sifted and fell in soundlessly behind her, till presently she was deep enough.

She curled and rolled herself round and round, pushing the snow, packing it, shaping the den. All the sides of it melted with her heat, then froze again into slippery walls. And the hot breath passed up through the way she had dug, melting the sides of the channel which also froze again and left a tube which would supply her with air until she came up in the spring.

Inside the snow and ice—inside her thick oily fur and the layer of blubber, she was warm, full fed and sleepy. She slept and waited.

In the fullness of time, the first familiar pang of birth trembled in her stomach. Pain fluttered like a butterfly and was gone.

She stirred, lifted her head, rearranged herself.

It came again, stronger, longer. She moved uneasily.

Then in long strong accomplishing strokes it was there—hard, forcing, contracting, out of her control. Moving to a crescendo. She grunted, tensed all her muscles, pressed and gasped. Another spasm, and on the smooth strong river of pain, she felt the first cub come out.

A wave of relief relaxed her.

There he lay mewing, so wet and tiny, hardly alive, and she nuzzled him delightedly, starting to clean him up.

But now another spasm—the same long final one as before, though easier—and the second cub was born.

It was over now. She felt the diminishing contractions, the subsidence of pain, pulsing quieter.

Now to clean them up. She licked and licked them, turning them over, rolling and caressing them; then life strengthened in them as they dried, as they fed. She lay in bliss, feeling her own life flowing from her heart.

Meanwhile in the world above, the sun had returned, first a green glow, then a rosy one, then touching the topmost peaks, days before the first sunrise.

Deep in the snow cave, the bear knew it as the snow grew luminous with the light pressing through.

One day she heard voices. The snow vibrated with footsteps, the ice ceiling cracked.

She rose, shook herself free of the cubs and stood ready in case the land-seals saw the warm yellow air hole that marked her den—in case one of them walked over her and fell in . . . .

She stood fierce, lean, ready, to defend her cubs, her heart pounding hot and loud as fever in her thin body.

Gradually the voices and the footsteps died away.

Presently it was time to come out into the world again. The cubs' eyes were open, their coats grown; they were walking, getting stronger every day. Now they must come out and face the world and swim and fight and catch seals. There was everything to teach them, and while they were still learning—still babies, they had to be kept safe and fed. All this she had to do alone. Other years she'd had a mate to help her, but this time he was gone— lost— Those white skins hanging by the camps—

She began to tear her way out, the giant paws and black nails breaking open the ice walls of their den. The ice gave, snow fell in.

They climbed out.

Clean frozen air, dazzling with sun, hit them like the stroke of an axe. Light entered the brain in needles through the eyes. Only gradually, as the pupils contracted, did it become possible to see.

Under an iridescent sun-halo, the arctic landscape blazed white and navy blue. Everything hit them at once—light, noise, wind—the blast of a new world.

Down there was the water—

The mother bear plunged joyfully into the buoyant cleanness. All the dirt and staleness of winter were washed away. It was like flight. She plunged and rose and shook and plunged again in sheer joy. So fresh, so clean, the salt cold water running through her teeth—

Then she resumed the heavy duties of parenthood, turned to the cubs. They were sitting on the edge, squeaking with fright, and she began urging them to come in. They kept feeling forward, then scrambling back. Suddenly one ventured too far down the ice, and slithered, shrieking, into the sea, where he bobbed up again like a cork.

His brother, seeing this, plucked up courage and plunged in too, in one desperate baby-jump, landing with a painful *smack!* and blinking in the spray.

They found they could swim.

Presently she pushed them up on to the ice again where they shook and dried, and the next thing was food. She left them while she killed a seal, and the three of them ate it.

After that there were lessons, how to fish, how to kill. Living was thin at first, for three hunters cannot move as silently as one, but they got along.

Until the day when land-seals approached them unseen from behind an ice ridge. The first they knew of it was an explosion, and one cub gasped and doubled up as he was hit. The bears dived for the water, even the wounded little one. He managed to keep up with them, and his mother and brother would die rather than desert him.

They all swam on, but slowly— slowly. Both cubs were still so small and *slow,* and they must hurry—

Blood ran in the sapphire water.

Other shots spattered beside them.

Anxiety roared in the she-bear's blood. Her heart was bursting. She pushed the cubs on, and turned to meet her enemies. Reared up on to the ice and galloped towards them, a charge that nothing could stop— not even death—if they'd stayed to face it, but they broke and ran.

The bear returned to her cubs.

The wounded one was sinking lower and lower in the water, breathing waves, and she managed to push him out at last on to distant ice. Then she licked him as he lay suffering in the snow, and his brother licked him too, whimpering with distress as he worked.

So that presently the blood stopped, and after a long time the suffering too. The cub sniffed the air. In the first real moment of recovery he consented to take food.

Pain went away from her heart.

Before them lay all the arctic lands, the snow in retreat. The floes, soft and friable from solar radiation, were being broken up by the waves. Plant life teemed in the water, the more open sea colored bright green by diatoms. Millions of wild flowers studded the rocky scree. There was everything to eat at once—lichen and moss and roots and halibut and seals. Salmon swam the green water, and cod. Seaweed washed round the rocks. On the land there were hares and young birds.

The summer gathered to almost tropical heat. Snow water dribbled into pools. Icicles glistened with wet, dropped, and broke like glass.

And the mother bear, in the snow, with her cubs did not know why she behaved as she did. There was pain and there was happiness, and these two things drove her according to unfathomable laws. When the summer ended, and the polar night began, she would do the same things over again, and her children after her.

What Do You Think?

1. What similarities can you find between the stories "Circle in the Dust" and "Polar Night"?
2. If the hyenas had not come, what other dangers do you think there may have been to Gajpati and the baby?
3. What lesson do you think Karim learned from this experience?
4. The author writes, "The big elephant stood and sucked his trunk in shame and remorse for wrongdoing." Do you think animals have feelings and thoughts like these? Explain your answer.
5. How does the use of color affect the story "Polar Night"? Give examples from the selection.
6. How do you think the bear knew that there was danger close by when she was eating the seal?
7. What do you think is probably the polar bear's greatest enemy? Explain your choice.

Taking a Closer Look

1. In the story "Circle in the Dust," what false conclusion did Karim come to when he returned to the camp? Why?
2. What tactics did Gajpati use in killing the first of the hyenas?
3. Why did the baby's mother and father not return till morning?
4. For what is the bear preparing at the beginning of the story "Polar Night"?
5. Why does the bear have to go to the sea for food in the winter?
6. This story is told from the bear's perspective. What things are described in "bear terms" and what are these things in "people terms"?
7. Explain in your own words the meaning of the image, "Life was squeezed out of the arctic desert by the polar night."

Putting Ideas to Work

Think of an incident you experienced or heard about which involved a time when an animal helped someone in an unusual way. Be ready to tell about that experience.

To Paint the Portrait of a Bird

Jacques Prevert, translated by Lawrence Ferlinghetti

First paint a cage
with an open door
then paint
something pretty
something simple
something beautiful
something useful
for the bird
then place the canvas against a tree
in a garden
in a wood
or in a forest
hide behind the tree
without speaking
without moving
Sometimes the bird comes quickly
but he can just as well spend
    long years before deciding
Don't get discouraged
wait
wait years if necessary
the swiftness or slowness of
    the coming
of the bird having no rapport
with the success of the picture
When the bird comes
if he comes

observe the most profound silence
wait till the bird enters the cage
and when he has entered
gently close the door with a brush
then
paint out all the bars one by one
taking care not to touch any of
    the feathers of the bird
Then paint the portrait of the tree
choosing the most beautiful of
    its branches
for the bird
paint also the green foliage and
    the wind's freshness
the dust of the sun
and the noise of insects in
    the summer heat
and then wait for the bird to begin
    to sing
If the bird doesn't sing
it's a bad sign
a sign that the painting is bad
but if he sings it's a good sign
a sign that you can sign
So then very gently you pull out
one of the feathers of the bird
and you write your name in
    a corner of the picture.

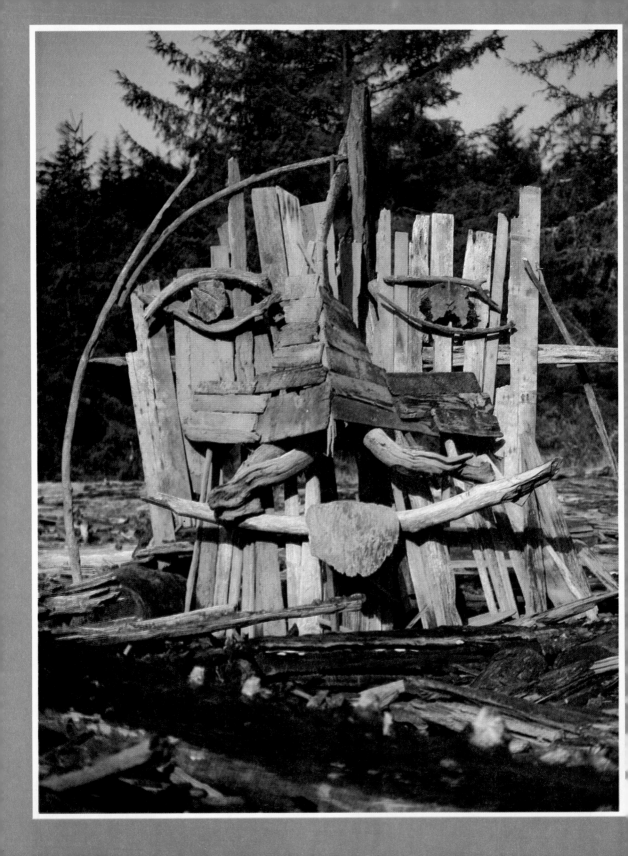

WHAT'S SO FUNNY?

Everyone likes to laugh. As you read this unit, you'll find many ways that authors create humor. So sit back and get ready to smile, to snicker, to laugh.

The Rhinoceros

The rhino is a homely beast,
For human eyes he's not a feast.
Farewell, farewell, you old rhinoceros,
I'll stare at something less prepoceros.

The Germ

A mighty creature is the germ,
Though smaller than the pachyderm.
His customary dwelling place
Is deep within the human race.
His childish pride he often pleases
By giving people strange diseases.
Do you, my poppet, feel infirm?
You probably contain a germ.

The Shrew

Strange as it seems, the smallest mammal
Is the shrew, and not the camel.
And that is all I ever knew,
Or wish to know, about the shrew.

Poems by Ogden Nash

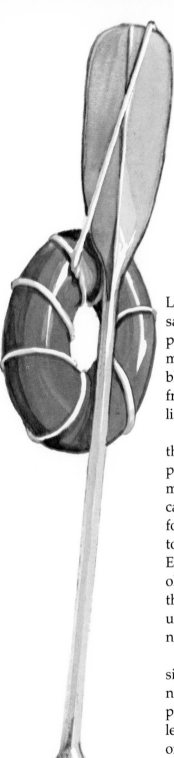

The Guinea Pig

Ruth McKenney

A guinea pig is a furry little animal.
But the term is also used to describe a person
who is being used to try something out on. How
is Ruth McKenney a guinea pig in this story?

I was nearly drowned, in my youth, by a Red Cross Lifesaving Examiner, and I once suffered, in the noble cause of saving human life from a watery grave, a black eye which was a perfect daisy and embarrassed me for days. Looking back on my agonies, I feel that none of my sacrifices, especially the black eye, was in the least worthwhile. Indeed, to be brutally frank about it, I feel that the whole modern school of scientific lifesaving is a lot of hogwash.

Of course, I've had rather bad luck with lifesavers, right from the beginning. Long before I ever had any dealings with professional lifesavers my sister nearly drowned me, quite by mistake. My father once took us to a northern Michigan fishing camp, where we found the life very dull. He used to go fishing for bass on our little lake all day long, and at night come home to our lodge, dead-beat and minus any bass. In the meantime Eileen and I, who were nine and ten at the time, used to take an old rowboat out to a shallow section of the lake and, sitting in the hot sun, feed worms to an unexciting variety of small, undernourished fish called gillies. We hated the whole business.

Father, however, loved to fish, even if he didn't catch a single fish in three weeks, which on this trip he didn't. One night, however, he carried his enthusiasm beyond a decent pitch. He decided to go bass fishing after dark, and rather than leave us alone in the lodge and up to who knows what, he ordered us to take our boat and row along after him.

Eileen and I were very bored rowing around in the dark, and finally, in desperation, we began to stand up and rock the boat, which resulted, at last, in my falling into the lake with a mighty splash.

When I came up, choking and mad as anything, Eileen saw me struggling, and, as she always says with a catch in her voice, she only meant to help me. Good intentions, however, are of little importance in a situation like that. For she grabbed an oar out of the lock, and with an uncertain gesture hit me square on the chin.

I went down with a howl of pain. Eileen, who could not see much in the darkness, was now really frightened. The cold water revived me after the blow and I came to the surface, considerably weakened but still able to swim over to the boat. Whereupon Eileen, in a noble attempt to give me the oar to grab, raised it once again, and socked me square on the top of the head. I went down again, this time without a murmur, and my last thought was a vague wonder that my own sister should want to murder me with a rowboat oar.

As for Eileen, she heard the dull impact of the oar on my head and saw the shadowy figure of her sister disappear. So she jumped in the lake, screeching furiously, and began to flail around in the water, howling for help and looking for me. At this point I came to the surface and swam over to the boat, with the intention of tipping it over.

Father, rowing hard, arrived just in time to pull us both out of the water and prevent me from attacking Eileen with the rowboat anchor. The worst part about the whole thing, as far as I was concerned, was that Eileen was considered a hero and Father told everybody in the lake community that she had saved my life. Her name was put in for a medal.

After what I suffered from amateur lifesaving, I should have known enough to avoid even the slightest contact with the professional variety of water mercy. I learned too late that being socked with an oar is as nothing compared to what the professional lifesavers can think up.

From the very beginning of that awful lifesaving course I took the last season I went to a girls' camp, I was a marked woman. The rest of the lifesavers were little, slender girls, but I was monstrously big for my fourteen years. I approximated, in poundage anyway, the average adult we energetic young lifesavers were scheduled to rescue, and so I was, for the teacher's purpose, the perfect guinea pig.

The first few days of the course were unpleasant for me, but not terribly dangerous. The elementary lifesaving hold, in case you haven't seen some hapless victim being rescued by our brave beach guardians, is a snakelike arrangement for supporting the drowning citizen with one hand while you paddle in to shore with the other. You are supposed to wrap your arm around the person's neck and shoulders, and keep the head well above water by resting it on your collarbone.

This is all very well in theory, of course, but the trick that none of Miss Folgil's little pupils could master was keeping the victim's nose and mouth above the waterline. Time and again I was held in a viselike grip by one of the earnest students with my whole face an inch or two under the billowing waves.

"No, no, Betsy," Miss Folgil would scream through her megaphone, as I felt the water rush into my lungs. "No, no, you must keep the head a little higher." At this point I would begin to kick and struggle, and generally the pupil would have to let go while I came up for air. Miss Folgil was always very stern with me.

"Ruth," she would shriek from her boat, "I insist! You must allow Betsy to tow you all the way in. We come to Struggling in Lesson Six."

This was but the mere beginning, however. A few lessons later we came to the section of the course where we learned how to undress under water in forty seconds. Perhaps I should say we came to the point where the *rest* of the pupils learned how to get rid of shoes and such while holding their breaths. I never did.

There was quite a little ceremony connected with this part of the course. Miss Folgil, and some lucky creature named as timekeeper and armed with a stopwatch, rowed the prospective victim out to deep water. The pupil, dressed in high, laced tennis shoes, long jeans, and a sweat shirt, then stood poised at the end of the boat. When the timekeeper yelled "Go!" the future boon to humanity dived into the water and, while holding her breath under the surface, unlaced her shoes and stripped down to her bathing suit. Miss Folgil never explained what connection, if any, this curious exercise had with saving human lives.

I had no sweat shirt of my own, so I borrowed one of my sister's. My sister was a slender little thing and I was, as I said, robust, which puts it politely. Eileen had some trouble wedging me into that sweat shirt, and once in it I looked like a stuffed sausage. It never occurred to me how hard it was going to be to get that sweat shirt off, especially when it was wet and soggy.

As we rowed out for my ordeal by undressing, Miss Folgil was snappish and bored.

"Hurry up," she said, looking irritated. "Let's get this over with quick. I don't think you're ready to pass the test, anyway."

I was good and mad when I jumped off the boat, and determined to make good and show that old Miss Folgil, whom I was beginning to dislike thoroughly. As soon as I was under water, I got my shoes off, and I had no trouble with the jeans. I was just beginning to run out of breath when I held up my arms and started to pull off the sweat shirt. I got it just past my neck so that my face was covered with heavy wet cotton, when it stuck.

I pulled frantically and my lungs started to burst. Finally I thought: Who needs this? Forget about the test and saving other people's lives, anyway. I came to the surface, a curious sight, my head enfolded in a water-soaked sweat shirt. I made a brief sound, a desperate glub-glub, a call for help. My arms were stuck in the shirt and I couldn't swim. I went down. I breathed in large quantities of water and cotton cloth.

I came up again, making final frantic appeals. Four feet away sat a professional lifesaver, paying absolutely no attention to somebody drowning right under her nose. I went down again, struggling with last panic-stricken feverishness, fighting water and a sweat shirt for my life. At this point the timekeeper pointed out to Miss Folgil that I had been under water for eighty-five seconds, which was quite a time for anybody. Miss Folgil was very annoyed, as she hated to get her bathing suit wet, but, a thoughtful teacher, she picked up her megaphone, shouted to the rest of the class on the beach to watch, and dived in after me.

If I say so myself, I gave her quite a time rescuing me. I presented a new and different problem, and probably am written up in textbooks now under the heading "What to Do When the Victim Is Entangled in a Tight Sweat Shirt." Miss Folgil finally towed my still-breathing body over to the boat, reached for her bowie knife, which she carried on a ring with her whistle, and cut Eileen's shirt straight up the front. Then she towed me with Hold No. 2 right in to the shore and delivered me up to the class for artificial respiration. I will never forgive the Red Cross for that terrible trip through the water, when I might have been hauled into the boat and rowed in except for Miss Folgil's overdeveloped sense of drama and pedagogy.

I tried to quit the lifesaving class after that, but the head councilor at the camp said I must keep on, to show that I was the kind of girl who always finished what she planned to do. Otherwise, she assured me, I would be a weak character and never amount to anything when I grew up.

So I stayed for Lesson 6: "Struggling." After that I didn't care if I never amounted to anything when I grew up. In fact, I hoped I wouldn't. It would serve everybody right, especially Miss Folgil. I came a little late to the class session that day and missed the discussion of theory, always held on the beach before the actual practice in the lake. That was just my hard luck. I was always a child of misfortune. I wonder that I survived my youth at all.

"We were waiting for you, Ruth," Miss Folgil chirped cheerily to me as I arrived, sullen and downcast, at the little group of earnest students sitting on the sand.

"What for?" I said cautiously. I was determined not to be a guinea pig any more. The last wave had washed over my helpless face.

"You swim out," Miss Folgil went on, ignoring my bad temper, "until you are in deep water—about twelve feet will do. Then you begin to flail around and shout for help. One of the students will swim out to you."

All of this sounded familiar and terrible. I had been doing that for days, and getting water in my nose for my pains.

"But when the student arrives," Miss Folgil went on, "you must not allow her to simply tow you away. You must struggle, just as hard as you can. You must try to clutch her by the head, you must try to twine your legs about her, and otherwise hamper her in trying to save you."

Now, *this* sounded like something. I was foolishly fired by the attractive thought of getting back at some of the fiends who had been ducking me in the name of science for the past two weeks. Unfortunately, I hadn't studied Chapter 9, entitled "How to Break Holds the Drowning Swimmer Uses." Worse, I hadn't heard Miss Folgil's lecture on "Be Firm with the Panic-Stricken Swimmer—Better a Few Bruises Than a Watery Grave." This last was Miss Folgil's own opinion, of course.

So I swam out to my doom, happy as a lark. Maybelle Anne Pettijohn, a tall, lean girl, was Miss Folgil's choice to rescue Exhibit A, the panic-stricken swimmer.

I laughed when I saw her coming. I thought I could clean up Maybelle Anne easily enough, but alas, I hadn't counted on Maybelle Anne's methodical approach to life. She had read Chapter 9 in our textbook, and she had listened carefully to Miss Folgil's inspiring words. Besides, Maybelle Anne was just naturally the kind of girl who ran around doing people dirty for their own good. "This may hurt your feelings," she used to say mournfully, "but I feel I have to tell you . . ."

When Maybelle Anne got near me, I enthusiastically lunged for her neck and hung on with both hands while getting her around her waist with my legs. Maybelle Anne thereupon dug her fingernails into my hands with ferocious force, and I let go and swam away, hurt and surprised. This was distinctly not playing fair.

"What's the idea?" I called out.

"It says to do that in the book," Maybelle Anne replied, treading water.

"Well, you lay off of that stuff," I said, angered, book or no book. Maybelle Anne was a Girl Scout, too, and I was shocked to think she'd go around using her fingernails in a fair fight.

"Come on, struggle," Maybelle Anne said, getting winded from treading water. I swam over, pretty reluctant and much more wary. Believe it or not, this time Maybelle Anne, who was two medals from being a Cadet or whatever it is Girl Scouts with a lot of medals get to be, bit me.

In addition to biting me, Maybelle Anne swung her arm around my neck, with the intention of towing me in to the shore. But I still had plenty of fight left and I had never been so mad in my life. I got Maybelle Anne under water two or three times, and I almost thought I had her when suddenly, to my earnest surprise, she hauled off and hit me as hard as she could, right in the eye. Then she towed me in, triumphant as anything.

Maybelle Anne afterward claimed it was all in the book, and she wouldn't even apologize for my black eye. Eileen and I fixed her, though. We put a little garter snake in her bed and scared the daylights out of her. Maybelle Anne was easy to scare anyway, and really a very disagreeable girl. I used to hope that she would come to a bad end, which, from my point of view, at least, she did. Maybelle Anne grew up to be a Regional Red Cross Lifesaving Examiner.

I'll bet she just loves her work.

What Do You Think?

1. In the first paragraph, the author clearly establishes her dislike of lifesaving training, yet she treats this serious subject with humor. What words or expressions in this paragraph contribute to the humorous effect?
2. When the author says that she was being used as a guinea pig, what does she mean?
3. What does Miss Folgil's attitude toward the author seem to be?
4. Why does the author mention that Maybelle Anne was a Girl Scout?
5. In the last sentence of the story, is the author paying Maybelle Anne a compliment? Why, or why not?

Taking a Closer Look

1. Why does the author dislike formal lifesaving training?
2. What was the author's first bad experience with lifesaving?
3. In the lifesaving course, why was the author often chosen to play the role of drowning victim in need of rescue?
4. What happened when the author tried to remove her sweat shirt in the water?
5. Why was the author eager to participate in the "Struggling" lesson?
6. What did Maybelle Anne grow up to be?

Putting Ideas to Work

Was Miss Folgil good at her job? Critically analyze her performance as a lifesaving instructor. Be sure to be specific.

Bamboo Beds and Running Water

Fern Babcock

One of the most vital attributes for a missionary is a sense of humor. The following events actually happened, all on one trip. Names and places have been changed to avoid offending anyone.

My Dear Family,

Two more weeks and I'll be with you! How I miss you—and Mom's cooking! Today I had cold potato patties with horseradish for *breakfast!*

Last time I wrote I was getting ready for an inland jungle trip. Now that I'm on the boat coming back to civilization and post offices, I'll have to write down some of my more exciting adventures.

We steamed upriver on an old ferryboat, the deck crowded with adults, kids, chickens, goats, and coconuts. Teacher Lal and I managed to squeeze into a small spot by the railing, and there we stayed for two days. The sun baked us, rain soaked us, and a nasty little goat drenched my foot!

When we landed at Laktal, the teacher took me to his house. It proved to be a one-room affair made of bamboo with a thatched roof that hung so low we had to stoop to enter. The villagers came to greet me, and brought rice and curry for supper. It tasted delicious, but was so full of chili peppers my mouth burned for hours. Now I know why Elder James warned me I'd need asbestos lips!

They go to bed at dark in Laktal since there's nothing to do, so by seven o'clock everyone began to get ready for bed by taking turns washing feet at the handpump beside the house. A cute little boy pumped water for me, and I washed my feet too.

While I was doing that, I noticed the teacher's two little girls shooing the chickens into the house for the night. Five hens and a rooster scurried inside. Then two boys came in, leading a big black goat and a small fuzzy brown one. They tied the goats to a bamboo stake in the far corner of the room. I sat by the door in the teacher's only chair, wondering how we'd all fit in the little 8- by 8-foot room. The two goats took up one corner; the chickens ran under everyone's feet, squawking when they got stepped on; and a whole family of long-tailed lizards seemed to inhabit the roof. I watched them run back and forth over our heads, and cringed as one fell and scooted off across the floor. A skinny brown dog slunk through the door and burrowed under the only bed so the chickens couldn't step on him.

The bed was like nothing I'd ever seen. It was made of split bamboo, laid rounded-side-up across a square frame to make a bed surface that looked like this: ᗧᗧᗧᗧᗧ . Four big bamboo legs held it about a foot off the floor, and the top end sported a fancy headboard. I wondered who would sleep on the bed. I soon found out. Since I was the guest, I must have the bed. The flat floor looked better to me, but everyone insisted so I spread my sleeping bag over the humpy bamboo.

The teacher, his wife, his old mother, and four children all unrolled reed mats and laid them on the floor, overlapping them until we had wall-to-wall mats except in the goats' corner and under the bed. I eyed the chickens wandering around, and decided on second thought that the bed was probably safer than the floor tonight. I soon had reason to wonder if I shouldn't change my mind.

As Teacher Lal pulled the door shut and blew out the smoky kerosene lantern, the heat, animal smells, and kerosene fumes began to get to me. I got an idea.

"Why don't I sleep outside under the mango tree?" I suggested. "It would make more room for everybody."

The children laughed and Teacher Lal chuckled.

"I don't think you'd like that, Pastor," he said. "Tigers sometimes come here at night. That's why we bring the goats in."

I gulped. "I guess I'll sleep in here," I agreed, and lay back on the bamboo bed. Staring into the darkness, I heard the lizards running and wondered if they ever fell on people. My question was answered before I could ask. Plunk! One landed on my chest and scampered off. I began for the first time to understand Mom's feelings about lizards!

As my eyes adjusted to the darkness, I suddenly realized where the chickens had roosted—on my bed's "fancy" headboard. I lay there staring up in disbelief at the back end of six chickens! You can imagine my thoughts! Quickly I sat up and carefully turned each chicken around so its *head* hung over my face! Somewhere in the hut I'm sure I heard snickering again!

Then the mosquitoes zoomed in, a whole platoon of them. While I swatted, the lizards began scurrying to get them too, and plopped onto the floor with alarming regularity. Grandma began snoring loudly and the dog rocked the bed as he tried to find a more comfortable place under it. Hours later I finally fell asleep wondering if cobras lived in thatch roofs!

The next day we hired a country boat for the trip to Kalikot Adventist School. It looked like a big canoe with rounded thatch over the center section. The thatch blocked the sun, but was so low I couldn't sit up inside, so I kind of half-sat, cross-legged and reclining, all day long. The boatman stood at the back of the boat poling us upstream. By the time I got to Kalikot, it was near evening and my legs felt like permanent pretzels. When I crawled out and tried to stand, I fell flat—much to the delight of the waiting students.

The principal helped me up, and I hobbled toward the old mission house. It was a huge two-story place, empty for years, and the mice and lizards protested my arrival.

"Now be careful when you close the shutters," the principal warned. "Snakes like to sun on the top of them and if you pull the shutters toward you, the snakes fall right on you. Shake the shutters first."

I promptly decided to leave the shutters entirely alone!

The bathroom was a marvel to behold. No nice ceramic box stood behind the toilet, but four feet above it a big iron water tank hung on the wall. A long flushing chain hung from it. The principal explained that there was no water piped into the house so the tank was dry. When I stood on a chair to examine the tank, a spider the size of a dinner plate looked me in the eye. I hurriedly climbed down and left him alone.

"We do have a sort of running water here," the principal joked. "When you ring this bell, a little boy will come running with water in a bucket!"

The rope-strung bed here looked better than the bamboo one I'd been bruised on the night before. When everyone had gone, I went to the bathroom to wash up for supper. It was so nice to see a real toilet again. Jungles and riverbanks aren't my idea of a bathroom at all!

I had just settled myself onto the nice plastic toilet seat when I thought I heard a rustle below me. Before I could get up, a little lizard whose home was evidently between the bowl and the seat, panicked and used my bottom as a bridge to the other side. He dived under the seat,

shot out on the floor and ran out a window, while I shot straight up into the air and klonked my head on that overhanging water tank.

I must have yelled, for the principal and two students were banging on the door in no time wanting to know what had happened.

"Nothing, nothing," I assured them. "I just banged my head."

From then on I checked under the seat every time.

The next Sunday I took my folding umbrella in case of a tropical downpour and got the school's boatman to pole me across the river to the village market. People stopped buying and selling to stare at me and to laugh at my reactions to their wares. I had just stopped to look at a monkey skin when it began to rain. How clever of me to have an umbrella, I thought, and pushed the button that unfolded and opened it. The crowd around me leaped back with a gasp. I grinned, closed it and popped it open again. Suddenly the friendly faces turned suspicious, and someone yelled a word that I later discovered meant "witch." He picked up a squash and threw it at the umbrella. It came to me very quickly that they'd never seen a folding umbrella before, and that the little thing growing big looked like black magic. I decided it was about time to return to the boat.

My brisk walk turned into a run as a rain of market vegetables showered around me. With the village at my heels, I dashed to the shore and leaped for the boat. My boatman saw the crowd and acted quickly, poling away from the bank as fast as he could. On the other side students washing their clothes in the river stopped to greet me with gales of laughter again. Their missionary certainly did funny things. Once I was sure I wasn't going to be "squashed" to death, I joined them and laughed at myself. Need I mention that I didn't try to investigate the village any more?

The last episode happened as I was trying to catch this ferry I'm on now. We were late, and pulled up to the dock just as the ferry steamed away. Mr. Lal and the boatman pulled our canoe alongside an open boat window and before I knew what was happening, they had thrown me and my luggage through the opening. Screams and shrieks filled the air as I landed in the lap of a fat lady, in the women's compartment! Knowing that was taboo, I jumped back toward the window,

climbed out, slid over the edge—and discovered Teacher Lal waving good-by from the canoe about thirty yards away. There I was, dangling over the side of the boat with nothing beneath me but water!

Fortunately, after they quit screaming, the ladies took pity on me and pulled me back in, muttering, I'm sure, about these crazy foreigners. Then they pushed me out of the compartment, and I made my way to the upper deck where I found a spot as far away from the goats as possible. One of my shoes is still slightly yellow-tan from my last goat encounter!

As you may imagine, I'll be delighted to get home to my own bed and a big dish of Mom's spaghetti. You three take care of each other till I get back to you.

Love, Dad

P.S. To Mom:
No, you may *not* use these stories in your next "mission" letter home.

What Do You Think?

1. Which of the incidents in this letter do you find the most amusing? Why?
2. What do you think would be the most uncomfortable of these experiences? What makes it worse than the others?
3. From what part of the world would you say this missionary is writing?
4. Why do you think his wife and children are not with him?
5. Most of the humor in this letter comes from things that are not usually mentioned in mission stories. Why do you think this is so?
6. Compare this selection with the article, "One Adventure after Another," on pp. 91-97. How are the two selections the same? How are they different?

Taking a Closer Look

1. Why didn't the missionary sleep outside?
2. What is meant by the phrase "asbestos lips" and why did the missionary need them?
3. Describe and explain the reaction of the people in the market place upon seeing a folding umbrella.

Putting Ideas to Work

Imagine you are the teacher, Mr. Lal. Write your impression of the foreign missionary's reaction to one of the incidents in this letter.

The Bear That Came to Supper

Robert Franklin Leslie

What happens when a 500-pound bear walks into your camp and decides to stay?

I met Bosco in the remote wilderness near Mount Robson in western Canada. At the end of a long day of backpacking I had made a lean-to in a clearing beside a stream and was preparing to catch supper. Then I looked up— and there he was; an enormous boar black bear, slowly circling the clearing within thirty yards.

He wasn't Bosco to me yet, and I viewed his presence with trepidation. My provisions were vulnerable if he was in a piratical mood, since I was unarmed. However, I decided to go about my fishing. The bear came along.

I've lived with wild creatures for thirty years, respecting their first fear—fast movements—and now I let him see the reason and the beginning in every slow, deliberate move I made. Soon he was sitting on his haunches less than five feet away, intensely interested in my activity. When I landed a fourteen-inch Loch Levin, I tossed it to him. He gulped it without bothering to chew. And when I flipped out the fly again he moved closer, planted his well-upholstered fanny on the turf beside my boot, and leaned half his 500 pounds against my right leg!

I plied the gray hackle along the riffles and got another strike. Before reeling in, I eased over a yard, convinced the bear would grab fish, line, rod—and maybe me. But he didn't. His patience and dignity were regal as he sat rocking back and forth, watching carefully. When I released the trout from the hook, he bawled a long-drawn-out "Maw!" I held the wriggling fish high by the lower lip, stepped over to my "guest," and shakily dropped the prize into his cavernous, red mouth.

When drizzly darkness set in, I was still fishing for that bear, fascinated as much by his gentle manners as by his insatiable capacity. I began to think of him in a friendly way as Big Bosco, and I didn't mind when he followed me back to camp.

After supper I built up the fire and sat on the sleeping bag under the lean-to. All this time Bosco had sat just outside the heat perimeter of the fire, but the moment I was comfortably settled he walked over and sat down beside me. Overlooking the stench of wet fur, I rather enjoyed his warmth as we sat on the sleeping bag under the shelter. I listened to the rain thumping on the tarp in time with the steady, powerful *cur-rump, cur-rump* of the heartbeat beneath his thick coat. When smoke blew our way, he snorted and sneezed, and I imitated most of his body movements, even the sneezing and snorting, swaying my head in every direction, sniffing the air as he did.

Then Bosco began licking my hands. Guessing what he wanted, I got him a handful of salt. Bosco enthusiastically nailed my hand to the ground with eight four-inch claws—claws capable of peeling the bark from a full-grown cedar, claws that could carry his 500-odd pounds at full gallop to the top of the tallest tree in the forest, claws that could rip a man's body like a band saw.

Finally the last grain of salt was gone and again we sat together. I wondered if this could be for real. I recalled Sam Ottley, trail foreman on the King's River in the Sierra Nevada, whom I had seen sharing tent and rations with a bear; but Sam's creature was old and toothless, no longer able to live off the country; this monster was the finest prime specimen I had ever seen.

Bosco stood up on all fours, burped a long, fishy belch, and stepped out into the rainy blackness. But he soon was back—with a message. He sat down near the sleeping bag and attempted to scratch that area of his rump just above his tail; he couldn't reach it. Again and again he nudged me and growled savagely at the itch. Finally I got the message and laid a light hand on his back. He flattened out to occupy the total seven feet of the lean-to as I began to scratch through the dense, oily hair.

Then the full significance of his visit hit me. Just above his stubby tail several gorged ticks were dangerously embedded in swollen flesh. Little by little I proved that the flashlight would not burn, so he allowed me to focus it on his body. When I twisted out the first parasite, I thought I was in for a mauling. His roar shook the forest. But I determined to finish the job. Each time I removed a tick, I showed it to him for a sniff before dropping it on the fire, and by the last one he was affably licking my hand.

A cold, sniffing nose awakened me several times during the night as the bear came and went. He left the sleeping bag wetter and muddier each time he crawled around over me, but he never put his full weight down when he touched any part of my body.

The next day I set off again, over a ridge, down through a chilly river, up the next crest, through thickets of birch and alder and down a wide, north-running river canyon. To my surprise, Bosco followed like a faithful dog, digging grubs or bulbs when we stopped to rest. That evening I fished for Bosco's supper.

As the days passed and I hiked north, I used a system of trout, salt, and scratch rewards to teach the bear to respond to the call, "Bosco!" Despite his perpetual devotion to food, he never lagged behind. One evening he walked over to the log where I was and began to dig at my boots. When I stood up he led me straight to a dead, hollow tree at which he clawed vigorously but unsuccessfully. Returning to camp, I covered my head with mosquito netting, tied shirt, pants, and glove openings, and got the hatchet. I built a smoke fire near the base of the tree and hacked away until the hollow shell crashed to earth, split wide open, and exposed the hive's total summer production. For my understanding and efforts I received three stinging welts. Bosco ate twenty pounds of honeycomb, beebread, and hundreds of bees. He snored most of that night at the foot of the sleeping bag.

At campsites Bosco never tolerated long periods of relaxation and reflection; and, true to my sucker form where animals were concerned, I babied his every whim. When he wanted his back scratched, I scratched; when he wanted a fish dinner, I fished; when he wanted to romp and roll with me in a meadow, I romped and rolled—and still wear scars to prove that he played games consummately out of my league.

During one particularly rough session, I tackled his right front leg, bowling him over on his back. As I sat there on his belly regaining wind, he retaliated with a left hook that not only opened a two-inch gash down the front of my chin but spun me across the meadow. When I woke up, Bosco was licking my wound. His shame and remorse were inconsolable. He sat with his ears back and bawled like a whipped pup when I was able to put my arm around his neck and repeat all the soft, ursine vocabulary he had taught me.

After that experience I let Bosco roll me around when he had to play, but I never raised another finger toward originality. If he got too rough, I played dead. Invariably he would turn me over, lick my face, and whine.

There were times when he spent his excess energy racing around in 100-yard circles, building up speed to gallop to the top of the tallest fir. When he returned to camp immediately afterward, I could detect absolutely no increase above his normal breathing rate. He panted only when we walked for long periods in full sun and he got thirsty.

It is not my intention either to attribute character traits to the bear that he could not possess or to exaggerate those he had. I simply studied him for what he was, and saw him manifest only the normal qualities of his species, which were formidable enough without exaggeration. Other than calling him Bosco, I never attempted human training upon him; conversely, I did everything possible to train myself to become a brother bear.

Like all sensitive mammals, Bosco had his full complement of moods. When serious, he was dead earnest; when exuberant, a volcano. Being a bear, he was by nature uninhibited; so I never expressed even a shade of the word *no*. The affection we developed for each other was spontaneous, genuine brotherly bear; when it occurred to him to waddle over my way on his hind legs, grab me up in a smothering bear hug, and express an overflowing emotion with a face licking, I went along with it for two reasons: first, I was crazy about the varmint; second, I nourished a healthy respect for what one swat from the ambidextrous giant could accomplish.

Although he was undisputed monarch of all his domain, I think Bosco considered me his mental equal in most respects. It wasn't long before he taught me to expand communication through a language of the eyes. How a bear can look you in the eye! Terrifying at first—it grows into the most satisfactory medium of all. Bosco and I would sit by the campfire, honestly and intimately studying each other's thoughts. Once in a while he'd reach some sort of conclusion and hang a heavy paw on my shoulder. And I'd do the same. It would have made an odd picture, but many times as I looked into those big yellowish-brown eyes, I felt an awed humility as if the Deity Himself were about to effect a revelation through this, another of His children.

Although his size and strength made Bosco almost invulnerable to attack by other animals, he had his own collection of phobias. Thunder and lightning made him cringe and whine. When whiskey jacks (Clark's nutcrackers) flew into camp looking for food, he fled in terror, the cacophonic birds power-diving and pecking him out of sight.

Bosco's phenomenal sense of smell amazed me. Trudging along behind me he would suddenly stop, sniff the air, and make a beeline for a big, succulent mushroom two hundred yards away, to

189

a flat rock across the river under which chipmunks had warehoused their winter seed supply, to a berry patch two ridges over.

One afternoon when we were crossing a heath where dwarf willows grew in scattered hedge-like clumps, Bosco suddenly reared up and let out a "Maw!" I could detect no reason for alarm, but Bosco stood erect and forbade me to move. He advanced, began to snarl—and pandemonium broke out. Every clump of willows sprouted an upright bear! Black bear, brown bear, cinnamon bear, and one champagne (all subdivisions of the same species).

But these were young bears, two-year-olds, and no match for Bosco. He charged his closest contestant with the fury of a Sherman tank, and before the two-year-old could pick himself up he dispatched a second bear and tore into a thicket to dislodge a third. At the end of the circuit my gladiator friend remembered me and scoured back, unscathed and still champion.

That night we sat longer than usual by the campfire. Bosco nudged, pawed, talked at great length, and looked me long in the eye before allowing me to retire. In my ignorance I assumed it was a rehash of that afternoon's battle. He was gone most of the night.

Along toward next midafternoon I sensed something wrong. Bosco didn't forage, but clung to my heels. I was looking over a streamside campsite when the big bear about-faced and broke into a headlong, swinging lope up a hill we had just descended. I did not call to him as he went over the crest full steam without once looking back.

That evening I cooked supper with one eye on the hillside, then lay awake for hours waiting for the familiar nudge. By morning I was desolated; I knew I should never again see big brother Bosco. He left behind a relationship I shall treasure.

What Do You Think?

1. In what ways is Bosco similar to the she-bear in the story "Polar Night"? In what ways are the two bears different?
2. Why do you think Bosco was so friendly? Use your imagination to guess what experiences he may have had that gave him a good impression of men.
3. The author says he didn't try to "attribute character traits to the bear which he could not possess." Do you think Bosco had unusual character traits? Compare him to the elephant in "Circle in the Dust."
4. Why do you think Bosco finally left the man?

Taking a Closer Look

1. What does the writer say is a wild animal's first fear? Why do you think this is so?
2. Explain how the bear climbs trees.
3. What does the writer mean by the expression "language of the eyes"?
4. What evidence is there in this story that the writer is experienced with wild animals?
5. Where did this story take place?
6. What did the author mean when he said that Bosco "played games consummately out of my league"?
7. What does the writer think was the major reason for the bear's visit?
8. What things did the bear fear?

Putting Ideas to Work

If you could be friends with any animal on earth, which would you choose? In a couple of paragraphs, explain your choice.

Art Buchwald

Fresh Air Will Kill You

Art Buchwald

Sometimes a writer exaggerates the truth to draw attention to greater truth. Watch for exaggerations in this article. How true do you think they are?

Smog, which was once the big attraction of Los Angeles, can now be found all over the country from Butte, Montana, to New York City, and people are getting so used to polluted air that it's very difficult for them to breathe anything else.

I was lecturing recently, and one of my stops was Flagstaff, Arizona, which is about seven thousand miles above sea level.

As soon as I got out of the plane, I smelled something peculiar.

"What's that smell?" I asked the man who met me at the plane.

"I don't smell anything," he replied.

"There's a definite odor that I'm not familiar with," I said.

"Oh, you must be talking about the fresh air. A lot of people come out here who have never smelled fresh air before."

"What's it supposed to do?" I asked suspiciously.

"Nothing. You just breathe it like any other kind of air. It's

supposed to be good for your lungs."

"I've heard that story before," I said. "How come if it's air, my eyes aren't watering?"

"Your eyes don't water with fresh air. That's the advantage of it. Saves you a lot in paper tissues."

I looked around and everything appeared crystal clear. It was a strange sensation and made me feel very uncomfortable.

My host, sensing this, tried to be reassuring. "Please don't worry about it. Tests have proved that you can breathe fresh air day and night without its doing any harm to the body."

"You're just saying that because you don't want me to leave," I said. "Nobody who has lived in a major city can stand fresh air for a very long time. He has no tolerance for it."

"Well, if the fresh air bothers you, why don't you put a handkerchief over your nose and breathe through your mouth?"

"Okay, I'll try it. If I'd known I was coming to a place that had nothing but fresh air, I would have brought a surgical mask."

We drove in silence. About fifteen minutes later he asked, "How do you feel now?"

"Okay, I guess, but I sure miss sneezing."

"We don't sneeze too much here," the man admitted. "Do they sneeze a lot where you come from?"

"All the time. There are some days when that's all you do."

"Do you enjoy it?"

"Not necessarily, but if you don't sneeze, you'll die. Let me ask you something. How come there's no air pollution around here?"

"Flagstaff can't seem to attract industry. I guess we're really behind the times."

The fresh air was making me feel dizzy. "Isn't there a diesel bus around here that I could breathe into for a couple of hours?"

"Not at this time of day. I might be able to find a truck for you."

We found a truck driver, and slipped him a five-dollar bill, and he let me put my head near his exhaust pipe for a half-hour. I was immediately revived and able to give my speech.

Nobody was as happy to leave Flagstaff as I was. My next stop was Los Angeles, and when I got off the plane, I took one big deep breath of the smog-filled air, my eyes started to water, I began to sneeze, and I felt like a new man again.

What Do You Think?

1. Exaggeration is often used in humorous writing. How does exaggeration play a part in this selection? Identify specific examples of exaggeration.
2. Why do you think the author would suggest that people who live in polluted places have to sneeze to live? Is there any truth in this idea?
3. Did the author really put his head near the exhaust pipe of a truck for half an hour? Explain your answer.
4. What is humorous about the statement, "I guess we're really behind the times"?
5. Which sentence in the entire article would you choose as a topic sentence? Why?

Taking a Closer Look

1. How does the author point out the negative aspects about air pollution in this article?
2. In what ways does the writer try to protect himself from fresh air?
3. According to this story why didn't Flagstaff have any air pollution?
4. What reason did the author give for having no tolerance for fresh air?
5. Why did Los Angeles make the writer feel better?

Putting Ideas to Work

Think of a situation that is not really funny. By turning phrases and carrying the idea to a ridiculous extreme, write a short humorous article on that subject.

Notes in an Outline

Preparing an outline is no laughing matter! It is a serious way to organize written information. An outline is a summary of a subject you are investigating. It can help you understand, remember, and use facts that you have collected.

An outline can summarize one or more paragraphs. When taking notes in outline form, first look for the main idea. Then seek the supporting details for the main idea in each paragraph. Here's the basic outline form:

I. **Main topic**
  A. **Subtopic of I**
    1. **Supporting detail**

Read the following paragraphs. They tell how Samuel Langhorne Clemens became Mark Twain.

Mark Twain (1835-1910) is the pen name of a great American author and humorist. He was born Samuel Langhorne Clemens in Missouri on November 30th. Clemens had a fiery temper combined with a biting sense of humor. And he loved the hustle and bustle of river life.

Clemens felt "Mark Twain" fit him better. The phrase *mark twain* is a river term for water that is barely safe to navigate. Clemens knew he was a grouch who sometimes scared people. So, he matched a name to his personality. That gave him a good laugh!

Outline notes for the two paragraphs could be organized like this:

I. Mark Twain (1835-1910)
  A. Pen name of Samuel L. Clemens
    1. Author-humorist
    2. Born in Missouri
    3. Temper, humor mix
    4. Loved river life
  B. "Mark Twain" fit him better
    1. River term
    2. Means: barely safe to navigate
    3. Name fits personality

This outline was organized using *key* words. The notes using the key words summarized both paragraphs. Roman numeral I gives the main topic. The subtopic, capital letter A, tells the first paragraph's theme. The four supporting details of subtopic A use Arabic numerals. The details summarize a few facts about Twain. This outline has been further developed. Capital letter B gives more information about the main topic. And the three Arabic numerals following subtopic B give the supporting details. Subtopics A and B complement each other. Note that the first word on each line of the outline is capitalized.

Now read the following passage.

Twain's Early Years

Mark Twain's youth was filled with excitement, tragedy, and hard work. When Twain was four, his family moved to Hannibal, Missouri, on the West Bank of the Mississippi River.

It was in Hannibal that Mark was introduced to the adventure of the Mississippi waterfront. Young Twain was fascinated by the excitement around the river. Steamboats, keelboats, and giant lumber rafts navigated the Mississippi. These colorful boats carried all kinds of interesting and sometimes dangerous characters. Some of these rowdy sea travelers were quick to settle an argument with fists or weapons. And tragedy was no stranger to Mark Twain personally. His family was poor and struggled to earn a living. When Mark was only eleven, his father died. (He had already lost a brother and a sister.) Young Twain had to work after school to help support the family. He labored as a delivery boy, grocery clerk, and blacksmith's helper. Twain hated all these jobs. When Mark was 13, he left his formal schooling behind to become an apprentice printer. But he still was searching for something else. The excitement of the Mississippi River churned within him. Twain kept thinking. He had no intention of staying put . . . ever!

Here is a partially filled-in outline about Twain's youth. You will try to complete it on a piece of notepaper. To complete the outline, it will help to remember these steps: reread, think, summarize, outline.

I. Twain's youth
  A. Excitement
    1.
    2.
  B. Tragedy
    1.
    2.
    3.

"Twain's youth" is the main topic of this outline. Two subtopics, "Excitement" and "Tragedy," have been filled in for you. Under each subtopic are Arabic numerals. These signal the placement of details that will support each subtopic.

To complete this outline, review the passage and find facts that support the subtopics "Excitement" and "Tragedy." Summarize these facts. Then copy the model outline on a sheet of paper and fill in the supporting details.

This outline can be expanded. Review the passage. Decide what subtopic and details should be added to your outline. Summarize and complete your outline.

The Owl-Critic

James Thomas Fields

"Who stuffed that white owl?" No one spoke in the shop,
The barber was busy, and he couldn't stop;
The customers, waiting their turns, were all reading
The "Daily," the "Herald," the "Post," little heeding
The young man who blurted out such a blunt question;
Not one raised a head, or even made a suggestion;
   And the barber kept on shaving.

"Don't you see, Mr. Brown,"
Cried the youth, with a frown,
"How wrong the whole thing is,
How preposterous each wing is,
How flattened the head is, how jammed down the neck is—
In short, the whole owl, what an ignorant wreck 'tis!
I make no apology;
I've learned owl-eology.
I've passed days and nights in a hundred collections,
And cannot be blinded to any defections
Arising from unskillful fingers that fail
To stuff a bird right, from his beak to his tail.
Mister Brown! Mister Brown!
Do take that bird down,
Or you'll soon be the laughing-stock all over town!"
   And the barber kept on shaving.

"I've *studied* owls,
And other night-fowls,
And I tell you
What I know to be true;
An owl cannot roost
With his limbs so unloosed;
No owl in this world
Ever had his claws curled,
Ever had his legs slanted,
Ever had his bill canted,
Ever had his neck screwed
Into that attitude.
He can't *do* it, because
'Tis against all bird-laws.
Anatomy teaches,
Ornithology preaches,
An owl has a toe
That *can't* turn out so!
I've made the white owl my study for years,
And to see such a job almost moves me to tears!
Mr. Brown, I'm amazed
You should be so gone crazed
As to put up a bird
In that posture absurd!
To *look* at that owl really brings on a dizziness.
The man who stuffed *him* don't half know his business!"
    And the barber kept on shaving.

"Examine those eyes.
I'm filled with surprise
Taxidermists should pass
Off on you such poor glass;
So unnatural they seem
They'd make Audubon scream,
And John Burroughs laugh
To encounter such chaff.
Do take that bird down;
Have him stuffed again, Brown!"
    And the barber kept on shaving.

"With some sawdust and bark
I could stuff in the dark
An owl better than that.
I could make an old hat
Look more like an owl
Than that horrid fowl,
Stuck up there so stiff like a side of coarse leather.
In fact, about *him* there's not one natural feather."

Just then, with a wink and a sly normal lurch,
The owl, very gravely, got down from his perch,
Walked around, and regarded his fault-finding critic
(Who thought he was stuffed) with a glance analytic,
And then fairly hooted, as if he should say:
"Your learning's at fault *this* time, anyway;
Don't waste it again on a live bird, I pray.
I'm an owl; you're another. Sir Critic, good day!"
   And the barber kept on shaving.

My Father and the Hippopotamus   *Leon Hugo*

One winter morning Father finally got his chance to show a
hippopotamus who was boss. He planned to teach the entire herd
a lesson about invading his farm, but he learned a thing or two
himself.

My father's farm was in the bushveld of the eastern Transvaal, about thirty miles from the Kruger National Park. Wild animals therefore were common in our daily lives. They were nearly all, in their peculiar ways, destructive. Jackals stole my mother's chickens, koodoo broke the fencing around the farm, giraffes entangled their necks in the telephone wires, and lions occasionally carried off a cow.

Against most wild beasts my father had to wage unceasing war. On the whole he won—except against the hippos. The Letaba River ran through one end of our farm, and during the winter, when in its lower reaches the water level dropped, hippos would move upstream from the game reserve and settle on our farm. They always had. They sneaked in during the night, sank softly into one of the deep pools in the river, and having done so announced their arrival with an amiable deep bellow. That would start my father's annual dance of rage on the veranda. It used to frighten me nearly out of my wits, but never the hippos, which was not surprising as they were a mile away. I still remember thinking: "If you could see my dad now, you hippos, you'd clear out before tomorrow. He's mad!"

My father may well have seemed so to me (my sister was too young to notice, and my mother used merely to sigh), but as I grew older I began to realize that his roarings and stampings were simply excessive face-saving devices. He knew, I grew to know, and the hippos must have guessed, that he could do nothing.

For one thing there were strict laws about the shooting of hippos; and for another, when on the mornings following their arrival my father stamped down to the river, there was never a sign of one. The reeds were crushed, of

course, and the riverbank looked as though it had been put through a mincing-machine, but none of us ever saw a single shining rump or head above the silent green surface.

My father always said that the animals were near. He could feel, he said, the calculating gaze of sleepy hippos lurking among the reeds on the opposite bank. Occasionally he would hear a sniff or a coarse gurgle, and that made him angrier than ever. He would walk up and down the bank daring any hippo to show its face, until my mother sent a message to say that breakfast was ready.

After these formalities there was nothing my father could do except see that fires round the lands were kept going during the night. These usually protected the crops from the hippos' darkling gambols, but during their two-month stay my father was an anxious and overworked man.

"Give me a herd of stampeding buffalo, rather," he once remarked bitterly. "At least you can see them. But these hippos! I wish," he added wistfully, "I could catch one—just one. I'd teach it who's boss. . . ."

His chance came, I remember, on a Sunday.

The hippos had been making a dreadful noise the night before: an army of swine would have been nightingales in comparison. The crashing splashes, the snorts, grunts, and squeals coming up to us through the dark in blasts of shattering sound, pointed to a hippopotamus frolic of unprecedented scope. To add to the pandemonium our two dogs, which were kept chained in the backyard, started howling. My father, with visions before him of a concerted hippo attack on his crops, if not on our very house, made four journeys on foot round his land to see that the farm hands were keeping the fires going; and although he took a powerful

201

flashlight with him—and the farm foreman carrying a rifle—caught only one gray fleeting form in the beam of the torch.

When he came in for the fourth time, he looked as though he had had enough. "They can eat everything," he muttered. "Everything—I don't care anymore."

"Oh, John, I'm sure it will be all right," said my mother. . . .

My father spoke very calmly. "Laurie," he said to me, "shut the dogs up."

My sister, as I walked out, said, "Daddy, has a hippo got a curly tail like a piggy's?" When I came in again she was crying and my father had gone to bed.

A tremendous yell woke me the next morning. I shot up in bed to hear flat feet pounding through the garden toward the house, the yell repeated, and then a burst of insane giggling. I was out in the passage in a moment and saw Matiba, our cook, still giggling as he banged on my parents' bedroom door.

"What is it?" my father growled.

Matiba managed to point to the garden. We hurried to the veranda. It was still early, but the sun had risen enough to make the garden fairly easy to see: particularly the cause of old Matiba's fright; for nature, as though to heighten the effect, had directed through the trees a shaft of golden light onto the fishpond. Cozily basking in this, half-submerged in the water, was a hippopotamus, fast asleep.

My mother called, "What is it, John?"

"A hippo," said my father, extraordinarily calm.

"A what?"

"I said a hippo," said my father.

"Where?" asked my mother.

"In your fishpond."

There was another pause from my mother, a long one. Then, "The poor goldfish!" we heard her gasp.

My father laughed shortly. "Laurie," he said, "fetch my rifle."

My mother was on the veranda when I got back. She looked pale. I handed my father the rifle. "You aren't going to shoot it, are you, John?" she said.

My father opened the breech. "I jolly well am," he answered grimly.

Sunlight had swept in a flood into the garden by then, and we could see our visitor down to the last wrinkle on its hide. It was a calf, a small one, weighing about eight hundred pounds, and it fitted snugly into the pond, like a round balloon wedged in a tin can. As my father raised the rifle to his shoulder the hippo moved. Water splashed out of the pond as it snuggled in more deeply; and then it yawned, opening its jaws to cavernous proportions and displaying a set of young but immense canines.

I waited, holding my breath for the report of the rifle.

"How will you get it out?" my mother asked.

A spasm ran through my father's body, and for a moment it looked as though he would still pull the trigger. But he did not. Slowly he lowered the rifle. "What did you say?" he said softly.

"How are you going to get it out?"

"Quite simple, dear," said my father patiently. "We'll pull it out."

"You couldn't."

"Couldn't?"

"You couldn't possibly drag a huge beast that weighs thousands of pounds out without ruining the fishpond."

I could see by the look on my father's face that my mother had presented a poser. "We'll hack it up first," he suggested.

"You will not," said my mother firmly. "I'm not having any hippos cut up in my front garden, and anyway I think it's horrid and cruel. He's only a calf."

My father said, "If you want the goldfish to have a playmate, dear, just say so and we'll leave little Jumbo to have his wallow."

"That's not a Jumbo," remarked my sister, who had joined us.

"You're quite right, darling," my mother told her. "Daddy's just being altogether ridiculous."

In the fishpond the hippo belched, not softly.

"No," my mother went on. "What you've got to do is get rid of it without ruining the pond or flowers. I've slaved for years in this garden, and I'm not going to stand by and let you destroy it just because you can't get rid of a baby hippo."

"You make me sound so ineffectual," my father grumbled, but he was, I think, secretly glad that he could not conscientiously go on with the killing. "Matiba," he said, "call the farm hands."

They came running from their quarters, all of them agog. Stealthily we crept up to one side of the sleeping hippo. As we drew closer we could hear it breathing, slow and deep, with the faintest rumbling snore.

"Now!" yelled my father, and the din started. In addition to ten or so full-blooded yells, empty paraffin tins clashed under smiting sticks and my father's rifle cracked five times as he fired into the air. Altogether it was a most discordant and satisfying noise, and it seemed to electrify our hippo.

It stood up in the pond. Drops shook from it in a silver shower and a goldfish slid from its rump into the water. And it bellowed. Awed by the majesty of the blast we fell silent. We looked at the hippo, it at us. There was something regal about a hippo, even a baby one. We squirmed under its angry gaze. Then, as we silently watched, it sniffed, blinked, and settled slowly back into the pond.

We started our noise again, of course, but shamefacedly and with much less gusto; in any case the more we shouted and banged, the deeper into the pond did the hippo try to get. Only a circlet of rump, its ears, eyes, and snout remained above the water eventually. We gave up after half an hour when jabs (with a very long pole) had produced no effect beyond indignant snorts and showers of spray.

"No good," my father whispered, as he and I returned to the house, and the farm hands, strangely quiet, to their quarters for the rest of their day. "We'll have to think of something else."

Breakfast was a silent meal. Even my sister, after mentioning sadly that hippos' tails were straight, said nothing. Shortly afterwards my mother left for town, but before driving off she asked my father to promise not to kill the hippo. Which he did rather irritably.

My father spent the greater part of the morning staring pensively at the hippo in the pond. Finally he said, "We'll have to drag it out, all the same," and went to fetch the truck. He brought it round, reversed it between the trees surrounding the garden to as near the pond as he could go.

"This is what we must do, Laurie," he said. "Tie this rope to the bumper and loop the other end round the blighter's neck. If I can't manage a dead one, a live hippo's going to find itself doing a quick sprint out of the pond."

First we tied the rope to the rear bumper; then my father made a wide noose of the other end and advanced slowly toward the pond. The hippo watched him suspiciously, snorting softly. It was wide-awake and clearly still annoyed.

I heard my father talking to it. "Steady now, boy. Don't worry, we don't want to hurt you. Just pull your head off at the worst. . . ." Carefully he inched forward to within about three yards of the pond. "Steady. . .!" He threw the rope. It was a good shot, and the noose dropped over the hippo's ears. For a second my father looked quite pleased. Then the hippo bellowed straight into his face and wrenched its head upwards. My father catapulted back into a bed of flowers where he lay; but in jerking its head the hippo had helped the noose to fall farther over its ears and round its neck.

It was some moments before I could bring my father to realize this happy accident. When he did,

though, he cheered up considerably, and after a few furtive flicks on the slack of the rope, the noose was reasonably tight round the hippo's neck.

"Well," my father remarked as we climbed into the truck, "that's nearly that." He revved the engine and slowly let out the clutch. The truck moved forward.

I could not see, sitting beside my father, but could feel when the rope tautened. We could hear too. Behind us, from the fishpond, came tremendous splashings and snorts of rage. The engine hummed, raced, roared; the wheels screamed in the earth. Then we shot away, bounded away rather, like an impala, and thundered along the car track toward the river.

My father yelled jubilantly. "He can run! Thirty—and not the slightest strain. . . ." A few seconds passed and then a worried look came into his face. He slowly braked.

Up to that moment my father had been exceptionally calm. But the strain began to tell on him then. He got very red in the face and started muttering through clenched teeth. As we drove back to the farmhouse I felt glad I was not that poor hippopotamus.

"You going to shoot him now, Dad?" I ventured.

"No!" my father roared. "I'll get him out alive if it takes me a week!"

The hippo was in the pond, the rope was still around its neck—the torn-off rear bumper skulked in a flower bed—and my sister was sitting on her haunches beside the pond gazing earnestly into the hippo's eyes. They seemed to be getting on well together; so well, in fact, that she strongly objected when my father, swooping on her like a bird of prey, carried her into the house and locked her up.

"Untie that rope!" he yelled at me as he disappeared through the doorway. Shaking, I ran to obey, but his rage had so unnerved me that by the time he came back I had not managed a single knot.

He pushed me aside, tried to untie the rope himself, tore his thumbnail, and cut the rope.

He passed me the severed end. "Hold this," he said. "I'm getting under the truck to tie it to the axle." He glared at the hippo. "Just let him try to pull the axle

off!" he snarled. "Hand me the rope when I'm ready."

He slid under the rear end of the truck. I was standing facing the pond. A sudden inexplicable gust of warm air struck the back of my neck and I swung around.

I question whether there is anything more conducive to a lightning upsurge of adrenalin than the sudden sight, from twelve inches, of an adult hippopotamus. The ancient wicked eyes, the enormous expanse of a two-and-a-half-ton amphibian, make for extremely rapid action. A tree was close at hand. I was up it in about a millionth of a second, staring down, goggle-eyed and dumb, at the hippopotamus cow that had appeared from nowhere at my shoulder. She gave me a perfunctory glance before turning. The part of my father that protruded from the back of the truck caught her eye. She bent her head to examine it.

206

It was horrible. There I was up the tree, quite speechless with fright, expecting her to open her mouth and bite my father. But she merely gave a long, interested sniff and my father said, "What are you doing, Laurie?" and wriggled pettishly. Then he said, "All right, give me the rope," and his hand strayed out. The hippopotamus sniffed at that.

My father, sensing that something was near and thinking it was the rope, said, "Give it to me," and grabbed. His fingers closed unerringly on the hippo's snout.

I found my voice at last. "Daddy," I squeaked, "get underneath! Get underneath!"

He did not. His hand seemed riveted to that snout; and some strange power, instead of sending him slithering for safety under the truck, brought him out into the open. They stared at one another for what seemed ages, my father and that female hippopotamus, deep into one another's eyes; then my father let go and giggled, while the hippo breathed long, slow exploratory breaths and twitched her ears. My father rose slowly to his feet, murmuring noncommittally, "Good chap, good old girl," only just restraining himself from patting her on the head. Then the hippo opened her mouth.

What happened next was too quick for me to see. It was a blur of action and there was my father just beneath me in the tree gasping, "Get higher, higher!" and I crying, "I can't, I'm stuck!" and my father appearing magically in the fork above my head and the hippo looking disappointedly up at him, as though she regretted not having tried a piece of human while the going was good. But if that was her thought it was only a passing one, for she turned almost immediately to the fishpond and grunted.

The calf squeaked in reply and squirmed. The mother—the new arrival must have been that—grunted again; the young hippo slowly emerged, leaving a trail of destruction through my mother's dahlias. As it reached her she bit it, not viciously but with enough vigor to make the calf squeal sharply, spring aside, and start off at a smart gallop for the river. Without a glance up at us, she followed.

As they reached the trees, the calf tossed its head and the noose flew free of its neck. In another moment the two animals had disappeared.

We climbed down and without a word to one another slunk into the house.

The first rain of the season fell that night, and the hippos left the river pool. They never came back. But five years had to pass before my father (avoiding my eye) dared boast that he had taught them a lesson.

What Do You Think?

1. In what ways were Father's roarings and stampings face-saving devices?
2. After the bumper was pulled off the truck, Laurie feels glad that she is not the hippopotamus. Why do you think she felt that way? How would you have felt?
3. How do you think Laurie and her father felt when they turned around and saw the mother hippo?
4. If you had been Laurie's father, how would you have tried to get the baby hippo out of the fishpond?
5. What three words would you choose to describe Laurie's father? Explain your choices.
6. How would you describe Laurie's mother?
7. Why do you think it was against the law to kill hippos?

Taking a Closer Look

1. What question did Mother ask that made Father think twice about shooting the hippo?
2. Did Father really want to kill the hippo? Give evidence from the story to support your answer.
3. In your own words describe the effect of the noise and prodding on the baby hippo.
4. How was the baby hippo finally removed from the fishpond?

Using Categorization

The human brain is sometimes likened to a computer. Both have the ability to store information in their memories. Computers, however, don't operate on their own. They need people to give them information and to tell them what to do with it. The human mind enables people to work on their own.

The brain arranges ideas or things in related groups. This grouping is called *categorization*, and it usually occurs automatically. The mind is continually grouping data whether you're aware of it or not.

Categorizing helps you to store information for later use. The system can be activated simply by hearing words that mean something to you. For example, the words *baseball*, *soccer*, *football*, and *hockey* will be quickly categorized by the brain as "sports."

The stories in this unit are grouped under the title "What's So Funny?" All the stories have something in common with the title. The same is true of the stories in the other units.

Jobs can be categorized, too. Try arranging the following occupations into two groups. Think about the type of work involved in each job. Try to think of a heading for each category. (Ask yourself, "What skills does a person need to do this work?")

> guidance counselor
> mechanic
> architect
> computer operator
> salesperson
> customer service representative

One group involves "people-oriented work." A guidance counselor, a customer service representative, and a salesperson are usually interested in working with people. The other group represents "object-oriented work." A mechanic, an architect, and a computer operator are usually skilled in working with things.

You can even categorize attitudes, or people's outlooks on life. Two attitude categories might be "optimism" and "pessimism." An optimistic person is someone who focuses on the joyful side of life. ("People will always be smarter than computers!") The pessimistic person tends to dwell on the gloomy side of life. ("Computers will take over the world, and people will become useless.")

Using the titles "Optimism" and "Pessimism," how would you classify each of the following statements?

1. I think the weather is clearing and the sun will soon shine.
2. My penny bank is half empty.
3. Our neighbor helped us to grow a large and varied vegetable garden.
4. My penny bank is half full.
5. It's so wet and dismal outside, I think the rain will go on forever.
6. Our neighbor talked us into planting too many vegetables in our garden.

Statements 1, 3, and 4 should be categorized under the title "Optimism." Statements 2, 5, and 6 should be categorized under "Pessimism." If you missed two, be optimistic—you got four right!

1. Food can be categorized in many ways. The following list is a food jumble. Classify the foods under the titles "Thirst-Quenchers," "Main Courses," "Vegetables," and "Breads." For the four question marks, add four foods of your own choice, one for each title.

roast	bran muffins
tomato juice	squash
baked potato	macaroni and cheese
broccoli	mushrooms
fruit punch	tossed salad
green beans	water
burger	taco
cheese	(?) your choice
corn	(?) your choice
rice	(?) your choice
milk	(?) your choice

2. Now that you have arranged the foods into the right categories, rearrange them into a 5-day dinner menu. Use a chart like the one below. Try not to use any food more than once. (A chart with one food from each group each day is correct!)

MENU PLANNER

FOOD TYPE	MON.	TUES.	WED.	THURS.	FRI.
THIRST-QUENCHER					
MAIN COURSE					
VEGETABLE					
BREAD					

Sizes

John Ciardi

If you were as big as a giant flea,
How much would you have to grow to be
The size of the tiniest head-to-tail
Very most midgety baby whale?

I mean to say—and it's no surprise—
Whatever you do about your size,
There's always something a size or two
Very much bigger or smaller than you.

I mean to say, what's big of some
Is small of others. Now get along home.
And whether you stay or wander far,
Be just the size of whatever you are.

How Beautiful with Mud

Hildegarde Dolson

Advertisers can make their products sound perfect, and in her quest for beauty, Hildegarde is willing to try just about anything.

Perhaps the surest way to tell when a female goes over the boundary from childhood into meaningful adolescence is to watch how long it takes her to get to bed at night. My own cross-over, which could be summed up in our family as "What on earth is Hildegarde doing in the bathroom?" must have occurred when I was in the eighth grade. Until then, I fell into bed dog-tired each night, after the briefest possible bout with toothbrush and washcloth. But once I'd become aware of the Body Beautiful as portrayed in advertisements in women's magazines, my absorption was complete and my attitude highly optimistic. I too would be beautiful. I would also be "Flower-fresh," "Fastidious and Dainty"—a triple-threat virtue obviously prized above pearls by the entire male sex, as depicted in the *Ladies' Home Journal.*

Somehow, out of my dollar-a-week allowance, I managed to buy Mum, Odorono, Listerine, and something called Nipso, guaranteed to remove excess hair from arms and legs. . . . I applied the Nipso painstakingly in the bathroom one night, with Sally, my younger sister, as my interested audience. The stuff had a rather overpowering, sickish-sweet scent, but this was a very minor drawback, considering the goal I had in mind. After Sally had been watching for a few minutes, she asked me to unlock the door and let her out. "Don't you want to see me wash it off?" I asked, rather hurt.

"No," Sally said. "It smells funny."

In the next hour, as my father, mother, and brothers followed their noses to the upstairs hall, there were more detailed descriptions of how Nipso affected the

olfactory senses. My brother Jimmy, being a simple child, merely said "Pugh" and went away. My father thought it was most like the odor of rotten eggs. But my younger brother Bobby said that it was more like a mouse that's been dead quite a while. Mother was more tactful, only remarking that Nipso obviously wasn't meant to be applied in a house people lived in. Since it certainly wasn't meant to be applied in a wooded dell, either, I was prevailed upon to throw the rest of the tube away.

I didn't mind too much, because I already had my eye on something that sounded far more fascinating than Nipso. This was a miraculous substance called Beauty Clay. Every time I read about it in a magazine advertisement, the words enveloped me in rapture. Even the story of its discovery was a masterpiece in lyrical prose. It seems this girl was traveling in an obscure European country (name on request) and ran out of those things ladies always run out of at the wrong time, such as powder and lotion. The worst part was that the girl really needed such artifices to cover up bumps. Through some intuitive process that escapes me at the moment, she had the presence of mind to go to a nearby hamlet, pick up a handful of mud, and plaster it on her face. Then she lay dozing in the sun, by a brook. When she came to, washed the claylike mud off her face, and looked at her reflection in the brook, she knew she had hit the jackpot. Boy, was she beautiful! Looking at the before-and-after pictures, I could see that this beauty was more than skin-deep, having benefited even her nose, eyes, and hair.

After pondering all this, I could well understand why a jar of the important Beauty Clay cost $4.98. In fact, it was dirt cheap at the price, and my only problem was how to lay my hands on $4.98. Certainly I had no intention of enlisting financial support from my parents. For one thing, it was too much money, and for another thing, parents ask too many questions. Far better, I thought, to let the transformation of their oldest daughter come as a dazzling surprise.

Due to the fact that I had such important things as Beauty Clay on my mind, it was understandable that my monthly marks in math should cause even more distress than usual in the bosom of my family. Each month, the school honor roll, consisting of the names of the ten highest students in each class, was published in the town newspaper. . . .

And each month, my own name was prominently absent. Appeals to my better nature, my pride, and the honor of the Dolsons did no good. I honestly meant well, and I even went so far as to carry books home from school and carry them back again the next morning. But math, implying as it did that x equals y, was simply beyond me. Finally my father said that if I got on the honor roll, he'd give me five dollars. Wobbly as I was in mathematics, it took me only a flash to realize this sum was approximately equal to $4.98, or the piddling price of the Beauty Clay. From there on in, I was straining every muscle. When I say that I got 89 in math and climbed to the bottom rung of the honor roll, I am stating a miracle simply. What is more important, I got the five dollars.

My father said that if I liked, he'd put most of it in my savings account. Bobby said, with even more enthusiasm, that he knew where I could get a bargain in a secondhand pistol. I declined both offers, marveling at the things men could think of to do with money, and made my way to Riesenman's drugstore. When Mr. Riesenman said he had no Beauty Clay, I was grieved. When he said he'd never even heard of the stuff, I was appalled. It took three trips to convince him that he must order it immediately, money on the line.

214

Then I went home and waited. With admirable restraint, I waited five days. After that, I made daily inquiries on my way home from school. If I was with friends, I'd say I had to do an errand for Mother and would catch up to them later. They must often have wondered, in the next thirty days, at the number of unobtainable items my mother demanded of a drugstore. Finally came the wonderful afternoon when Mr. Riesenman said, "Here you are, Hildegarde." His jovial air may have been due to the fact that he was rid of me at last. My own joy was primitive and unconfined. At last I'd got hold of a rainbow.

It took a week more before I could achieve the needed privacy for my quick-change act. Mother was taking Jimmy and Sally downtown to get new shoes, Bobby was going skiing, and my father, as usual, would be at the office. I got home to the empty house at twenty minutes of four, and made a beeline for the Beauty Clay. According to the directions, I then washed off all makeup, which in my own case was a faint dash of powder on my nose, and wrapped myself in a sheet "to protect that pretty frock," or, more accurately, my blue-serge middy blouse. Then I took a small wooden spatula the manufacturer had thoughtfully provided, and dug into the jar.

The Beauty Clay was a rather peculiar shade of grayish-green, and I spread this all over my face and neck—"even to the hairline where tell-tale wrinkles hide." The directions also urged me not to talk or smile during the twenty minutes it would take the clay to dry. The last thing in the world I wanted to do was talk or smile. That could come later. For now, a reverent silence would suffice. In fact, as the thick green clay dried firmly in place, it had to suffice. Even though my face and neck felt as if they'd been cast in cement, the very sensation reassured me. Obviously, something was happening. I sat bolt upright in a chair and let it happen.

After fifteen minutes of this, the doorbell rang. I decided to ignore it. The doorbell rang again and again, tingling at my conscience. Nobody at our house ever ignored doorbells, and I was relieved when it stopped. In my eagerness to see who had been calling on us, I ran to my window, opened it, and leaned out. The departing guest was only the man who brought us country butter each week, I was glad to note. Hearing the sound of the window opening above him, he looked up. When he saw me leaning out, his mouth dropped open and he let out a hoarse, awful sound. Then he turned and ran down the steep hill at incredible speed. I couldn't imagine what had struck him to act so foolishly.

It wasn't until I'd remembered that I understood. Swathed in a sheet, and with every visible millimeter of skin a sickly gray-green, I scared even myself.

According to the clock, the Beauty Clay had been on the required twenty minutes, and was now ready to be washed off. It occurred to me that if twenty minutes was enough to make me beautiful, thirty minutes or even forty minutes would make me twice as beautiful. Besides it would give me more lovely moments of anticipation, and Mother wouldn't be home till after five.

By the time my face was so rigid that even my eyeballs felt yanked from their sockets, I knew I must be done, on both sides. As I started back to the bathroom, I heard Bobby's voice downstairs yelling "Mom!" With the haste born of horror I ran back and just managed to bolt myself inside the bathroom as Bobby leaped up the stairs and came down the hall toward his room. Then I turned on the faucet and set to work. The directions had particularly warned, "Use only gentle splashes to remove the mask—no rubbing or washcloth." It took several minutes of gentle splashing to make me realize this was getting me nowhere fast. Indeed, it was like splashing playfully at the Rock of Gibraltar. I decided that maybe it wouldn't hurt if I rubbed the beauty mask just a little, with a nailbrush. This hurt only the nailbrush. I myself remained embedded in Beauty Clay.

By this time, I was getting worried. Mother would be home very soon and I needed a face—even any old face. Suddenly it occurred to me that a silver knife would be a big help, although I wasn't sure just how. When I heard Bobby moving around in his room, I yelled at him to bring me a knife from the dining-room sideboard. Rather, that's what I intended to yell, but my facial

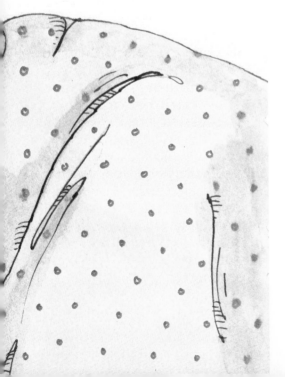

muscles were still cast in stone, and the most I could do was grunt. In desperation I ran down to the sideboard, tripping over my sheet as I went, and got the knife. Unfortunately, just as I was coming back through the dusky upstairs hall, Bobby walked out of his room and met me, face to face. The mental impact on Bobby was terrific. To do him justice he realized almost instantly that this was his own sister, and not, as he had at first imagined, a sea monster. But even this realization was not too reassuring.

I had often imagined how my family would look at me after the Beauty Clay had taken effect. Now it had taken effect—or even permanent possession of me—and Bobby was certainly reacting, but not quite as I'd pictured it.

"Wh-what?" he finally managed to croak, pointing at my face.

His concern was so obvious and even comforting that I tried to explain what had happened. The sounds that came out alarmed him even more.

Not having the time or the necessary freedom of speech to explain any further, I dashed into the bathroom and began hitting the handle of the knife against my rocky visage. To my heavenly relief, it began to crack. After repeated blows, which made me a little groggy, the stuff had broken up enough to allow me to wriggle my jaw. Meanwhile, Bobby stood at the door watching, completely bemused.

Taking advantage of the cracks in my surface, I dug the blade of the knife in, and by scraping, gouging, digging, and prying, I got part of my face clear. As soon as I could talk, I turned on Bobby. "If you tell anybody about this, I'll . . . ," I said fiercely.

Whether it was the intensity of my threat or a latent chivalry aroused by seeing a lady tortured before his very eyes, I still don't know, but Bobby said, "Cross my heart. . . ."

He then pointed out that spots of the gray-green stuff were still very much with me. As I grabbed up the nailbrush again, to tackle these remnants, he asked in a hushed voice. "But what is it?"

"Beauty Clay," I said. "I sent away for it."

Bobby looked as though he couldn't understand why anyone would deliberately send away for such punishment when there was already enough trouble in the world. However, for the first time in a long, hideous half hour, I remembered why I'd gone through this ordeal, and I now looked into the mirror expecting to see results that would wipe out all memory of suffering. The reflection that met my eye was certainly changed all right, varying as it did between an angry scarlet where the skin had been rubbed off, to the greenish splotches still clinging.

Maybe if I got it all off, I thought. When it was all off, except those portions wedded to my hair, I gazed at myself warily, all hope abandoned. My face was my own—but raw. Instead of the Body Beautiful I looked like the Body Boiled. Even worse, my illusions had been cracked wide open, and not by a silver knife.

"You look awfully red," Bobby said. I did indeed. To add to my troubles, we could now hear the family assembling downstairs, and Mother's voice came up, "Hildegarde, will you come set the table right away, dear?"

I moved numbly.

"You'd better take off the sheet," Bobby said.

I took off the sheet.

Just as I reached the stairs, he whispered, "Why don't you say you were frostbitten and rubbed yourself with snow?"

And in a way I had been frostbitten, to the quick. Lying in bed that night, still smarting, I tried to think up ways to get even. It wasn't clear to me exactly whom or what I had to get even with. All I knew was that I was sore and unbeautiful, and the loser of five dollars. With the hot and cold fury of a woman stung, I suddenly conceived my plan of revenge. It was so simple and logical and yet brilliant that my mind relaxed at last. Someday I too would write advertisements.

What Do You Think?

1. Imagine how the girl felt when she feared that she might never get the clay off her face. Think of at least five words describing the feelings you might have in the same situation.
2. What do you think Hildegarde learned from her experience?
3. What double meaning does the expression "dirt cheap" have in regards to the Beauty Clay?
4. Why do you think Hildegarde told her friends that she was on an errand for her mother to the drugstore? Tell about a time when you "made up" an excuse like this.
5. Tell about a time when you eagerly waited for something, only to be very disappointed by it when you got it.

Taking a Closer Look

1. What three reasons did Hildegarde have for not asking her parents for money to buy the Beauty Clay?
2. According to the author, how can you tell when a girl crosses over from childhood to adolescence?
3. What are the olfactory senses?
4. How did Hildegarde finally raise the money for the Beauty Clay?
5. What caused the man who delivered butter to run down the hill and away from the house?
6. What did the writer mean when she said, "My illusions had been cracked wide open, and not by a silver knife"?

Putting Ideas to Work

Compare at least three products whose advertising promises better skin. Look at the ingredients listed on the packages. Then compare the cost of the three products. Discuss your findings with the class.

Mrs. Dunn's Lovely, Lovely Farm

Myron Levoy

Mr. Warfield knew something was going on. But Amelia, Adeline, and Agatha had a surprise in store for him.

Mrs. Dunn had always wanted a farm. Back in the old country, she had lived in the great city of Dublin[1] with its crowded streets and noisy carts over the cobblestones, with its men forever looking for work, and its thin children, forever hungry.

She had made her husband promise that when they came to America they would save every penny they possibly could, so that in time they could buy a farm. A lovely farm with chickens and cows and potatoes, with the smell of sweet clover and the giggle of a brook always beyond the door. Where their children, Cathy and Neil, could have good fresh food, could grow and run and tumble. A lovely, lovely farm.

When they arrived in New York, with other thousands from Ireland and Italy and Hungary and Russia, they moved into a little apartment on the third floor of a building near Second Avenue. One of their neighbors was named DeMarco and another was named Kandel. In Dublin everyone had Irish names; this was something new and different, and a little frightening. But the neighbors said Hello and smiled and warned them about Mr. Warfield, the terrible, horrible landlord. And Mr. and Mrs. Dunn felt much better, because in Dublin the landlords had been terrible and horrible too. Things were becoming familiar very quickly.

The next task was for Mr. Dunn to find work. After much searching, he found a job hauling coal. He helped send the coal roaring like a river down a metal chute into the basements of buildings. Sometimes he would stand on the mound of coal in the back of the truck and coax it down through a square hole into the chute. And sometimes he would stand on the coal pile down in the cellar, clearing the coal away from the bottom of the chute so that more coal and still more coal could come roaring down into the coal bin.

Mr. Dunn would come home every night looking just like a great lump of coal himself. But after a good washing and a hot dinner, Mr. Dunn looked almost like Mr. Dunn again.

And though they could pay the rent and buy coats for the winter, and could afford a little more milk and butter than they could in Dublin, they couldn't seem to save much money. After a year, Mrs. Dunn counted four dollars and ninety-two cents in her secret empty cereal box, and Mr. Dunn had eight dollars and twelve cents in his shaving mug.

At that rate, they would never have enough for a farm. There were new shoes needed, and a new blanket, and a bigger stew pot, and this, and that, and the other. So Mrs. Dunn made a firm decision. They must buy their farm now, as much of it as they could, or the money would

---

[1] Dublin: capital city of Ireland

221

vanish like a mist over the chimneys of Dublin. And Mr. Dunn had to admit she was right.

That very next day, Mrs. Dunn bought a hen. They had told her at the market that it was a good dependable laying hen, a Rhode Island Red, the best. Mrs. Dunn wrapped the hen in a scarf, tucked it under her arm, and carried it five blocks back to her kitchen. Then she put the hen on the floor and watched it strut on the yellow linoleum.

The children named it Amelia for no special reason, and fed it cereal and corn and crusts of bread. Mr. Dunn brought home scraps of wood from the coal yard and built a coop. Then with more wood and some chicken wire, he built a little barnyard filled with dirt and pebbles in which Amelia could scratch. And he took some old felt hats and shaped them into nice, soft nests.

Soon, Amelia was joined by Agatha, and then Adeline. Now there were two eggs, sometimes three, every morning in the hatnests, fresh and delicious. Cathy and Neil loved Agatha and Amelia and Adeline as if they were their own sisters. Each hen was different: Amelia was very, very proud and strutted as if she were a rooster; Agatha was a busybody, forever poking into everything; Adeline was shy and loved to sit in the coop and preen. Soon, the other children in the building started bringing the three hens little presents: Aaron Kandel brought pieces of *matzo*[1] which Adeline particularly loved; Fred Reinhardt brought scraps of thick pumpernickel bread; and Vincent DeMarco brought dried chick-peas.[2] And sometimes, Mrs. Dunn would give one of the children a freshly laid egg to take home.

Now, it was time for the vegetables, for who ever heard of a farm without vegetables? Mr. Dunn built large, deep boxes, filled them with earth, and planted seeds. Then he put them on the fire escape outside the bedroom window. When the fire-escape landing was covered with boxes, he put new boxes on the iron stairs leading up to the next landing. Soon, the fire escape was blooming with the green shoots of tomato plants, string beans, potatoes, onions, and parsley. And on every windowsill were pots of herbs and spices: rosemary, thyme,[3] mint, chives.

On weekdays, Mrs. Dunn carefully weeded and watered the fire-escape garden and fed the chickens. And on Sundays, after he had tried to wash the last of the coal from his face and hands for the third time, Mr. Dunn would repair the chicken wire, and prop up the growing vegetables with tall sticks and string, and build new boxes. Then

---

[1] matzo (mät′zə): unleavened bread
[2] chick-peas: a legume
[3] thyme (tīm)

he and Mrs. Dunn would walk from room to room, admiring the pots of herbs and spices, the vegetables, the chickens, and the mushrooms growing in flat boxes on the kitchen shelves.

But one day, Mr. Warfield, the terrible, horrible landlord came to collect the rents. As he was about to enter the building, a sun shower drenched his hat. He took off the hat and looked at it with disbelief, for there wasn't a cloud in the sky. Perhaps a tenant had spilled some dishwater on him from above. He looked up and shook his fist toward the top of the building, at the hidden enemy.

His mouth dropped in astonishment and he forgot to bring down his fist, for up above, three stories up, was a hanging garden twining about the metal bars of the fire escape. A lady was watering the green mirage with a watering can, and some of it had dripped down the fire escape from landing to landing until it finally splashed on Mr. Warfield's head.

"This is an outrage!" Mr. Warfield muttered to himself. "It's completely unreasonable."

Then he plunged into the building and rushed toward the stairs.

"Ah, Mr. Warfield," said Mrs. Callahan at the first landing, "and when, pray tell, are you going to fix m'stove? The thing's got only one burner working. Do you expect me to pay m'rent when I can't cook soup and stew at the same time?"

"Oh please!" said Mr. Warfield, "I'll see you later. I've got a madhouse here. A madhouse! Let me go by, Mrs. Callahan."

"And what might be the trouble, if I may ask?" said Mrs. Callahan.

"Somebody's growing a tree on the fire escape!"

"Ah, to be sure, to be sure." And with that, Mrs. Callahan nudged her little girl, Noreen, standing next to her. Without a word, Noreen turned and raced up the two flights of stairs to warn her friend Cathy Dunn that Warfield, the monster landlord, was on his way up. "And tell me now, Mr. Warfield, but how would a tree gain the necessary nourishment on a fire escape, do you know?"

"I intend to find out, Mrs. Callahan, if you'll let me get by!"

"But m'stove, Mr. Warfield. I'm paying rent for three rooms and four burners."

"Yes, yes, yes, yes! Very reasonable request. We'll have it fixed in seventy-two hours. Now please let me get—"

"Seventy-two hours, is it? Make it twenty-four," said Mrs. Callahan.

"But that's only one *day*. That's unreasonable. Make it . . . forty-eight hours."

"Thirty-six, Mr. Warfield, or I'll have the Board of Health, I will."

"Forty!"

"Thirty-eight!"

"All right! We'll have it fixed within thirty-eight hours! Now let me *through!*"

And Mr. Warfield raced up the

flight of stairs to the second landing.

"Hello, Mr. Warfield!" Mrs. Grotowski called. "I dreamt about you last night! And what did I dream?"

"I don't care!" said Mr. Warfield. "Let me go by!"

"I'll *tell* you what. I dreamt that I took the money for your rent and tore it up into little shreds. Then I put a little salt on it, stirred in some nice milk, and made you eat every dollar of it until you choked. And *why?*"

"Please, Mrs. Grotowski! This isn't the time for your dreams!"

"I'll tell you why. Because you promised to have my apartment painted two months ago. Two months! Where are the painters? Did they join the Foreign Legion? Or is it possible that they've gone over Niagara Falls in a barrel?"

"We'll have the painters soon."

"When?"

"Soon. Very soon."

"How soon?"

"Very, very soon. Let me go by, Mrs. Grotowski, before I lose my temper."

"This week! I want them *this* week."

"Next week."

"By Friday!"

"By next Wednesday, Mrs. Grotowski."

"By next Monday, Mr. Warfield."

"Tuesday."

"All right. But it better be Tuesday," said Mrs. Grotowski.

"Tuesday. Absolutely, positively Tuesday."

Meanwhile, up in the Dunns' apartment, people were flying back and forth. Cathy and Neil had each grabbed a chicken and raced out the door. One chicken went into the DeMarco apartment, the other clucked away in Mrs. Kandel's kitchen. But the chicken left behind, Amelia—or was it Adeline?—had gotten so excited from all the rushing about that she'd flown up to the ceiling and was now roosting comfortably on top of the chandelier in the living room. Mr. Dunn wasn't at home, but Mrs. Dunn took vegetable boxes off the fire-escape landing and slid them under the bed. And from the apartment above, Mrs. Cherney climbed out of her bedroom window onto the fire escape, took more boxes off the iron stairs, and hid them in her own apartment. But try though they did, there just wasn't enough time to hide everything.

For Mr. Warfield had finally reached the third floor and was pounding at the Dunns' door. Three Rhode Island Reds answered with a cascade of *berawk-bawk-bawks:* one in Mrs. Kandel's kitchen, one in Mrs. DeMarco's bathroom, and one on Mrs. Dunn's chandelier. But Mr. Warfield knew they weren't chickens, because that would be impossible. It was the children making chicken noises at him. Why did they all hate him? He was a good man. Fair. Reasonable. Wasn't he always reasonable? . . . But what

224

was *this?* There were feathers in the hallway. Children having a pillow fight? Very likely. Ah well, children must play. No harm. Not like trees on the fire escape!

Then Mr. Warfield pounded on the door again; not the dainty tap-tap of a salesman, nor the thump-thump of a bill collector, but the Shaboom-Shaboom of a landlord. And again, from three apart-ments, three children in a superb imitation of three chickens, *berawk-bawked* away at Mr. War-field.

Why? thought Mr. Warfield. Why? He had three children of his own and they *loved* him. Didn't they? Of course they did.

At last the door opened a crack, and Mrs. Dunn's hand appeared with an envelope holding the rent

225

money. She waved the envelope up and down at Mr. Warfield. Mr. Warfield took the envelope, but also pushed firmly on the door.

"Mrs. Dunn, I'd like a word or two with you," he said.

"I'm feeling a bit ill today, Mr. Warfield, sir. Would you be so kindly as to stop back next week."

"Mrs. Dunn! There is a tree growing on your fire escape!"

"You're blessed. There's many a blind man would trade this very building for your keen eyesight. But still, a tree cannot truly grow on a fire escape. Good day to you now."

"Good day my foot! I demand to see the condition of that fire escape. As landlord, I have the right to enter and inspect the premises at reasonable hours. I'm a reasonable man and I would never come at an unreasonable hour."

"Why it's nearly four o'clock. I've got to do m'husband's supper. 'Tis not a reasonable hour at all," said Mrs. Dunn.

"Either you let me enter, madam, or I'll call the police. *And* the fire department. A tree on the fire escape is a fire hazard. Let me in!"

"Tomorrow."

"NOW!" shouted Mr. Warfield. And with that, the chicken on the chandelier clucked again. "Did you hear that, Mrs. Dunn?"

"Sounded like a cuckoo clock. Cuckoo, cuckoo. 'Tis four o' the clock, you see."

"Nonsense. You have a *chicken* in there! My building has

chickens!" At that, all three hens in all three apartments *berawk-bawked* again. Then Mr. Warfield pushed his way past Mrs. Dunn and stormed into her living room.

"My chandelier!" shouted Mr. Warfield.

" 'Tisn't *your* chandelier. I've paid the rent. 'Tis *my* chandelier," said Mrs. Dunn.

Mr. Warfield rushed through to the bedroom and stared at the remains of the farm on the fire escape. "My fire escape!" His face was flushed, his eyes were bulging. "Unbelievable! Mrs. Dunn, what are these weeds supposed to *be*?"

"That? Why that's onions, Mr. Warfield."

"*This* is an *onion?*"

"Oh, you can't see it. The onion's beneath the dirt. Least I hope 'tis."

"And *this?*" he said, pointing.

"That's supposed to be potatoes. But I fear for them. The soil's not deep enough."

"Incredible!" he said. "Don't you like geraniums, Mrs. Dunn? I thought people liked to grow geraniums. Look out the window, across the street. See the windowsills? There and there. And over there. Everyone *else* is growing geraniums."

"That's a good *idea*, Mr. Warfield," said Mrs. Dunn. " 'Twould brighten up the house. I'll fetch some seed tomorrow."

"No, no. I didn't mean . . . Mrs. Dunn, look here. This is a firetrap! And that chicken—"

"I have two more, visiting with the neighbors."

"Well, that, Mrs. Dunn, is a relief. I thought *all* the tenants had gone insane."

"No, 'tis only m'self. But I do think I'm as sane as you, if not a bit saner. Because you see, I shall have the freshest vegetables in the city of New York. I already have the freshest eggs."

"Those chickens, in an apartment, are a health hazard. You'll have to remove them! Sell them to a farmer or a butcher."

"I shan't. They stay right here."

"That's unreasonable. I'm a reasonable man, Mrs. Dunn. Say something reasonable, *ask* something reasonable, and I'll say: *that's* reasonable."

"Very well. Why don't you pretend that you hadn't come at all today. Then you wouldn't have seen anything, would you, and your mind would rest easy," said Mrs. Dunn.

"Completely unreasonable! And *that's* why you tenants don't like me. Because *I'm* reasonable, and you're all *un*reasonable. Simple as that."

"Oh, I like you, Mr. Warfield."

"Nonsense."

"Any landlord who would offer me the use of his roof for a fine little garden must be a very likable *and* reasonable man."

"I didn't offer you any roof, Mrs. Dunn."

"You were going to. I saw it on the tip of your lips."

"My *lips?*"

"And you were going to say how much better 'twould be if the chickens had a much bigger coop up there on the roof."

"I was never going to say—"

"Tut, tut, Mr. Warfield," said Mrs. Dunn. "You've as good as said it. And I was going to answer that for such generosity you should surely receive some fresh string beans and onions and potatoes in season. And you were going to say, 'Ah, and how lovely the roof would look with greenery all about.' And I was about to answer, 'Yes, Mr. Warfield, and the tenants would surely look at you most affectionately.' Would they not, now?"

"*Hmmm,*" said Mr. Warfield, thinking.

"Reasonable or unreasonable?" asked Mrs. Dunn.

"*Hmmm* . . . well . . . I'd have to give this some thought."

"But you're a man of *action*, Mr. Warfield. You pound on the door like a very tiger."

"Yes. Well . . . it's not *un*reasonable," said Mr. Warfield. "If you didn't already *have* any chickens or trees or onions, I would say No. But since you *do* have all this *jungle* of creatures and vines . . . I would, after careful consideration, being after all a human being, I would . . . *ahem, ahem* . . . say . . . *ahem* . . . yes."

"Oh, you are a darling man, Mr. Warfield. A darling, *darling* man."

227

"Here, Mrs. Dunn! Watch your language! I mean to say! *Darling* man?"

"Oh, back in the old country, it only means you're nice, that's all."

"Oh. Now remember, Mrs. Dunn, a bargain's a bargain. I expect one tenth of everything you grow as my roof rent. Is that a deal?"

" 'Tis a deal."

"Except the onions. You can keep them all. I hate onions. My whole family hates onions."

And with that, Mr. Warfield slammed his hat on his head, only to find it was still wet from Mrs. Dunn's watering can. Without a word, he turned and stalked out to the living room. At that moment, Amelia—or was it Adeline?—up on the chandelier decided it was time to come down. For there, on top of Mr. Warfield's head, was her nest-shaped-like-a-hat, moving by. And down she came, wings beating, feathers flying, on top of Mr. War-field's head. "Oh, no!" shouted Mr. Warfield as he raced to the hallway with the chicken flapping on top of him.

"She likes you!" called Mrs. Dunn. "She knows you have a good heart! Chickens can tell right off!"

But Mr. Warfield didn't hear this very clearly, for as he raced out to the hallway and down the stairs, all three chickens started their *berawk-bawking* again, and the loudest of all was the one on top of Mr. Warfield. He finally escaped by leaving his nest-shaped-like-a-hat behind.

And so Mrs. Dunn moved everything to the roof, and Mr. Dunn added still more boxes for vegetables. Cathy and Neil and their friends went up to the roof every afternoon to feed the chickens and water the plants. And Mrs. Dunn had her lovely, lovely farm—or at least she thought she did, which comes to the same thing in the end.

What Do You Think?

1. Do you think Mrs. Dunn's idea about having a farm in the middle of New York City is a good one? Why or why not?
2. What kind of a person is Mrs. Dunn? What one word would you choose to describe her?
3. Why does Mrs. Dunn think she is saner than Mr. Warfield? Do you agree with her? Why or why not?
4. Why do you think Mr. Warfield puts so much importance on being "reasonable"?
5. Was Mr. Warfield reasonable in his wishes to remove the chickens from the apartment and the plants from the fire escape? Explain your answer.

Taking a Closer Look

1. From what country did Mrs. Dunn come?
2. What led Mrs. Dunn to the conclusion that they had to begin buying their farm immediately?
3. Give examples from the story of how Mrs. Dunn was able to adapt to her surroundings.
4. How did the neighbors help keep Mr. Warfield from getting to Mrs. Dunn's apartment in a hurry?
5. How did Mrs. Dunn manage to influence Mr. Warfield?
6. What agreement did Mrs. Dunn and Mr. Warfield make at the end of this story?

Putting Ideas to Work

Pretend that you live in a city apartment and want to have a garden. Write a paragraph or two telling what you might do.

Reading Bus and Train Schedules

Learning to read a schedule is nothing to clown around about. The first step is to know where to get a train or bus schedule. The station is the place. Ask at the information booth or at the ticket or fare window. Sometimes, the bus driver or train conductor carries the route schedule.

Do all schedules look and read the same? Yes and no. They all give times, dates, and names of stops. They all help you to plan the quickest route or closest destination. Some tell fares and where to call for further assistance. Some also tell exceptions, such as "must have exact change."

HARVARD SQUARE-DUDLEY

VIA MASSACHUSETTS AVENUE
FARE 25¢   EXACT CHANGE REQUIRED

	WEEKDAY		SATURDAY		SUNDAY	
	Leave Harvard	Leave Dudley	Leave Harvard	Leave Dudley	Leave Harvard	Leave Dudley
MORNING		4:44	5:10	4:44	5:50	5:20
		5:04	5:30	5:04	every 30 min. until	every 30 min. until
	5:10	5:24	5:46	5:20	9:20	8:50
	5:30	5:40	6:01	5:35	every 20 min.until	every 20 min.until
	5:50	5:55	6:14	5:48	11:40	10:50
	6:06	6:07	6:27	6:01	11:55	11:05
	6:20	6:19	6:40	6:14		11:20
	6:35	6:31	6:53	6:27		11:35
	6:47	6:43	7:06	6:40		11:50
	6:59	every 10 min. or less until	7:19	6:51		
	7:11	10:00	7:33	7:04		
	every 10 min. or less until	10:16	7:46	7:17		
	9:51	every 11 min. until	7:59	7:29		
	every 11 min. until	11:55	8:12	7:42		
	11:52		8:25	7:55		
			8:39	8:08		
			every 13 min. until	8:21		
			9:44	8:34		
			every 11 min. until	8:47		
			11:56	8:59		
				9:12		
				every 11 min. until		
				11:56		
AFTERNOON	12:03	12:06	12:08	12:07	12:10	12:05
	every 11 min. until	12:17	every 11 min. until	every 11 min. until	12:25	every 11 min. until
	12:58	12:28	5:49	5:48	12:40	5:46
	every 10 min. or less until	every 10 min. or less until			12:51	
	5:53	5:58			1:01	
					every 11 min. until	
					5:58	
EVENING	6:00	6:08	6:00	6:00	6:10	6:01
	every 10 min. or less until	6:18	6:11	6:12	6:22	6:16
	7:00	6:30	6:22	6:25	6:35	6:31
	7:20	every 15 min. until	6:33	6:40	6:50	6:46
	7:30	12:00	6:45	7:00	7:05	7:03
	every 15 min. until	12:30	every 15 min. until	7:12	7:20	7:20
	12:30	1:00	12:00	7:29	7:35	every 20 min. until
	1:00		12:15	7:45	7:50	12:00
	1:24		12:30	every 15 min. until	every 20 min. until	12:30
			1:00	12:00	12:30	1:00
			1:24	12:30	1:00	
				1:00	1:24	

NOTES:
LIGHT TYPE IS A.M.
BOLD TYPE IS P.M.

HOLIDAYS:
June 18—See WEEKDAY
July 4, Sept. 3—See SUN

THIS DIAGRAM SHOWS THE APPROXIMATE TRAVEL TIME IN MINUTES BETWEEN STOPS, SUBJECT TO TRAFFIC CONDITIONS.

13-18 min.
Harvard Sq.
Camb. City Hall
Central Sq.
MIT
Auditorium
Boylston St.
Prudential Ctr.
Symphony Hall
(Green Line)

10-15 min.
Horticultural Hall
Boston Arena
Northampton
Dudley

THE TOTAL TRIP TIME IN ONE DIRECTION IS: 23 - 33 MINUTES.

FOR ASSISTANCE CALL 555 - 3200

Train No.	Name	How often	NEW YORK (Pennsylvania Station) NY	RYE NY	NEW HAVEN CT	NEW HAVEN CT	KINGSTON RI	PROVIDENCE RI	ROUTE 128	BOSTON MA (South Station)	SERVICES
		Miles	0	27		75	161	188	220	232	
			Dp	Dp	Ar	Dp	Dp	Dp	Dp	Ar	
66	The Zoom	Daily	3:10a	3:50a	4:45a	5:05a	6:47a	7:25a	8:03a	8:25a	⬛ ιΟι ✳
84	The Lollygag	Ⓐ Daily	7:10a	7:48a	8:45a	8:55a	10:26a	10:54a	11:27a	11:50a	ιΟι ⊛
93	The Sonic Storm	Daily	9:10a	9:48a	10:45a	10:55a	12:29p	12:57p	1:29p	2:07p	⬛ ιΟι
101	The One Choo	Daily	11:10a	Lightning Service	12:45p	12:55p	2:24p	2:50p	3:21p	3:57p	⬛ ιΟι ✳
123	The Whoosh	Daily	1:05p	1:43p	2:40p	2:50p	4:26p	4:54p	5:24p	6:06p	⬛ ιΟι ✳
137	The Dawdler	Daily	3:10p	—	4:45p	4:55p	6:24p	6:50p	7:20p	8:00p	⬛ ιΟι
146	The Two Choo	Ⓔ Fr and Su only	4:10p	—	5:38p	5:53p	8:22p	7:41p	8:23p	8:50p	⬛ ιΟι
154	The Thunderbolt	Daily	5:10p	Lightning Service	6:42p	6:52p	10:07p	8:50p	9:20p	10:00p	⬛ ιΟι $

NOTE—Due to track work in progress, passengers might be asked to push train.

--- SYMBOLS ---

- ≣ Streamlined Rail Diesel Car.
- ® All-reserved train.
- ⬛ Sleeping or Club Car Service available. At-your-seat Food and Beverage Service available in club cars.
- ▦ Complete Dining and Beverage Service.
- ιΟι Tray Food and Beverage Service.
- ▲ Snack and Beverage Service.
- ✳ Checked Baggage Service; consult agent for further information and exceptions.

- ⊛ Amblongus pie served.
- $ As conductor receives fares, all tickets will be punched in presence of passengers.

CIRCLED LETTERS
- Ⓐ Will *not* operate July 4 and Sept. 5.
- Ⓔ Will operate July 4 *instead of* July 3, and Sept. 5 *instead of* Sept. 4.

Schedules tend to be arranged in different diagram-type forms. The two most common are *maps* and *timetables*. The maps show all routes and where to make connections to other lines. The timetables are arranged in columns and show routes, times, and names of starting and stopping points.

Also be sure to check for any symbols—they give important information. For example, a symbol will tell you whether a bus or train is "express" (no stops until destination) or a "local" (stops at every station). If you want to reach the end of the line in a hurry and you board a local, you will arrive at the end of your wits!

The bus-schedule example gives both timetable and map information. The type of print used (light or heavy) is its main symbol. Once you decide if you're coming or going, choose the time and day of departure. Then, check to see how often the bus runs. Use both the map and the minutes scale at the bottom of the schedule to find out how long the trip will take.

Now look at the train schedule on page 231. Compare it with the bus schedule. The train schedule gives more information because it involves greater distances. Symbols are defined. It is important to find where on the schedule the symbols are placed. If a particular train doesn't offer a service you need, you might want to adjust your travel plans.

Now is the time to get a pencil. Discover a part of North America by traveling through these questions. Tell which schedule you used to answer each question.

1. What is the earliest bus leaving Harvard Sq. (in Cambridge, Massachusetts) on Sunday morning? Will the driver make change?

2. When does the last bus leave Dudley on weekday nights? If you want to take this trip on July 4, what should you do?

3. Why can't you take "The Two Choo" on Wednesday? What do "Dp" and "Ar" mean?

4. What time should you leave New York City if you want to reach Providence, Rhode Island, at 8:50 p.m.? What is the name of the station in New York?

5. How many minutes does it take

to go from Providence, RI, to Boston, MA, on "The Zoom"? Is "The Whoosh" faster?

6. Approximately how many minutes does it take to travel from Harvard Sq. to Boylston St.? Will this trip take more time at 5 p.m. on Friday? Why or why not?

7. If you left Harvard Sq. on the 7 p.m. bus Tuesday, what is the earliest time you could reach Dudley? Where did you look to find this information on the bus schedule?

8. Name three trains that do not stop at Rye, NY, going from Pennsylvania Station. How many miles is it from New York City to Rye, NY?

9. Is there food service on "The Lollygag"? If so, what kind is it? Does "The Lollygag" provide a sleeping car?

10. You want to travel from Pennsylvania Station in New York to South Station in Boston. A friend is picking you up at 4 p.m. You need your bags checked, and you're tired and hungry. You can't leave New York before 11 a.m.

   a. Pick the best train for your needs. Tell the name and the number of the train. Explain why you picked that particular train.

   b. How many miles is it between New York and Boston by train?

Richard Armour

From the pen of a
humorous author,
social studies can
be given quite
a twist.

The Discovery of America

America was founded by Columbus in 1492. This is an easy date to remember because it rhymes with "ocean blue," which was the color of the Atlantic in those days. If he had sailed a year later the date would still be easy to remember because it would rhyme with "boundless sea."

Columbus fled to this country because of persecution by Ferdinand and Isabella, who refused to believe the world was round, even when Columbus showed them an egg. Ferdinand later became famous because he objected to bullfights and said he preferred to smell flowers if he had to smell anything. He was stung in the end by a bee.

Before Columbus reached North America, which he named after a man called American Vesuvius, he cried "Ceylon! Ceylon!" because he wanted to see India, which was engraved on his heart, before he died. When he arrived, he cried again. This time he cried "Excelsior!" meaning "I have founded it." Excelsior has been widely used ever since by persons returning with chinaware from China, with indiaware from India, and with underware from Down Under.

Columbus was mistaken in thinking he had reached India when actually he had not got even as far as Indiana. There is still a great deal of confusion about the East and the West. As Columbus discovered, if you go west long enough you find yourself in the east, and vice versa. The East and the West are kept apart by the Date Line, just as the North and South are kept apart by the Masons' Dixon Line. In the New World most of the eastern half of the country is called the Middle West, although it is known as the East by those who live in the Far West.

Accompanied by his devoted followers, the Knights of Columbus, Columbus made several other voyages in search of India. Try as he might, however, he kept discovering America, and finally returned to Spain to die. He lived for a time in Madrid, but spent his last days in Disgrace.

Further Explorations

After Columbus proved the world was round, a great many people went around it. Marco Polo, who was one of the earlier explorers, had the misfortune to live several centuries before Columbus. Therefore, although he got around a good deal, he did not get completely around. He went far to the north, however, and is remembered for his discovery of the Polo regions.

The chief rivals in exploration were England and Spain. The struggle between England and Spain came to a climax in an epic sea battle off the Azores known as the Last Fight of the Revenge. In this decisive conflict, Sir Richard Grenville and Alfred Lord Tennyson proved conclusively that the lighter English warships could get more miles to the galleon.

England has ruled the waves ever since and has kept the sun from setting anywhere on her empire, thus providing a longer working day than in other countries.

The Virginia Colony

All this time there was not much happening in the New World, except that it was steadily growing older.

This period, known as the Doldrums, came to an end in fifteen-something-or-other when Sir Walter Raleigh, a man with a pointed beard and a pointless way of muddying his cloak, established a colony in America in the hope of pleasing the Queen, whose favor he had been in but was temporarily out of.

Although he claimed the new land in the name of Elizabeth, he called it Virginia, which aroused Elizabeth's anger and caused her to confine Sir Walter in a tower. While imprisoned, Sir Walter made good use of his time by writing a history of the world on such scraps of paper as he could find.

He had barely completed his history when he lost his head.

The Virginia Colony was lost for a time, and its name was changed to The Lost Colony, but it was subsequently found at

about the place where it was last seen. Its original name of Virginia was restored because Elizabeth no longer cared, being dead.[1]

Captain John Smith

Captain John Smith was the first of a long line of Smiths who came to the New World to keep up with the Joneses.

He was captured by the great Indian Chief, Powhatan, and was about to be killed when Popocatepetl, the fiery young daughter of the Chief, stepped in. We are not told what she stepped in, but she saved Captain John Smith's life, for which he thanked her.

The Pilgrims

The Pilgrims were a branch of the Puritans, and were proud of their family tree. Being unhappy under King James, they left England and went to Leyden, a city in Holland noted for the discovery of electricity in a jar. (Electricity was subsequently lost for a while, but was rediscovered, by accident, when Benjamin Franklin was told to go fly a kite, and did.) After several years in Holland, the Pilgrims decided to set out for the New World. This decision to move is known as Pilgrims' Progress.

The ship on which they sailed was the *Mayflower*. In stormy weather the travelers descended below the heaving decks, thus becoming the *Mayflower* descendants. There they passed the weary hours comparing genealogies.

It was a long and perilous voyage across the Atlantic. Several times they were blown off their course. But finally, in 1620, which was a doubly Memorable Year because it was also the year in which they set sail, they sighted the rocky coast. The rock on which they landed they called Plymouth Rock because it reminded them of another rock of the same name in England. They built a small picket fence around it and made it a national shrine.

The first four men ashore became our fourfathers.

---

[1]The end of Elizabeth is known as the Elizabethan Period.

What Do You Think?

1. Was Ferdinand of Spain really famous for the reasons that the author gives? If the king of Spain didn't act in that way, then who did?
2. What was the real reason for Columbus's voyage to America? Why is the author's version funny?
3. The author says that Columbus "lived for a time in Madrid, but spent his last days in Disgrace." What is funny about this statement?
4. What was Powhatan's daughter really named? Why do you think the author changed the name of the "fiery young daughter"? (Hint: Use a dictionary or encyclopedia to find out what Popocatepetl really is.)
5. Some people today take great pride if they can prove that their ancestors crossed the ocean on the *Mayflower*. How does the author use this fact humorously?
6. A pun is a humorous play on words—one word is substituted for another word with the same or similar sound. An example: "The first four men ashore became our fourfathers" (instead of "forefathers"). Can you find another pun in this story?

Taking a Closer Look

1. For what reason did Ferdinand supposedly become famous?
2. In this version of history, why did Columbus go to America?
3. Where did Columbus die?
4. For what is Marco Polo supposedly remembered?
5. According to the author, what did Popocatepetl do?
6. What did the "*Mayflower* descendants" do?

Putting Ideas to Work

Write a funny version of some historical event. Some possibilities: Paul Revere's ride; the first Olympic games in Greece; Mackenzie's explorations of the Canadian wilderness; the astronauts landing on the moon.

Mark Twain

Is He Dead?

Mark Twain

The travel guide tries to make things interesting for the tourists. Watch what happens when Mark Twain decides to make things "interesting" for the guide.

In this place I may as well jot down a chapter concerning those necessary nuisances, European guides. Many a man has wished in his heart he could do without his guide, but, knowing he could not, has wished he could get some amusement out of him as a remuneration for the affliction of his society. We accomplished this latter matter, and if our experience can be made useful to others they are welcome to it.

Guides know about enough English to tangle everything up so that a man can make neither head nor tail of it. They know their story by heart—the history of every statue, painting, cathedral, or other wonder they show you. They know it and tell it as a parrot would—and if you interrupt and throw them off the track, they have to go back and begin over again. All their lives long they are employed in showing strange things to foreigners and listening to their bursts of admiration. It is human nature to take delight in exciting admiration. It is what prompts children to say "smart" things, and do absurd ones, and in other ways "show off" when company is present. It is what makes gossips turn out in rain and storm to go and be the first to tell a startling bit of news. Think, then, what a passion it becomes with a guide, whose privilege it is, every day, to show to strangers wonders that throw them into perfect ecstasies of admiration! He gets so that he could not by any possibility live in a soberer atmosphere. After we discovered this, we *never* went into ecstasies anymore—we never admired anything—we never showed any but impassible faces and stupid indifference in the presence of the sublimest wonders a guide had to display. We had found their weak point. We have made good use of it ever since. We have made some of those people savage at times, but we have never lost our own serenity.

The doctor asks the questions generally because he can keep his countenance, and look more like an inspired idiot, and throw more imbecility into the tone of his voice than any man that lives. It comes natural to him.

The guides in Genoa are delighted to secure an American party, because Americans so much wonder and deal so much in sentiment and emotion before any relic of Columbus. Our guide there fidgeted about as if he had swallowed a spring mattress. He was full of animation—full of impatience. He said:

"Come wis me, genteelmen! Come! I show you ze letter-writing by Christopher Colombo! Write it himself! Write it wis his own hand! Come!"

He took us to the municipal palace. After much impressive fumbling of keys and opening of locks, the stained and aged document was spread before us. The guide's eyes sparkled. He danced about us and tapped the parchment with his finger:

"What I tell you genteelmen! Is it not so? See! Handwriting Christopher Colombo! Write it himself!"

We looked indifferent—unconcerned. The doctor examined the document very deliberately, during a painful pause. Then he said, without any show of interest:

"Ah—Ferguson—what—what did you say was the name of the party who wrote this?"

"Christopher Colombo! Ze great Christopher Colombo!" Another deliberate examination.

"Ah—did he write it himself or—or how?"

"He write it himself! Christopher Colombo! His own handwriting, write by himself!"

Then the doctor laid the document down and said:

"Why, I have seen boys in America only fourteen years old that could write better than that."

"But zis is ze great Christo——"

"I don't care who it is! It's the worst writing I ever saw. Now you mustn't think you can impose on us because we are strangers. We are not fools, by a good deal. If you have got any specimens of penmanship of real merit, trot them out! And if you haven't, drive on!"

We drove on. The guide was considerably shaken up, but he

made one more venture. He had something which he thought would overcome us. He said:

"Ah, genteelmen, you come wis me! I show you beautiful, oh, magnificent bust Christopher Colombo! Splendid, grand, magnificent!"

He brought us before the beautiful bust—for it *was* beautiful—and sprang back and struck an attitude:

"Ah, look genteelmen! Beautiful, grand—bust Christopher Colombo! Beautiful bust, beautiful pedestal!"

The doctor put up his eyeglass—procured for such occasions:

"Ah—what did you say this gentleman's name was?"

"Christopher Colombo! Ze great Christopher Colombo!"

"Christopher Colombo——the great Christopher Colombo. Well, what did *he* do?"

"Discover America! Discover America!"

"Discover America. No—that statement will hardly wash. We are just from America ourselves. We heard nothing about it. Christopher Colombo—pleasant name—is—is he dead?"

We have made it interesting for this Roman guide. Yesterday we spent three or four hours in the Vatican again, that wonderful world of curiosities. We came very near expressing interest sometimes—even admiration—it was very hard to keep from it. We succeeded, though. Nobody else ever did in the Vatican museums. The guide was bewildered—nonplused. He walked his legs off nearly, hunting up extraordinary things, and exhausted all his ingenuity on us, but it was a failure; we never showed any interest in anything. He had reserved what he considered to be his greatest wonder till the last—a royal Egyptian mummy, the best preserved in the world, perhaps. He took us there. He felt so sure this time that some of his old enthusiasm came back to him:

"See, genteelmen! Mummy! Mummy!"

The eyeglass came up as calmly, as deliberately as ever.

"Ah—Ferguson—what did I understand you to say the gentleman's name was?"

"Name? He got no name! Mummy! 'Gyptian mummy!"

"Yes, yes. Born here?"

"No! *Gyptian* mummy!"

"Ah, just so. Frenchman, I presume?"

"No! *Not* Frenchman, not Roman! Born in Egypta!"

"Born in Egypta. Never heard of Egypta before. Foreign locality, likely. Mummy—mummy. How calm he is—how self-possessed. Is, ah—is he dead?"

We make it exceedingly interesting for this Ferguson. However, he has paid us back partly, without knowing it. He came to the hotel this morning to ask if we were up, and he endeavored as well as he could to describe us, so that the landlord would know which persons he meant. He finished with the casual remark that we were lunatics. The observation was so innocent and so honest that it amounted to a very good thing for a guide to say.

There is one remark (already mentioned) which never yet has failed to disgust these guides. We use it always when we can think of nothing else to say. After they have exhausted their enthusiasm pointing out to us and praising the beauties of some ancient bronze image or broken-legged statue, we look at it stupidly and in silence for five, ten, fifteen minutes—as long as we can hold out, in face—and then ask:

"Is—is he dead?"

That conquers the serenest of them. It is not what they are looking for—especially a new guide. Our Roman Ferguson is the most patient, unsuspecting, long-suffering subject we have had yet. We shall be sorry to part with him. We have enjoyed his society very much. We trust he has enjoyed ours, but we are harassed with doubts.

What Do You Think?

1. Why is it that even though travelers often feel as though the guide is a nuisance, they can't do without him?
2. Could this selection be a criticism of American tourists? Why or why not?
3. Using details from the story, tell whether you agree that guides are like gossips and show-off children.
4. Do you think the tourists were fair in their treatment of guides?

Taking a Closer Look

1. Do you think that the doctor needed to wear glasses in order to see well? Support your answer with information from the story.
2. Why does Mark Twain think that having a guide call him a lunatic is a good thing?
3. How would you describe Mark Twain's attitude toward guides?
4. What did Mark Twain and his friends do to irritate the guides?
5. Why did the doctor generally ask the questions for this group of tourists?

Putting Ideas to Work

Think about a country that you would like to visit. What would you want to see and do if you were to go there? Write a short paragraph and be ready to share it with the class.

REAL IMAGININGS

"Imaginings" can be large or small. They can be special experiences of the once-in-a-while, or they can be woven into the day-to-day. How are the characters in this unit affected by real imaginings?

Castles in the Air

Henry David Thoreau

If you have built
castles in the air,
your work need not be lost;
that is where they should be.
Now put the foundations under them.

A Trip for Mrs. Taylor

Hugh Garner

How far away does someplace have
to be if you're "going on a trip"
to get there? What makes a trip
exciting?

Mrs. Taylor got out of bed at five o'clock that morning, an hour ahead of her usual time for getting up. She moved around her attic room with the stealth of a burglar, making herself her morning cup of tea on the hot plate, and dressing quietly so as not to disturb her landlady, Mrs. Connell, on the floor below.

She dressed her tiny self carefully, putting on a clean white slip and her black Sunday frock. After she had drunk her tea and eaten a slice of thinly margarined toast she washed her cup and saucer in some water she had drawn from the bathroom the evening before, and put them away on her "kitchen" shelf in the clothes closet. Then she tiptoed down the steep stairs to the bathroom and washed her face and hands—"a lick and a spit" as she called it.

When she returned to her room her seventy-six-year-old face shone with wrinkled cleanliness and the excitement of the day. She combed her thinning gray hair and did it up with pins into an unsevere bun at the back of her head.

She took her old black straw hat from its paper bag and put it on, primping a bit before the dime-store mirror on the wall, smiling at herself and wishing that her false teeth were a little whiter.

All through her preparations she had been taking hurried glances at the alarm clock on the dresser. But now, when she was ready to go, she saw that she still had nearly two hours before train time. The train left at seven o'clock Standard Time, which was eight o'clock Daylight Saving, and here it was only a quarter to six. Still, it would take a half-hour to get downtown to the station, and she couldn't afford to be late on this day of days.

She opened her small cardboard suitcase and carefully checked its contents once again. There was a clean change of underwear, a towel and soap, some handkerchiefs, two pairs of black stockings, Bert's picture in its frame, and one of the two boys in uniform, her blouse and blue skirt, and the red velvet dress that Mrs. Eisen had given her the year before. The dress didn't fit her, but she liked its rich color and the feeling of wealth it gave, just to possess it.

She sat down on the edge of the bed and let the wonderful coming events of the day take over her thoughts. The idea for the trip had come to her about a week before, on the day she had received her July old-age pension check. She had been down to the main post office, mailing a set of hand-crocheted runners[1] to her daughter-in-law, Ruth, in Montreal when the idea struck her. Seeing all the holiday crowds hurrying into the station had prompted her to go in and inquire about train times.

The hurry and excitement of the place had brought back the memories of those happier times when she and Bert and young Johnnie—yes, and young Bert, too, who was killed in Italy— had gone away sometimes in the summer. Their trips hadn't been long ones, and their destination was usually the home of her now-dead cousin Flora in Jamesville. But they had been filled with all the hustle and bustle of getting ready, packing cheese and peanut-butter sandwiches for their lunches, and making sure Bert had the tickets. There had been the warm picnicky feeling going to the station on the streetcar, trying to keep young Bert from kneeling on the seat and brushing his

---

[1] runners: long narrow strips of fabric used to protect furniture

248

feet on the man beside him (she wiped away a tear at the memory) and the awareness that she *belonged* to the crowds around her.

That was the thing she had missed most during the past few years, the feeling of being one with those about her. Her loneliness and the striving to live on her old-age pension made mere existence a hardship. Mrs. Connell, her landlady, was a kindly soul, not much younger than herself, but she had no idea of what it was like to be cooped up month after month in a dreary little room, without even a radio to keep you company, without even a cat or a dog or a canary—nothing but the four walls, an electric plate, a bed, and a dresser.

Of course, she told herself, she could have gone to live with Johnnie and Ruth in Montreal, but she'd seen too much of that sort of thing in the past. When Johnnie had married down there after the war she had felt a sinking in the stomach at the thought that he, too, was leaving her. "Come on down there with me, Ma," he had said, but she had sensed the reluctance behind his words. "I'm not going to be a built-in baby-sitter for my grandchildren," she had answered, trying to cover her sense of loss and disappointment under her bantering words. She was independent, a woman who had run her own home for years, and brought up her two boys on the small and undependable wages of a laborer husband. But sometimes her independence melted under her silent tears, and she wished that once, just once, somebody would need her again.

But today was not the time for such gloomy thoughts. She glanced at the clock and saw that it was after seven. She stood up, straightened her hat once more, and picking up the heavy suitcase, made her way from the room, closing the door silently behind her. She had no wish to waken Mrs. Connell and have to answer to the surprised questions of that lady. This trip was going to be a secret one, known only to herself.

She hurried down the street through the warmth of the summer morning as fast as the heavy bag would allow her. When she reached the streetcar stop she put the suitcase down on the sidewalk and searched in her purse for a car ticket. There was very little money left from her pension check. But by

doing without a few things to eat over the past week she had managed to save the expenses for the trip.

When the streetcar came along she climbed aboard and sat down near the front of the car. She was aware of the stares from the men and women who were going to work, and she felt important for the first time in months. There was something friendly in the glances they gave her, and perhaps even a slight envy that she should be going away while they could only look forward to another stifling day in their offices and factories.

The downtown streets at this hour of the day were strange to her, but there was a tired camaraderie among the people getting on and off the car which brought back memories she had almost forgotten. Once again she saw herself as a young woman going to work as they were, stepping down from the open-sided cars they had in those days, proud of her narrow waist and new high-buttoned boots. She felt almost young again and smiled apologetically as a thin girl in slacks nearly tripped over her suitcase.

As they neared the station several people carrying pieces of luggage boarded the car, and Mrs. Taylor smiled at them as if they were partners in a conspiracy. Most of them smiled back at her, and she felt that the anticipation and preparation for a journey was only bettered by its actual beginning.

When she stepped from the streetcar a young man in army uniform took her suitcase from her, and holding her by the arm, led her across the street.

"This is a heavy bag for you to be carrying," he said in a conversational tone.

"It is a little heavy," she answered, "but I haven't far to go."

"Everybody seems to be going away today," he said. "I guess I won't get a seat on the northbound train."

"That's a shame," Mrs. Taylor answered, trying to keep up with the soldier's long strides. "Are you on leave?"

"Sort of. I was down here on a forty-eight-hour pass from camp. I should have been back last night."

"I hope you don't get into trouble," she said. She felt suddenly sorry for the young man—only a boy really. She wanted to tell him that both her sons had been overseas during the war, and that young Bert had been killed. But then she thought he might think she was bragging, or trying to make him feel bad because he'd been too young to go.

As they entered the station, she said to the young soldier, "I can manage now, thank you," and he stopped and placed the bag on the floor.

"If you're taking the northbound train I'll carry the suitcase to the gates for you," he offered.

"No. No, thank you. I'm taking the Montreal train," she answered.

"Well then, I'll have to leave you. Good-bye. Have a nice holiday," he said.

"Yes," she whispered, her voice cracking with emotion. As he walked away she shouted after him, "Good luck, son!" She watched him disappear into the crowd and felt a nameless dread for what might be before him. He was such a nice, polite young boy, but what was more he was the first person outside Mrs. Connell and the man at the grocery story that she had spoken to all week.

The man at the ticket window seemed surprised as she bought her ticket, but he stamped it on the back and handed it to her without a word. When she asked him where to get the Montreal train he pointed across the station to a queue of people lined up before a pair of gates. She picked up her suitcase and made her way toward it.

The crowd was a good-natured one, as she had known it would be, and she spent several minutes taking stock of the other travelers. It was unbelievable that so many people had awakened this morning as she had done, with the idea of catching the same train. All night as she had tossed and turned in anticipation of the morning these other people had probably been doing the same thing, unknown to her. The knowledge that they all shared the same sense of immediacy seemed to bring them closer together, and they were united in their impatience to be going.

But Mrs. Taylor was not impatient. She knew the value of time—she who had so little of it left—and this waiting with the others in the crowded station was as exciting to her as reaching the end of her trip—more so in fact.

She looked about her at the young people with their overnight bags and their tennis rackets. She looked at the older men carrying haversacks[2] and fishing rods, each seeming a little sheepish like children caught playing hookey. She listened to the three girls in the brand-new clothes whispering

---

[2]haversacks: bags like knapsacks but worn over one shoulder

252

together ahead of her in the line. She watched the young couple with the baby in the go-cart standing outside the queue, smiling at one another and talking together in French. And she looked at the two priests in white panama hats[3] who nodded solemnly and looked hot and cool at the same time in their black jackets.

This was what she had looked forward to all week! It was just

―――――――――
[3]panama (pan′ə mä′) hats: natural-colored, handmade hats made from leaves of a plant of South and Central America

as she had expected it to be, and she didn't care if the gates never opened. The best part of any journey was the waiting for the train.

There was the sound of a small scuffle behind her, and a young woman's tired voice said, "Garry, stop that right now!"

Mrs. Taylor turned and saw a slight dark girl wearing a shabby suit trying vainly to hold a young baby in her arms while she tugged at a little boy who was swinging on the end of a harness. The boy was trying desperately to break away.

"Here, young man, where do you think you're going!" Mrs. Taylor said sternly, bending down and catching him around the waist. The child stopped struggling and looked at her in surprise.

"He's been a little rascal all morning," his mother said. "He knows I can't do much with him while I've got the baby in my arms."

"Now you just stand still!" Mrs. Taylor warned, letting him go and smiling at the young woman to show that she did not mean to override her authority.

"He'll stop for you," the girl said. "At home he'll do anything for his grandma, but when he knows I've got the baby to look after, he takes advantage of it."

Mrs. Taylor nodded. "I know. I had two boys myself," she said. "Is the baby a boy, too?"

"Yes. Four months."

Mrs. Taylor reached over and pulled the light blanket from the baby's face. "He's a big boy for four months, isn't he?" she asked.

She learned that the young woman's name was Rawlinson, and that she was on her way to New Brunswick to join her husband, who was in the Air Force. The girl's mother had wanted to come down to the station with her, but her arthritis[4] had kept her at home. She also learned that the baby's name was Ian, and that his mother was twenty-two years old.

She in turn told the girl that she had lived alone since her oldest boy's marriage, and that Johnnie now lived with his wife

---

[4]arthritis (är thrī′tis): inflammation of joints of the body

and a young daughter in Montreal. In answer to the other's questions she also told the young woman that her husband and youngest son were dead, that she received the old-age pension, and that it wasn't enough in these days of high prices.

Mrs. Rawlinson said that a friend of her mother's went to the same church as Mrs. Taylor. Mrs. Taylor didn't recognize the woman's name, although she thought she knew who the girl meant: a stout woman with short-bobbed bluish hair who wore a Persian lamb coat in the winter.

She realized now that she had been starved for conversation, and she was so grateful for having met the young woman with the children.

"They should be opening the gates pretty soon," said the girl, looking at her wristwatch. "The train is due to leave in twenty minutes."

From the loudspeaker came the voice of the stationmaster announcing that the northbound train was due to leave. Mrs. Taylor thought about the nice young soldier who had overstayed his pass.

The little boy, Garry, indicated that he wanted to go to the toilet.

"Wait till we get on the train, dear," his mother pleaded desperately.

Mrs. Taylor said eagerly, "I'll hold the baby while you take him, if you like."

"Will you? That's swell!" the young woman exclaimed. She handed the baby over, and Mrs. Taylor cradled him in her arms, while the young mother and the little boy hurried away.

She pulled back the blanket once again from the baby's face and saw that he was awake. She placed her finger on his chin and smiled at him, and he smiled back at her. The moment took her back more years than she cared to remember, back to a time when young Bert was the same age. She was filled with the remembered happiness of those days, and she thought, "I'd give up every minute more I have to live just to be young again and have my boys as babies for one more day." Then to hide the quick tears that were starting from her eyes she began talking to the baby in her arms, rocking back and forth on her heels in a gesture not practiced for years.

When the woman and the little boy returned she gave up the baby reluctantly. She and the young woman stood talking together like old friends, or like a mother and daughter-in-law. They discussed teething troubles, the housing shortage, and how hard it was to raise a family these days. They were so engrossed in their new-found friendship that they failed to notice when the man opened the gates.

The crowd began pushing them from behind, and Mrs. Taylor picked up her suitcase in one hand and grasped Garry's harness with the other. Then, followed by Mrs. Rawlinson and the baby, they climbed the set of iron stairs to the platform.

Mrs. Taylor's feet were aching after the long wait at the gates, but her face shone with happiness as she steered the small boy alongside the train. The boy's mother drew up to her, and they walked together to the day-coach steps where a conductor waited to help them aboard.

"You've got your hands full there, Granny," he said, picking up the little boy and putting him in the vestibule of the car.

She was pleased that he mistook her for the children's grandmother, and she beamed at him, not attempting to correct his mistake.

Inside the coach she led the way to a pair of seats that faced each other at the end of the car, and dropped into one with a tired sigh. Then she held the baby while its mother took the harness off Garry and placed her small case and shopping bags on the luggage rack.

"Am I ever glad to get aboard!" Mrs. Rawlinson exclaimed. "I'd been dreading the wait at the station. Now I've only got to change trains in Montreal and I'll be all set."

"It's quite a job traveling with children," Mrs. Taylor sympathized. "Don't worry, I know. I've done enough of it in my day," she said with slight exaggeration.

Mrs. Rawlinson laid the baby on the seat beside her, before sitting back and relaxing against the cushions. The coach soon filled up, and several people eyed their double seat in envy. Mrs. Taylor was glad she had been able to get well up in the queue at the gates.

256

When the train started she moved over close to the window and pointed out to the little boy the buildings and streets they passed, and the tiny inconsequential people they were leaving behind them. Young Garry shouted excitedly, "Choo-choo!" at every engine they passed in the yards.

The city looked hot and uncomfortable in the morning sun. Mrs. Taylor was surprised that all the little ant-like people didn't simply jump on a train and get away from it. It was remarkable that the ones she could see walking the streets were strangers to her now, as if there was no connection between

257

them and the people on the train. They were a race apart; an earth-bound race separated from herself by movement and time, and the sense of adventure of her and her fellows.

She picked out landmarks as the train gathered speed. She saw the streets she had lived on as a girl, now turned into industrial sites. She saw the spinning mill where she had once worked. She saw the soot-blackened park where she and Bert had walked so many years ago. . . .

"We won't be getting into Montreal until suppertime," Mrs. Rawlinson said from the opposite seat, intruding upon her memories.

"No."

"I'll bet you'll be glad to get there and see your granddaughter."

Mrs. Taylor shook her head. "I'm not going to Montreal today," she said sadly. "I can't afford to go that far."

"But—but couldn't your son send you the fare?" asked the girl.

She had to protect Johnnie, who wasn't really mean, just forgetful. "Oh, he could, but I've never really cared to go that far," she replied.

"Well—well, where are you going then?" the young woman asked, her curiosity getting the best of her.

"Not very far. Just up the line a piece," Mrs. Taylor answered, smiling. "It's just a short trip."

The train seemed to flow across the bridges marking the streets. Soon the industrial areas were left behind, and they began rushing through the residential districts.

Mrs. Taylor was enthralled with the sight of the rows of houses as seen from the rear; yards waving with drying clothes, and every house having an individuality of its own. She only recognized some of the familiar streets after the train had passed them, they looked so different when seen from her fast-moving point of vantage.

In a few minutes the train began to slow down for an outlying station, and the conductor came along the car collecting tickets. When Mrs. Taylor handed him hers, he asked, "Are you getting off here, madam?"

"Yes, I am," Mrs. Taylor replied, coloring with embarrassment.

"Have you any luggage?"

She pointed to the suitcase at her feet, ashamed to face the stares of those who were watching her.

"Fine. I'll carry it off for you," the conductor said calmly, as if old ladies took ten-cent train rides every day of the week.

She stood up then and said good-bye to the little boy, letting her hand rest for a long minute on his tousled head. She warned him to be a good boy and do what his mother told him.

"You must think I'm crazy just coming this far," she said to Mrs. Rawlinson. "You see, I've wanted to take a trip for so long, and this was sort of—pretending."

The young woman shook the surprised look from her face. "No, I don't, Mrs. Taylor," she said. "I wish you were coming all the way. I don't know what I'd have ever done without you to help me with Garry."

"It was nice being able to help. You'll never know how much I enjoyed it," Mrs. Taylor answered, her face breaking into a shy smile. "Good-bye, dear, and bless you. Have a nice journey."

"Good-bye," the young woman said. "Thanks! Thanks a lot!"

Mrs. Taylor stood on the station platform and waved at the young woman and her son, who waved back at her as the train began to move again. Then she picked up her bag and walked along the platform to the street.

When she boarded a streetcar the driver looked down at her and said, "You look happy; you must have had a swell vacation."

She smiled at him. "I had a wonderful trip," she answered.

And it had been wonderful! While all the others in the train would get bored and tired after a few hours of travel, she could go back to her room and lie down on the bed, remembering only the excitement and thrill of going away, and the new friends she had made. It was wonderful, just wonderful, she said to herself. Perhaps next month, if she could afford it, she would take a trip to the suburbs on the Winnipeg train!

What Do You Think?

1. List some of the details in the story that suggest that Mrs. Taylor has very little money.
2. Why was Mrs. Taylor pleased when the conductor mistook her for the children's grandmother?
3. Describe how "imaginings" made the trip a wonderful experience for Mrs. Taylor.
4. Would you like to be the kind of person Mrs. Taylor was? Explain what you mean.

Taking a Closer Look

1. What prompted Mrs. Taylor to make the trip?
2. Why didn't Mrs. Taylor live with her son Johnnie?
3. What did she miss most since she had moved to the room in Mrs. Connell's house?
4. How did Mrs. Taylor help the young mother, Mrs. Rawlinson? How did Mrs. Rawlinson help Mrs. Taylor?
5. How far did Mrs. Taylor go on the train?

Putting Ideas to Work

Imagine that you are Mrs. Rawlinson, the young mother. What are your thoughts about Mrs. Taylor as she leaves the train?

To everything there is a season: a time to laugh . . .

A Time to Cry

Sally McMillan

Ron refused to believe it because it was just impossible. Dad couldn't die; he was still a young and healthy man. No matter what Mom and the preacher and everybody said, Dad couldn't be dead. Everyone kept talking about some car accident, but accidents happened to other people—not to his dad.

Several times Ron and Dad had discussed driving. Ron could hardly contain his impatience to get behind the wheel, but Dad told him he had to wait until he turned sixteen and acted like a responsible adult. He said that a good driver should never follow too close to another car, or run through stop signs, or go over the speed limit. Dad always lived up to his own advice about driving, so Ron knew that all the talk about Dad dying in an accident was sheer foolishness.

It must be some kind of sick joke. The kids at school always played jokes on him and, even though he always managed to get good grades, their tricks embarrassed him so badly that he felt like the dumbest person in the class. No doubt they had schemed night and day to come up with this joke and intended to make him feel ridiculous. But he knew Dad would come back soon so he wouldn't give them the pleasure of embarrassing him this time.

The day of the funeral Ron kept waiting expectantly for someone to laugh and humiliate him and then he could be positive it wasn't really true. But Mom cried the whole time. Didn't she know about the joke—the stupid joke?

The minister droned on and on about Dad and enumerated all the good things Dad had done. He doesn't have to keep talking like Dad will never do another good thing, thought Ron. He's on a business trip right now, but he'll be home in a couple of days. I know he will.

Then the preacher rambled on about how Dad had fallen asleep believing in Jesus and would continue sleeping until Jesus comes. Ron choked back a laugh. Obviously, even though the preacher had said a lot of true things about Dad, he really didn't know him very well. Dad never slept in—not even on Sundays. Sometimes Ron would wake up early and hear his dad in the kitchen whistling and banging pots while he fixed breakfast so that Mom could lounge in bed for a few extra minutes. Sometimes Dad went out bird-watching at five-thirty in the morning. How could the preacher think that Dad would sleep till Jesus comes?

Finally the service was over. Ron still waited for someone to laugh and admit that the whole fiasco was just a joke, but instead everyone went quietly out of the church and to the cemetery. They lowered the coffin into the ground and Mom cried some more.

The next day Mom told him he could stay home from school for a couple of days until he adjusted to Dad being gone. But he protested, "No need to stay home, I'm going to school." He thought to himself, I've got to go to school so that I can have a good report card to show Dad when he gets home.

At school everybody acted a little awkward around him. They all kind of smiled at him and a couple of people attempted to make small talk.

262

They're just acting nice to make me think they feel sorry for me, thought Ron. Well, I refuse to let this stupid game make me believe Dad is dead.

Ron felt so angry that he tried to find some way to get back at them for saying his dad was dead, but his mind seemed numb. At least I'll finally get my chance to laugh at them, he thought. When Dad gets back they'll be sorry they ever tried to trick me. Dad's just on a business trip; he'll be back soon.

But the days dragged on and Dad didn't come back. Sometimes an aching down deep inside that felt like a rotten emptiness and a bitter fullness at the same time nearly overwhelmed Ron. Maybe Dad really never would come back.

Why did Dad go away without saying good-by? Before he left on a business trip he always told Ron where he was going, how long he planned to stay, and what kind of birds there were in the place where he had business. Dad and Ron did a lot of things together, but bird-watching had become their favorite shared hobby.

Maybe he had done something to make Dad angry. Maybe Dad had gone off without saying good-by because he neglected taking out the trash when Mom told him to; or maybe because he didn't always do his homework before he went out to practice baseball. Well, Ron thought, I guess I can do the stuff he wants if that will make him come home.

Once, Mom gave him a curious glance when he came straight home from school, emptied the trash, and then did all his homework right away. But he didn't try to explain anything and he didn't care what she thought. He'd prove that he could handle responsibility and then when Dad came back he wouldn't just go off and leave without saying good-by again.

Once Mom talked to him. "You don't have to keep on acting brave," she said. "It's all right to cry. The Bible says there's a time to be born, and a time to die; a time to laugh, and a time to cry." But she just didn't understand that Dad wasn't dead. Why should he cry?

The aching inside grew larger and kept eating at him. Sometimes it hurt so bad to think about Dad that Ron almost felt paralyzed. A lot of days after school he went home and after he did his chores he just sat on the front porch—waiting. He didn't go out to the woods to look at birds anymore, and he didn't like doing his math homework anymore because Dad had always helped him with math. Why didn't Dad come back?

Mitsy, the girl who sat next to him at school, started acting friendly. He had often thought he would like to know her better but that was before. Now he nearly exploded every time she talked to him or asked him to help her with a math problem. Finally he couldn't stand it anymore. "No, I won't help you," he screamed when she asked him if he knew how to do the homework. "Why don't you mind your own business and just leave me alone." He threw his math book in his desk and slammed it shut. "You're just trying to be nice to me because of my dad, but you could never be that nice."

Ron felt something huge and frightening inside of him getting so big that it was about to swallow him. Before the teacher could

say anything, he jumped out of his desk, almost turned it over, and ran for the door. He ran down the hall, out the front door, and all the way home.

He looked for Dad's car in the driveway as he always did, but he knew before he looked that he wouldn't see it and he had a gnawing feeling that he might never see it again. He kicked open the front door and headed straight to Mom and Dad's bedroom. There on the dresser he saw the pair of binoculars he'd given Dad for his birthday. Dad always took the binoculars when he went on a business trip. He looked for birds and wrote down a list of the ones he'd seen so that he and Ron could look them up in the field guide.

Ron had successfully ignored the binoculars for the last few weeks by just pretending that they didn't exist, that he couldn't even see them on the dresser, but now Ron grabbed the binoculars and ran to his room. He slammed the door, then threw himself on the bed, hoping he'd land hard enough to break a spring. Mom wasn't home from work yet, but she undoubtedly would be angry when she found out that he had run away from school. She just didn't seem to understand. She still cried sometimes but she had started acting as if life were normal—as if she could just go on living even though Dad was dead.

He had said it—Dad was dead. Ron turned the binoculars over in his hand then carefully set them on his own dresser next to his field guide to birds. He felt as though everything that had happened in the last few weeks had all been trapped up inside and now it exploded like a volcano. He couldn't deny or pretend any longer—Dad was dead. Ron hugged his knees, turned his face toward the wall, and let the tears come.

Dad would never come back again. Dad could never go for long walks with him, or watch the birds, or help him with math. Never, never again. The tears kept coming and Ron quit trying to stop them. He cried so hard that the bed shook. "Dad is dead," the words came out in choking sobs.

He didn't hear Mom come in, but when she put her arms around him he clung to her and felt relieved that she was crying too.

And later, when the tears were dry and gone, he looked up into her face and said, "I guess there is a time to cry."

What Do You Think?

1. Ron goes through several stages before he accepts his father's death. The first is denial—he won't admit that his father is really dead. Try to find at least three other ways in which Ron deals with his father's death.
2. Why did Mom give Ron a curious glance when he came straight home from school, emptied the trash, and did all his homework right away?
3. Why do you think that Mitsy's questions made Ron so angry? Was he really angry at Mitsy?
4. Why did Ron refuse to believe that his father had died?
5. What similarities do you see between the loss of a parent through death and the breaking of a home through divorce? How would you cope with either situation?

Taking a Closer Look

1. What do you think was the fullness and bitterness that seemed to be building up inside Ron?
2. How did the students at school usually treat Ron?
3. What hobby had Ron and his father shared? How did this hobby lead to Ron's acceptance of his father's death?
4. What change had come over Ron by the end of the story?

Putting Ideas to Work

Using a Bible concordance, find five references in the Bible that would be comforting to someone who has lost a loved one.

A Mother in Mannville

Marjorie Kinnan Rawlings

In this story, a boy from an orphanage
and a woman who writes become friends.
"Imaginings" are the woman's business;
she makes a living at it. How does the boy
weave imaginings into his life?

The orphanage is high in the Carolina mountains. Sometimes in winter the snowdrifts are so deep that the institution is cut off from the village below, from all the world. Fog hides the mountain peaks, the snow swirls down the valleys, and a wind blows so bitterly that the orphanage boys who take the milk twice daily to the baby cottage reach the door with fingers stiff in an agony of numbness.

"Or when we carry trays from the cookhouse for the ones that are sick," Jerry said, "we get our faces frostbit, because we can't put our hands over them. I have gloves," he added. "Some of the boys don't have any."

He liked the late spring, he said. The rhododendron[1] was in bloom, a carpet of color, across the mountainsides, soft as the May winds that stirred the hemlocks. He called it laurel.[2]

"It's pretty when the laurel blooms," he said. "Some of it's pink and some of it's white."

I was there in the autumn. I wanted quiet, isolation, to do some troublesome writing. I wanted mountain air to blow out the malaria from too long a time in the subtropics. I was homesick, too, for the flaming of maples in October, and for corn shocks and pumpkins and black-walnut trees and the lift of hills. I found them all, living in a cabin that belonged to the orphanage, half a mile beyond the orphanage farm. When I took the cabin, I asked for someone to come and chop wood for the fireplace. The first few days were warm, I found what wood I need-

---

[1]rhododendron: an evergreen shrub with leathery leaves and pink, purple, or white flowers
[2]laurel: a small evergreen tree with smooth, shiny leaves

267

ed about the cabin, no one came, and I forgot the order.

I looked up from my typewriter one late afternoon, a little startled. A boy stood at the door, and my pointer dog, my companion, was at his side and had not barked to warn me. The boy was probably thirteen years old, but undersized. He wore overalls and a torn shirt, and was barefooted.

He said, "I can chop some wood today."

I said, "But I have a boy coming from the orphanage."

"I'm the boy."

"You? But you're small."

"Size doesn't matter, chopping wood," he said. "Some of the big boys don't chop good. I've been chopping wood at the orphanage a long time."

I visualized mangled and inadequate branches for my fires. I was well into my work and not inclined to conversation. I was a little blunt.

"Very well. There's the ax. Go ahead and see what you can do."

I went back to work, closing the door. At first the sound of the boy dragging brush annoyed me. Then he began to chop. The blows were rhythmic and steady, and shortly I had forgotten him, the sound no more of an interruption than a consistent rain. I suppose an hour and a half passed, for when I stopped and stretched, and heard the boy's steps on the cabin stoop, the sun was dropping behind the

farthest mountain, and the valleys were purple with something deeper than the asters.

The boy said, "I have to go to supper now. I can come again tomorrow evening."

I said, "I'll pay you now for what you've done," thinking I should probably have to insist on an older boy. "Fifty cents an hour?"

"Anything is all right."

We went together back of the cabin. An astonishing amount of solid wood had been cut. There were cherry logs and heavy roots of rhododendron, and blocks from the waste pine and oak left from the building of the cabin.

"But you've done as much as a full-grown person," I said. "This is a splendid pile."

I looked at him, actually, for the first time. His hair was the color of the corn shocks, and his eyes, very direct, were like the mountain sky when rain is pending—gray, with a shadowing of that miraculous blue. As I spoke a light came over him, as though the setting sun had touched him with the same suffused glory with which it touched the mountains. I gave him a dollar.

"You may come tomorrow," I said, "and thank you very much."

He looked at me, and at the money, and seemed to want to speak, but could not, and turned away.

"I'll split kindling tomorrow," he said over his thin ragged shoulder. "You'll need kindling and medium wood and logs and backlogs."

At daylight I was half wakened by the sound of chopping. Again it was so even in texture that I went back to sleep. When I left my bed in the cool morning, the boy had come and gone, and a stack of kindling was neat against the cabin wall. He came again after school in the afternoon and worked until time to return to the orphanage. His name was Jerry; he was thirteen years old, and he had been at the orphanage since he was four. I could picture him at four, with the same grave gray-blue eyes and the same—independence? No, the word that comes to me is "integrity."

The word means something very special to me, and the quality for which I use it is a rare one. My mother had it—there is another of whom I am almost sure—but almost no one of my acquaintance possesses it with the clarity, the purity, the simplicity of a mountain stream. But the boy Jerry had it. It is bedded on courage, but it is more than brave. It is honest, but it is more than honesty. The ax handle broke one day. Jerry said the wood shop at the orphanage would repair it. I brought money to pay for the job and he refused it.

"I'll pay for it," he said. "I broke it. I brought the ax down careless."

"But no one hits accurately every time," I told him. "The fault was in the wood of the handle. I'll see the man from whom I bought it."

269

It was only then that he would take the money. He was standing back of his own carelessness. He was a free-will agent and he chose to do careful work, and if he failed, he took the responsibility without subterfuge.

And he did for me the unnecessary thing, the gracious thing, that we find done only by the great of heart. Things no training can teach, for they are done on the instant, with no predicated experience. He found a cubbyhole beside the fireplace that I had not noticed. There, of his own accord, he put kindling and "medium" wood, so that I might always have dry fire material ready in case of sudden wet weather. A stone was loose in the rough walk to the cabin. He dug a deeper hole and steadied it, although he came, himself, by a short cut over the bank. I found that when I tried to return his thoughtfulness with such things as candy and apples, he was wordless. "Thank you" was, perhaps, an expression for which he had had no use, for his courtesy was instinctive. He only looked at the gift and at me, and a curtain lifted, so that I saw deep into the clear well of his eyes, and gratitude was there, and affection, soft over the firm granite of his character.

He made simple excuses to come and sit with me. I could no more have turned him away than if he had been physically hungry. I suggested once that the best time for us to visit was just before supper, when I left off my writing. After that, he waited always until my typewriter had been some time quiet. One day I worked until nearly dark. I went outside the cabin, having forgotten him. I saw him going up over the hill in the twilight toward the orphanage. When I sat down on my stoop, a place was warm from his body where he had been sitting.

He became friends, of course, with my pointer, Pat. There is a strange communion between a youth and a dog. Perhaps they possess the same singleness of spirit, the same kind of wisdom. It is difficult to explain, but it exists. When I went across the state for a week-end, I left the dog in Jerry's charge. I gave him the dog whistle and the key to the cabin, and left sufficient food. He was to come two or three times a day and let out the dog, and feed and exercise him. I should return Sunday night, and Jerry would take out the dog for the last time Sunday afternoon and then leave the key under an agreed hiding place.

My return was belated and fog filled the mountain passes so treacherously that I dared not drive at night. The fog held the next morning, and it was Monday noon before I reached the cabin. The dog had been fed and cared for that morning. Jerry came early in the afternoon, anxious.

"The superintendent said nobody would drive in the fog," he said. "I came just before bedtime last night and you hadn't come. So I brought Pat some of my breakfast this morning. I wouldn't have let anything happen to him."

"I was sure of that. I didn't worry."

"When I heard about the fog, I thought you'd know."

He was needed for work at the orphanage and he had to return at once. I gave him two dollars in payment, and he looked at it and went away. But that night he came in the darkness and knocked at the door.

"Come in, Jerry," I said, "if you're allowed to be away this late."

"I told maybe a story," he said. "I told them I thought you would want to see me."

"That's true," I assured him, and I saw his relief. "I want to hear about how you managed with the dog."

He sat by the fire with me, with no other light, and told me of their two days together. The dog lay close to him, and found a comfort there that I did not have for him. And it seemed to me that being with my dog, and caring for him, had brought the boy and me, too, together, so that he felt that he belonged to me as well as to the animal.

"He stayed right with me," he told me, "except when he ran in the laurel. He likes the laurel. I

took him up over the hill and we both ran fast. There was a place where the grass was high and I lay down in it and hid. I could hear Pat hunting for me. He found my trail and he barked. When he found me, he acted crazy, and he ran around and around me, in circles."

We watched the flames.

"That's an apple log," he said. "It burns the prettiest of any wood."

He was suddenly impelled to speak of things he had not spoken of before, nor had I cared to ask him.

"You look a little bit like my mother," he said. "Especially in the dark, by the fire."

"But you were only four, Jerry, when you came here. You have remembered how she looked, all these years?"

"My mother lives in Mannville," he said.

For a moment, finding that he had a mother shocked me as greatly as anything in my life has ever done, and I did not know why it disturbed me. Then I understood my distress. I was filled with a passionate resentment that any woman should go away and leave her child. A fresh anger added itself. A child like this one. The orphanage was a wholesome place, the executives were kind, good people, the food was more than adequate, the boys were healthy, a ragged shirt was no hardship, nor the doing of clean

271

labor. Granted, perhaps, that the boy felt no lack. But at four he would have looked the same as now. Nothing, I thought, nothing in life could change those eyes. His quality must be apparent. I burned with questions I could not ask. In any, I was afraid, there would be pain.

"Have you seen her, Jerry—lately?"

"I see her every summer. She sends for me."

I wanted to cry out. "Why are you not with her? How can she let you go away again?"

He said, "She comes up here from Mannville whenever she can. She doesn't have a job now."

His face shone in the firelight.

"She wanted to give me a puppy, but they can't let any one boy keep a puppy. You remember the suit I had on last Sunday?" He was plainly proud. "She sent me that for my birthday. The year before that"—he drew a long breath, savoring the memory—"she sent me a pair of skates."

"Roller skates?"

My mind was busy, making pictures of her, trying to understand her. She had not, then, entirely deserted or forgotten him. But why, then—I thought, "I must not condemn her without knowing."

"Roller skates. I let the other boys use them. They're always borrow-

ing them. But they're careful of them."

What circumstance other than poverty—

"I'm going to take the money you gave me for taking care of Pat," he said, "and buy her a pair of gloves."

I could only say, "That will be nice. Do you know her size?"

"I think it's eight and a half," he said.

He looked at my hands.

"Do you wear eight and a half?" he asked.

"No. I wear a smaller size, a six."

"Oh! Then I guess her hands are

bigger than yours."

I hated her. Poverty or no, there was other food than bread, and the soul could starve as quickly as the body. He was taking his money to buy gloves for her big hands, and she lived away from him, in Mannville, and contented herself with sending him skates.

"She likes white gloves," he said. "Do you think I can get them for a few dollars?"

I decided that I should not leave the mountains without seeing her and knowing for myself why she had done this thing.

The human mind scatters its interests as though made of thistledown,[3] and every wind stirs and moves it. I finished my work. It did not please me, and I gave my thoughts to another field. I should need some Mexican material.

I made arrangements to close my Florida place. Mexico immediately, and doing the writing there, if conditions were favorable. Then, Alaska with my brother. After that, who knew what or where.

I did not take time to go to Mannville to see Jerry's mother, nor even to talk with the orphanage officials about her. I was a trifle abstracted about the boy, because of my work and plans. And after my first fury at her—we did not speak of her again—his having a mother, any sort at all, not far

---

[3] thistledown: feathery growth that forms on ripe thistle seeds

away, in Mannville, relieved me of the ache I had had about him. He did not question the separation. He was not lonely. It was none of my concern.

He came every day and cut my wood and did small helpful favors and stayed to talk. The days had become cold, and often I let him come inside the cabin. He would lie on the floor in front of the fire, with one arm across the pointer, and they would both doze and wait quietly for me. Other days they ran with a common ecstasy through the laurel, and since the asters were now gone, he brought me back vermilion maple leaves, and chestnut boughs dripping with imperial yellow. I was ready to go.

I said to him, "You have been my good friend, Jerry. I shall often think of you and miss you. Pat will miss you too. I am leaving tomorrow."

He did not answer. When he went away, I remember that a new moon hung over the mountains, and I watched him go in silence up the hill. I expected him the next day, but he did not come. The details of packing my personal belongings, loading my car, arranging the bed over the seat, where the dog would ride, occupied me until late in the day. I closed the cabin and started the car, noticing that the sun was in the west and I should do well to be out of the mountains by nightfall. I stopped by the orphanage and left the cabin key and money for my light bill with Miss Clark.

"And will you call Jerry for me to say good-by to him?"

"I don't know where he is," she said. "I'm afraid he's not well. He didn't eat his dinner this noon. One of the boys saw him going over the hill into the laurel. He was supposed to fire the boiler this afternoon. It's not like him; he's unusually reliable."

I was almost relieved, for I knew I should never see him again, and it would be easier not to say good-by to him.

I said, "I wanted to talk with you about his mother—why he's here—but I'm in more of a hurry than I expected to be. It's out of the question for me to see her now too. But here's some money I'd like to leave with you to buy things for him on his birthday. It will be better than for me to try to send him things. I could so easily duplicate—skates, for instance."

She blinked her eyes.

"There's not much use for skates here," she said.

Her stupidity annoyed me.

"What I mean," I said, "is that I don't want to duplicate things his mother sends him. I might have chosen skates if I didn't know she had already given them to him."

She stared at me.

"I don't understand," she said. "He has no mother. He has no skates."

274

What Do You Think?

1. Why does the author recount the incident about the broken ax handle? What did this tell her about Jerry?
2. How do you know that Jerry enjoyed the author's company?
3. What do you think Jerry felt when the author said she was going away? What information in the story supports your opinion?
4. Why do you think Jerry invented a mother living in Mannville?

Taking a Closer Look

1. Why did the author go to the cabin near the orphanage?
2. Describe Jerry's appearance. What was surprising about his abilities?
3. How did Jerry react to the broken ax handle?
4. What was the author's reaction when she first heard that the boy had a mother in Mannville?
5. Why was the woman at the orphanage confused by the author's desire not to duplicate gifts for Jerry?

Putting Ideas to Work

Imagine that you are Jerry. The woman at the orphanage has told you about her conversation with the author. Write a note to the author explaining why you invented a mother living in Mannville.

Preparing an Outline

When you do research, you will find that several paragraphs are usually needed to thoroughly explain a topic. The first paragraph usually states the main idea of the selection. The remainder of the article contains information that is related in some way to the main idea. These are subtopics. The paragraphs will also include many supporting details.

A well-prepared outline provides a summary of several paragraphs you have read. It can help you to understand, recall, and report information.

Skim *Tides of Calm, Waves of Terror*. Read the titles, and look for key words. They are clues to the main idea.

Tides of Calm, Waves of Terror

Throughout history, people have been drawn to the sea. The steady ebb and flow of the tides has both calmed and fascinated us. Sometimes, the rhythm of the tides becomes restless with power. These create huge waves that spill across shorelines. They can be terrifying and tragic. *Spring tides, tidal bores,* and *storm waves* are some of the intriguing water phenomena.

Spring Tides

The rise and fall of ocean waters seems constant. About twice a month (on the days of the new and full moons), the tides rise very high. This is because the sun, the moon, and Earth are in line with each other. The gravity of the sun and the moon tugs at Earth. The combined gravitational pull is greater than usual and causes high tides. They are called spring tides and are predictable because we know the cycles of the moon.

Tidal Bores

Another predictable high-water phenomenon is the tidal bore. Bore in this case means "high wall." Tidal bores are not dull! The bore is a towering wall of fast-moving water, which runs in advance of the incoming tide. Bores rise from 1 to 10 feet (0.3 to 3 meters). Tidal bores are formed in shallow rivers and bays where there are wide differences between high and low tides. High walls occur where large amounts of the ocean tide are funneled into the mouth of a river. As the tidewaters meet the outpouring of the river, they are held back temporarily, until so much tidal water builds up that a wall of water develops. Finally, the force of the incoming tide is so great that the wall, or bore, rushes rapidly up the river.

Tsunamis—The Storm Waves

Tsunami (sü′ näm′ē) means "storm wave" in Japanese. Storm waves are often referred to as tidal waves. But tides do not cause them. Storm waves are caused by undersea earthquakes and volcanic eruptions. Sometimes, they occur due to a hurricane deep over the ocean. These waves of terror are deadly. There have been stories of 100-foot waves (30 meters) moving at 500 miles (800 kilometers) per hour! And they're neither regular nor predictable like spring tides or tidal bores. However, once an underwater disturbance has created a monster wave, scientists are able to predict when the tsunami will reach a coastal area. A wave travels about the same distance in an hour that an earthquake travels in a minute. Seismographs (sīz′mə graf: a device that measures and records earth tremors) help predict when the storm wave will strike an area. However, until we know more about predicting earthquakes and volcanic eruptions, people will not have more than a few hours' warning.

Review the basic outline form.

I. Main topic
  A. Subtopic
    1. Supporting detail
    2. Supporting detail
  B. Subtopic
    1. Supporting detail
    2. Supporting detail

Remember, Roman numeral I signals the main topic. Capital letters signal subtopics. Arabic numerals signal supporting details. The first word in each line is capitalized.

On notebook paper, try to prepare an outline using this format. First, carefully read *Tides of Calm, Waves of Terror*. Choose key words that summarize the article. Use these phrases to make your outline. You may have more subtopics and supporting details than shown in the model outline form. By the way, tsunamis are hardly noticed if you're traveling deep in the ocean (they resemble the ripples caused by tossing a pebble in a pool). So, smooth sailing through the outline!

Bridging the Gap

Earl G. Robbins

Everyone has an imagination, but sometimes it needs an extra boost to start moving. What assistance does Ned's imagination get in this story?

The old man leaned heavily on the strong young lad. He pointed his bent and weather-worn walking stick toward the distant hill. "This is the right direction, Ned. Take me there," he said.

"But Gramps," the boy protested, "there's nothing there anymore! Time and weather have rotted and caved the old house in. Only brambles remain, they say."

"Nonsense! Nonsense!" the old man scoffed. "They are wrong! Wrong! Everything is as it used to be. You lead. I'll direct." He limped toward the distant hill.

"The briars and bushes will be too rough for you, Gramps," the boy grumbled. "And it's no use. You come here every year and find nothing but that old grave marker." He held back stubbornly.

"No, Ned. No! Take me there," the old man pleaded. "You'll discover it today."

278

Reluctantly, the boy turned toward the remote ridge. He kicked and stomped brambles and briars, and flailed bushes with a heavy stick. "Why? Why?" he chafed, "does Gramps come here year after year to search for that old shack of a house and rotted-down barn that disappeared decades ago? The only thing he ever does is rub moss from that old half-hidden tombstone, stand by the grave and read the inscription:

Amos Robb
1839-1895
Indiana Infantry

"Wasted time! Wasted energy," he fumed, beating his way over fallen logs and dead treetops.

The old man shuffled after the boy, coughing and wheezing. "Lead on, Ned. I know the spot. You'll find it today." Briars tore his wrinkled skin and jerked at his scraggly beard. He rested on a half-decayed tree stump beside the overgrown path.

Ned stumbled upon a narrow leaf-covered stream that blocked his way. Carelessly, he splashed through its shallow water, sloshing and slipping over rough stones and floating driftwood. Upon reaching the far side of the little branch, he turned to look into the settling water. A dark, gloomy, defiant figure stared sternly up at him. He left the stream, beating his way through rank weeds, tall grass and roses, grown wild. He stomped up a slope, still questioning the sense of wasting a long afternoon, searching for the ramshackle farmstead, only to placate the whims of a doting old man.

Far back in the woods, Gramps gazed dreamily in the direction of his former home. "That big maple was a mere sapling the spring morning that Paul and Teddy nailed a horseshoe on it to make a hitching tree for Dan's high-stepping trotter when he came courting Chrissie. Chrissie's gone now. Bless Chrissie," he mumbled, "Bless her." He picked up his stick as if to follow the boy. He stood on wobbly legs and called softly, "Seek on, Ned. Search to the top of the hill. It's there. You'll find everything today. You must! It's your time!"

The tired old man looked into the distance, to the place where he had worked, rested and loved. Fifty years passed over his being like a gently slow-moving cloud, airy and light, sprinkled here and there by dark threatening thunderheads. He rested once more on the tree stump. "Fifty years . . . fifty years," he murmured, smiling contentedly. He looked longingly toward the little knoll. "Ah, there's Pop! coming in from the barn, a milk pail on his arm—same old crumpled hat. Oh, how I like the strong smell of its sweaty band." His face shone with youthful joy. "There's Betty! in her blue-flowered bonnet, the one that matches her pretty eyes." He dreamed on. "Someone's moving in the parlor. It's Mom! She's lighting the evening lamp. See! There! That's right. She's turning up the wick. I can see her tired angelic face as she places it at the window." He roused himself half awake.

"Look up, Ned! Look high for the slanting gabled roof. It's there.

I can see it from here. I see it all, the house, the barn and all the people. Just beyond the maple, boy, near the wild plum grove. You're almost upon it. You'll find it this time!"

Ned climbed to a low plateau beyond the shoe-scarred maple. He meditated upon his grandfather's yearning to visit this varmint-infested wilderness, now retaken by scrub oak, sassafras[1] and sumac.[2] A skinny half-grown rabbit dashed across his path, followed closely by a long hungry-looking snake. The snake stopped and lashed its tongue out at Ned, as if to back him off the ridge. It slunk and slithered away when he moved toward it with his up-raised stick.

As Ned moved up the rise, near the top, he stopped to look around and get his bearings. He stepped into a shallow hole covered with leaves and caught the toe of his shoe on the crimped handle of a battered kettle. He dug his foot deep into the soft black earth. A corroded plowshare, the rusted barrel of a rifle and bits of an old tub lay buried in the moldy mass. He examined each carefully and thoughtfully. With the plowshare, he turned over leaves, brush and earth in search of other signs of human habitation.

At the highest point of the nearly level plateau, close by the plum trees, he lifted a long heavy limb from his path. And there it was! A square outline of stone, firm and solid. "Here it is, Gramps! Here it is!" he hollered. "I've found it! I've found it! Come and see, Gramps! Come and see!" He walked around and upon the foundation. He examined and studied the stones, how each fit into place and held all together. "Hurry, Gramps! Hurry and see these stones! They would support a hundred houses and they will stand here a thousand years!" He moved to the center of the structure and envisioned how the old house had been, laying it out, room by room, seeing where people had eaten, slept, worked, rested, loved and lived. He poked his stick into crevices and corners, hoping to find other artifacts left by those who had used this place

---

[1]sassafras (sas'ə fras): a kind of tree having fragrant yellow flowers and bluish-black fruit
[2]sumac (sü'mak): a kind of shrub or small tree having divided leaves and clusters of red or white fruit

years earlier. He surveyed the landscape surrounding the foundation, meditating upon those early people. In his mind, he saw the bubbling life-giving spring, the barn and buildings around it. He looked again at the foundation.

At one end of the embedded stones, he discovered the low hearth of a fallen chimney. He rested upon it, thinking of people hovered around the hearth on a cold winter night. A light reflected into his eyes from where the fireplace had been. He reached to find its cause. There, half-hidden in rank weeds, lay fragments of a shattered mirror. He picked up a piece and held it out from him studying his own features. The eyes in the mirror questioned his right to use it and his reason for being at this place. He cringed and turned the mirror from his face. He felt alone, naked and neglected and yet surrounded by hordes of people. Even Gramps, he thought, had failed him; or maybe he had failed Gramps. His mind swirled with wonder and bewilderment at his surroundings and at the people who once used this house as their own, their place of being, their home. "What has this old out-of-the-way place and its people to do with me?" he scowled. "They had nothing and they were going no place. Bowed, stooped, struggling, sweating all their days just to eke out a skimpy existence; and always slaving, working."

He saw himself parading proudly on courts and playing fields achieving scholarships, honors and accolades with half the effort and energy these people had given for nothing, nothing but a life consumed by toil and drudgery. "So these were my ancestors!" he said mockingly, looking vainly into the mirror. He drew back, startled by the defiant belligerent eyes of the youth, now almost a man, that looked accusingly at him. He turned abruptly away, unable to meet the penetrating stare of the taunting eyes. . . . "Is this me? Is this Ned Robb? Is this to be my life, thinking only of self and self-glorification? Is this how I am to look to myself and to be when I am as old as Gramps? Is this all there is to be for me, Ned Robb? Is this all?" he shrank with shame and humility. He fumbled nervously with the mirror, turning it over and around in his hand, thinking of the people who might have used it decades earlier. Again, he turned his face to the little looking glass. Those people he had thought of with scorn and contempt nodded at him. All seemed alike, as one. Yet each held some distinct identification that set him or her apart as a special individual, a person unlike all others. As one, the constrained group seemed to say, "We understand. We, too, faced the mirror." They smiled knowingly out to him. He felt welcome and at ease among them. He searched for those he might have known or could recognize from descriptions he had received from Gramps. And then, to one side and alone, he visualized his own mother standing before this mirror on the eve of her wedding, questioning, perhaps, her own self, her beauty, her fitness and the wisdom of this life-long decision. Or maybe it was Gramps' mother. He hungered for knowledge of them and others of his people, people of his own blood and bone; people who had laid this foundation and built their lives around it. He remembered stories, joyful and sad, about the old farmstead: births, deaths, marriages . . . happy and carefree; separations . . . sad and cruel.

A sandy-whiskered old man, his left sleeve dangling at the elbow, marched challengingly to the front of the attentive crowd. He stood stoic and stiffly before Ned searching him, questioning him, neither approving nor disapproving of Ned's intrusion of his premises. Ned recognized the rugged old man as founder of the clan, the old monarch who purchased the little plot of unproductive, water-logged land; paying for it with his sweat and blood, two years in war and half of his left arm; that Mariah and their two sons might have a home, a place to call their own.

Standing quietly now, in the fading evening light, Ned's thoughts turned to other ancestors, nearer and farther away. He felt their presences hovering around the old farmstead and himself. He seemed to belong to them and to this place. . . . The past merged with the present. Generations marched and mingled before him and after him. He pondered soberly upon his own future, what it would be, how it would fit into place with the lives of those people who had gone before him, and those that would come after him. All seemed nebulous, uncertain, unattached, far away, and yet upon him. . . . He reexamined the mirror. The people—his people—children, youths, adults, older people, smiled warmly to him. . . . Carefully, he placed the sliver of mirror in his pocket and walked to the center of the foundation.

The hum of a plane, high in the darkening sky, interrupted his reveries. He watched it disappear beyond the eastern wood, its lights blinking brightly as it cut through clouds and shadows. He remembered his grandfather back in the bush. "Gramps!" he called. "Gramps! It's growing late. Come! Come and tell me more. . . ."

The old man smiled, not moving from his seat. "Directly, Ned. Directly. I'll be along directly," he said calmly. "I've seen it all, the house, the barn and all the people. I knew you would find it today, Ned. It was your time." He picked up his stick, raised his body slowly and shuffled in the direction of his grandson's voice.

What Do You Think?

1. Why do you think Gramps liked to return to the site of the old house each year?
2. What did Gramps mean when he told Ned, "You'll find everything today. You must! It's your time"?
3. How did the mirror serve as a link between Ned and his family's past?
4. How was Ned changed by what he found on the plateau?
5. How did the site of the old house stimulate the imagination of Gramps? Of Ned?

Taking a Closer Look

1. Did Ned want to help his grandfather search for the old house? Give evidence from the story that supports your opinion.
2. What things did Ned find on the plateau?
3. What feelings did Ned have when he first looked into the mirror?
4. When Ned looked into the mirror, he saw the reflection of his own eyes. What words does the author use to describe those eyes?
5. Who did Ned imagine he saw in the mirror?

Putting Ideas to Work

Imagine the conversation between Ned and Gramps as they walked home. List several questions that you think Ned could ask Gramps about their ancestors.

Let Your Imagination Picture

Ellen G. White

As your senses delight
  in the attractive loveliness
  of the earth,
think of the world
  that is to come,
  that shall never know
  the blight of sin and death;
where the face of nature
  will no more wear
  the shadow of the curse.
Let your imagination picture
  the home of the saved,
  and remember that it will be
  more glorious than
  your brightest imagination can portray.
In the varied gifts of God in nature
  we see but the faintest gleaming
  of His glory.

It is written,
  "Eye hath not seen,
  nor ear heard,
  neither have entered
  into the heart of man,
  the things which God hath prepared
  for them that love Him."
1 Corinthians 2:9.

The Big Wave

Pearl Buck

A Television Play

Generation to generation, there is a continuity to life and to people's views of life. How do the characters in this play help each other to appreciate the past? How do they use their experience to understand the present and to prepare for the future?

Characters
NARRATOR
KINO UCHIYAMA (kē'nō ōō chē yä' mä), a farmer's son
MOTHER
FATHER, the farmer
SETSU (se'tsōō), Kino's sister
JIYA (jē'yä), a fisherman's son
JIYA'S FATHER, the fisherman

OLD GENTLEMAN, a wealthy land-owner
GARDENER
FIRST MAN
SECOND MAN
WOMAN
CHILD

Act I

A scene in Japan, sea and mountainside, and in the distance Mount Fuji.
Dissolve To: A small farmhouse, built on top of the terraces. This, as the Narrator *speaks, dissolves to the inside of the house, a room with the simplest of Japanese furniture.*
NARRATOR: Kino lives on a farm. The farm lies on the side of a mountain in Japan. The fields are terraced by walls of stone, each of them like a broad step up the mountain. Centuries ago, Kino's ancestors built the stone walls that hold up the fields. Above the fields stands this farmhouse, which is Kino's home. Sometimes he feels the climb is hard, especially when he has been working in the lowest field and is hungry.
Dissolve To: Kino comes into the room. He is a sturdy boy of about thirteen, dressed in shorts, and a Japanese jacket, open on his bare chest.

288

Mother *hurries in. She is a small, serious-looking woman dressed in an everyday cotton kimono,[1] sleeves tucked up. She is carrying a jar of water.*

MOTHER: Dinner is ready. Where is your father?

KINO: Coming. I ran up the terrace. I'm starving.

MOTHER: Call Setsu. She is playing outside.

KINO [*turning his head*]: Setsu!

FATHER: Here she is. [*He comes in, holding by the hand a small roguish girl.*] Getting so big! I can't lift her anymore. [*But he does lift her so high that she touches the rafters.*]

SETSU: Don't put me down; I want to eat my supper up here.

FATHER: And fall into the soup?

KINO: How would that taste?

SETSU [*willfully*]: It would taste nice.

MOTHER: Come, come—[*They sit on the floor around the little table.*

----

[1]kimono (kə mōʹnə): a loose outer garment held in place by a sash, worn by Japanese men and women

The mother serves swiftly from a small bucket of rice, a bowl of soup, a bowl of fish. She serves the father first, then Kino, then Setsu, then herself.]

FATHER: Kino, don't eat so fast.

KINO: I have promised Jiya to swim in the sea with him.

MOTHER: Obey your father.

FATHER [*smiling*]: Let him eat fast. [*He puts a bit of fish in Setsu's bowl.*] There—that's a good bit.

KINO: Father, why is it that Jiya's father's house has no window to the sea?

FATHER: No fisherman wants windows to the sea.

MOTHER: The sea is their enemy.

KINO: Mother, how can you say so? Jiya's father catches fish from the sea and that is how his family lives.

FATHER: Do not argue with your mother. Ask Jiya your question. See what he says.

KINO: Then may I go?

FATHER: Go.

Montage: Film. A sandy strip of seashore at the foot of the mountain. A few cottages stand there. Dissolve To: Jiya, a tall slender boy. He stands at the edge of the sea, looking up the mountain.

JIYA [*calling through his hands*]: Kino!

KINO: Coming. [*He is running and catches Jiya's outstretched hand, so that they nearly fall down. They laugh and throw off their jackets.*]

KINO: Wait—I am out of breath. I ate too much.

JIYA [*looking up the mountain*]: There's Old Gentleman standing at the gate of his castle.

KINO: He is watching to see whether we are going to sea.

JIYA: He's always looking at the sea—at dawn, at sunset.

Dissolve To: Old Gentleman, standing on the rock, in front of his castle, halfway up the mountain. The wind is blowing his beard. He wears the garments of an aristocrat. Withdraw the cameras to the beach again.

JIYA: He is afraid of the sea— always watching!

KINO: Have you ever been in his castle?

JIYA: Only once. Such beautiful gardens—like a dream. The old pines are bent with the wind, and under them the moss is deep and green and so smooth. Every day men sweep the moss with brooms.

KINO: Why does he keep looking to the sea?

JIYA: He is afraid of it, I tell you.

KINO: Why?

JIYA: The sea is our enemy. We all know it.

KINO: Oh, how can you say it? When we have so much fun. . . .

JIYA: It is our enemy. . . .

KINO: Not mine—let's swim to the island.

JIYA: No. I must find clams for my mother.

KINO: Then let's swim to the

sandbar. There are millions of clams there.

JIYA: But the tide is ready to turn. . . .

KINO: It's slow—we'll have time.

They plunge into the sea and swim to the sandbar. Jiya has a small, short-handled hoe hanging from his girdle.² He digs into the sand. Kino kneels to help him. But Jiya digs for only a moment; then he pauses to look out over the sea.

KINO: What are you looking for?

JIYA: To see if the sea is angry with us.

KINO [*laughing*]: Silly—the sea can't be angry with people.

JIYA: Down there, a mile down, the old sea god lives. When he is angry he heaves and rolls, and the waves rush back and forth. Then he gets up and stamps his foot, and the earth shakes at the bottom of the sea . . . I wish I were a farmer's son, like you. . . .

KINO: And I wish I were a fisherman's son. It is stupid to plow and plant and cut sheaves, when I could just sit in a boat and reap fish from the sea!

JIYA: The earth is safe.

KINO: When the volcano is angry the earth shakes too.

JIYA: The angry earth helps the angry sea.

KINO: They work together.

JIYA: But fire comes out of the volcano.

Meanwhile, the tide is coming in and swirls about their feet.

JIYA [*noticing*]: Oh—we have not half enough clams. . . .[*They fall to digging fanatically.*]

Dissolve To: The empty seashore and the tide rushing in. A man paces the sand at the water's edge. He wears shorts and a fisherman's jacket, open above his bare breast. He calls, his hands cupped about his mouth.

JIYA'S FATHER: Ji————ya!

There is only the sound of the surf. He wades into the water, still calling. Suddenly he sees the boys, and he beckons fiercely. They come in, and he gives a hand to each one and pulls them out of the sea.

JIYA'S FATHER: Jiya! You have never been so late before.

JIYA: Father, we were on the sandbar, digging clams. We had to leave them.

JIYA'S FATHER [*shaking his shoulders*]: Never be so late!

KINO [*wondering*]: You are afraid of the sea, too?

JIYA'S FATHER: Go home, farmer's boy. Your mother is calling you.

In the distance a woman's voice is calling Kino's name. He hears and runs toward the mountain.

JIYA: Father, I have made you angry.

JIYA'S FATHER: I am not angry.

JIYA: Then why do you seem angry?

---

²girdle: a belt, sash, or cord worn around the waist

JIYA'S FATHER: Old Gentleman sent down word that a storm is rising behind the horizon. He sees the clouds through his great telescope.

JIYA: Father, why do you let Old Gentleman make you afraid? Just because he is rich and lives in a castle, everybody listens to him.

JIYA'S FATHER: Not because he is rich—not because he lives in a castle, but because he is old and wise and he knows the sea. He doesn't want anybody to die. [*He looks over the sea, and his arm tightens about his son, and he mutters as though to himself.*] Though all must die. . . .

JIYA: Why must all die, Father?

JIYA'S FATHER: Who knows? Simply, it is so.

They stand looking over the sea.

Act 2

Montage. Film of the Japanese scene as in Act 1.

NARRATOR: Yet there was much in life to enjoy. Kino had a good time every day. In the winter he went to school in the fishing village, and he and Jiya shared a bench and writing table. They studied reading and arithmetic and learned what all children must learn in school.

But in the summer Kino had to work hard on the farm. Even Setsu and the mother had to help when the rice seedlings were planted in the watery terraced fields. On those days Kino could not run down the mountainside to find Jiya. When the day was ended he was so tired he fell asleep over his supper.

There were days when Jiya, too, could not play. Schools of fish came into the channel between the shore and the island, and early in the morning Jiya and his father sailed their boats out to sea to cast their nets at dawn. If they were lucky, their nets came up so heavy with fish that it took all their strength to haul them in, and soon the bottom of the boat was flashing and sparkling with wriggling fish.

Sometimes, if it were not seed-time or harvest, Kino went with Jiya and his father. It was exciting to get up in the night and put on his warm padded jacket; for even in summer the wind was cool over the sea at dawn. However early he got up, his mother was up even earlier to give him a bowl of hot rice soup and some bean curd[3] and tea before he went. She packed him a lunch in a clean little wooden box—cold rice and

---

[3]bean curd: a soft soybean cheese

292

fish and a radish pickle. Down the stone steps of the mountain path, Kino ran straight to the narrow dock where the fishing boats bobbed up and down with the tide. Jiya and his father were already there, and in a few minutes their boat was nosing its way past the sandbar toward the open sea. Sails set, and filling with wind, they sped straight into the dawnlit horizon. Kino crouched down in the bow, and his heart rose with joy and excitement. It was like flying into the sky. The winds were so mild, the sea lay so calm and blue, that it was hard to believe that it could be cruel and angry. Actually it was the earth that brought the big wave.

One day, as Kino *helped his father plant turnips, a cloud came over the sun.*

Dissolve To: A field, and Kino *and his father. The volcano is in the background.*

KINO: Look, Father, the volcano is burning again!

FATHER [*straightens and gazes anxiously at the sky*]: It looks very angry. I shall not sleep tonight. We must hurry home.

KINO: Why should the volcano be angry, Father?

FATHER: Who knows? Simply, the inner fire burns. Come—make haste.

They gather their tools.

Dissolve To: Night. The threshing floor outside the farmhouse. Kino's Father *sits on a bench outside the door. He gets up and walks to and fro and gazes at the red sky above the volcano. The* Mother *comes to the door.*

MOTHER: Can you put out the volcano by not sleeping?

FATHER: Look at the fishing village! Every house is lit. And the lamps are lit in the castle. Shall I sleep like a fool?

MOTHER: I have taken the dishes from the shelves and put away our good clothes in boxes.

FATHER [*gazing down at the village*]: If only I knew whether it would be earth or sea. Both work evil together. The fires rage under the sea, the rocks boil. The volcano is vent unless the sea bottom breaks.

KINO [*coming to the door*]: Shall we have an earthquake, Father?

FATHER: I cannot tell.

MOTHER: How still it is. There's no wind. The sea is purple.

KINO: Why is the sea such a color?

FATHER: Sea mirrors sky. Sea and earth and sky—if they work against men, who can live?

KINO [*coming to his Father's side*]: Where are the gods? Do they forget us?

FATHER: There are times when the gods leave men alone. They test us to see how able we are to save ourselves.

KINO: What if we are not able?

FATHER: We must be able. Fear

293

makes us weak. If you are afraid, your hands tremble, your feet falter. Brain cannot tell hands what to do.

SETSU [*her voice calling from inside the house*]: Mother, I'm afraid!

MOTHER: I am coming. [*She goes away.*]

FATHER: The sky is growing black. Go into the house, Kino.

KINO: Let me stay with you.

FATHER: The red flag is flying over the castle. Twice I've seen that red flag go up, both times before you were born. Old Gentleman wants everybody to be ready.

KINO [*frightened*]: Ready for what?

FATHER: For whatever must be.

A deep-toned bell tolls over the mountainside.

KINO: What is that bell? I've never heard it before.

FATHER: It rang twice before you were born. It is the bell inside Old Gentleman's temple. He is calling to the people to come up out of the village and shelter within his walls.

KINO: Will they come?

FATHER: Not all of them. Parents will try to make their children go, but the children will not want to leave their parents. Mothers will not want to leave fathers, and the fathers will stay by the boats. But some will want to be sure of life.

The bell continues to ring urgently. Soon from the village comes a straggling line of people, nearly all
of them children.

KINO [*gazing at them*]: I wish Jiya would come. [*He takes off his white cloth girdle and waves it.*]

Dissolve To: Jiya *and his* Father *by their house. Sea in the background, roaring.*

JIYA'S FATHER: Jiya, you must go to the castle.

JIYA: I won't leave you and Mother.

JIYA'S FATHER: We must divide ourselves. If we die, you must live after us.

JIYA: I don't want to live alone.

JIYA'S FATHER: It is your duty to obey me, as a good Japanese son.

JIYA: Let me go to Kino's house.

JIYA'S FATHER: Only go–go quickly.

Jiya *and his* Father *embrace fiercely, and* Jiya *runs away, crying, to leap up to the mountainside.*

Dissolve To: Terrace and farmhouse, and center on Kino *and his* Father, *who put out their hands to help* Jiya *up the last terrace. Suddenly* Kino *screams.*

KINO: Look—at the sea!

FATHER: May the gods save us.

The bell begins to toll, deep, pleading, incessant.

JIYA [*shrieking*]: I must go back—I must tell my father. . . .

FATHER [*holding him*]: It is too late. . . .

Film. The sea rushes up in a terrible wave and swallows the shore. The water roars about the foot of the mountain.

Jiya, *held by* Kino *and his* Father

*stares transfixed and then sinks
unconscious to the ground. The bell
tolls on.*

Act 3

NARRATOR: So the big wave came,
swelling out of the sea. It lifted
the horizon while the people
watched. The air was filled with
its roar and shout. It rushed
over the flat, still waters of the
sea; it reached the village and
covered it fathoms deep in
swirling, wild water—green,
laced with fierce white foam.
The wave ran up the mountainside, until the knoll upon which
the castle stood was an island.
All who were still climbing the
path were swept away, mere
tossing scraps in the wicked
waters. Then with a great
sucking sigh, the wave ebbed
into the sea, dragging everything with it—trees, rocks,
houses, people. Once again it
swept over the village, and
once again it returned to the
sea, sinking into great stillness.
*Upon the beach, where the village
stood, not a house remained, no
wreckage of wood or fallen stone
wall, no street of little shops, no
docks, not a single boat. The beach*

295

was as clean as if no human being had ever lived there. All that had been was now no more.

Dissolve To: Inside the farmhouse. The farm family is gathered about the mattress on which Jiya *lies.*

MOTHER: This is not sleep. . . . Is it death?

FATHER: Jiya is not dead. His soul has withdrawn for a time. He is unconscious. Let him remain so until his own will wakes him.

MOTHER: [*rubbing* Jiya's *hands and feet*]: Kino, do not cry.

Kino *cannot stop crying, although silently.*

FATHER: Let him cry. Tears comfort the heart. [*He feels* Kino's *hands and cheeks.*] He is cold. Heat a little rice soup for him and put some ginger in it. I will stay with Jiya.

Mother *goes out.* Setsu *comes in, rubbing her eyes and yawning.*

FATHER: Sleepy eyes! You have slept all through the storm. Wise one!

SETSU [*coming to stare at* Jiya]: Is Jiya dead?

FATHER: No, Jiya is living.

SETSU: Why doesn't he open his eyes?

FATHER: Soon he will open his eyes.

SETSU: If Jiya is not dead, why does Kino stand there crying?

FATHER: As usual, you are asking too many questions. Go back to the kitchen and help your mother.

Setsu *goes out, staring and sucking*

her thumb. Father *puts his arm around* Kino.

FATHER: The first sorrow is the hardest to bear.

KINO: What will we say to Jiya when he wakes? How can we tell him?

FATHER: We will not talk. We will give him warm food and let him rest. We will help him to feel he still has a home.

KINO: Here?

FATHER: Here. I have always wanted another son, and Jiya will be that son. As soon as he knows this is his home, we must help him to understand what has happened. Ah, here is Mother, with your hot rice soup. Eat it, my son—food for the body is food for the heart, sometimes.

Kino *takes the bowl from his* Mother *with both hands and drinks. The parents look at each other and at him, sorrowfully and tenderly.* Setsu *comes in and leans her head toward her* Mother.

Dissolve To: The same room, the same scene except that Mother *and* Setsu *are not there.* Father *sits beside* Jiya's *bed,* Kino *is at the open door.*

KINO: The sky is golden, Father, and the sea is smooth. How cruel. . . .

FATHER: No, it is wonderful that after the storm the sea grows calm again, and the sky is clear. It was not the sea or sky that made the evil storm.

296

KINO [*not turning his head*]: Who made it?

FATHER: Ah, no one knows who makes evil storms. [*He takes Jiya's hand and rubs it gently.*] We only know that they come. When they come we must live through them as bravely as we can, and after they are gone we must feel again how wonderful life is. Every day of life is more valuable now than it was before the storm.

KINO: But Jiya's father and mother —and the other fisherfolk— so good and kind—all of them —lost. [*He cannot go on.*]

FATHER: We must think of Jiya— who lives. [*He stops.* Jiya *has begun to sob softly in his unconsciousness.*]

FATHER: Quick, Kino—call your mother and Setsu. He will open his eyes at any moment, and we must all be here—you to be his brother, I, his father, and the mother, the sister—

Kino *runs out,* Father *kneels beside* Jiya, *who stirs, still sobbing.* Kino *comes back with* Mother *and* Setsu. *They kneel on the floor beside the bed.* Jiya's *eyelids flutter. He opens his eyes and looks from one to the other. He stares at the beams of the roof, the walls of the room, the bed, his own hands. All are quiet except* Setsu, *who cannot keep from laughing. She claps her hands.*

SETSU: Oh, Jiya has come back. Jiya, did you have a good dream?

JIYA [*faintly*]: My father, my mother—

MOTHER [*taking his hands in both hers*]: I will be your mother now, dear Jiya.

FATHER: I will be your father.

KINO: I am your brother, Jiya. [*He falters.*]

SETSU [*joyfully*]: Oh, Jiya, you will live with us.

Jiya *gets up slowly. He walks to the door, goes out, and looks down the hillside.*

Dissolve To: The peaceful empty beach. Then back to the farmhouse and Jiya, *standing outside and looking at the sea.* Setsu *comes to him.*

SETSU: I will give you my pet duck. He'll follow you—he'll make you laugh.

MOTHER [*leaving the room*]: We ought all to eat something. I have a fine chicken for dinner.

KINO [*coming to Jiya*]: Mother makes such good chicken soup.

SETSU: I'm hungry, I tell you.

FATHER: Come, Jiya, my son.

Jiya *stands still dazed.*

KINO: Eat with us, Jiya.

JIYA. I am tired—very tired.

KINO: You have been sleeping so long.

JIYA [*slowly*]: I shall never see them again. [*He puts his hands over his eyes.*] I shall keep thinking about them—floating in the sea.

MOTHER [*coming in*]: Drink this bowl of soup at least, Jiya, my son.

Jiya *drinks and lets the bowl fall. It is wooden and does not break.*

JIYA: I want to sleep.

FATHER: Sleep, my son. Sleep is good for you. [*He leads* Jiya *to the bed and covers him with a quilt.*]

FATHER [*to them all*]: Jiya is not yet ready to live. We must wait.

KINO: Will he die?

FATHER: Life is stronger than death. He will live.

Act 4

NARRATOR: The body heals first, and the body heals the mind and the soul. Jiya ate food, he got out of bed sometimes, but he was still tired. He did not want to think or remember. He only wanted to sleep. He woke to eat, and then he went to sleep again. In the quiet, clean room Jiya slept, and the mother spread the quilt over him and closed the door and went away. All through these days Kino did not play about as he once had. He was no longer a child. He worked hard beside his father in the fields. They did not talk much, and neither of them wanted to look at the sea. It was enough to look at the earth, dark and rich beneath their feet.

One evening Kino climbed the mountain behind the house and looked up at the volcano. The heavy cloud of smoke had gone away, and the sky was clear. He was glad that the volcano was no longer angry, and he went down again to the house. On the threshold his father was smoking his usual evening pipe. In the house his mother was giving Setsu her evening bath.

KINO [*dropping down on the bench beside his father*]: Is Jiya asleep, again?

FATHER: Yes, and it is a good thing for him. When he sleeps enough, he will wake and remember.

KINO: But should he remember?

FATHER: Only when he dares to remember his parents will he be happy again.

[*A silence*]

KINO: Father, are we not very unfortunate people to live in Japan?

FATHER: Why do you think so?

KINO: The volcano is behind our house and the sea is in front. When they work together to make earthquake and big wave, we are helpless. Always, many of us are lost.

FATHER: To live in the presence of death makes us brave and strong. That is why our people never fear death. We see it too often, and we do not fear it. To die a little sooner or a little later does not matter. But to live bravely, to love life, to see how beautiful the trees are and the mountains—yes, and even the sea—to enjoy work because it produces food—in these ways we are fortunate people. We love life because we live in danger. We do not fear death, for we understand that death and life are necessary to each other.

KINO: What is death?

FATHER: Death is the great gateway.

KINO: The gateway—where?

FATHER: Can you remember when you were born?

KINO: I was too small.

FATHER [*smiling*]: I remember very well. Oh, hard you thought it was to be born. You cried and you screamed.

KINO [*much interested*]: Didn't I want to be born?

FATHER: You did not. You wanted to stay just where you were, in the warm dark house of the unborn, but the time came to be born, and the gate of life opened.

KINO: Did I know it was the gate of life?

FATHER: You did not know anything about it, and so you were afraid. But see how foolish you were! Here we were waiting for you, your parents, already loving you and eager to welcome you. And you have been very happy, haven't you?

KINO: Until the big wave came. Now I am afraid again because of the death the big wave brought.

FATHER: You are only afraid because you don't know anything about death. But someday you will wonder why you were afraid, even as today you wonder why you once feared to be born.

KINO: I think I understand—I begin to understand. . . .

FATHER: Do not hurry yourself. You have plenty of time. [*He rises to his feet.*] Now what do I see? A lantern coming up the hill.

KINO [*running to the edge of the threshold*]: Who can be coming now? It is almost night.

FATHER: A visitor—ah, why, it's Old Gentleman!

Old Gentleman *indeed is climbing the hill. He is somewhat breathless in spite of his long staff. His Manservant carries the lantern, and, when they arrive, steps to one side.*

OLD GENTLEMAN [*to Manservant*]: Is this the house of Uchiyama, the farmer?

MANSERVANT: It is—and this is the farmer himself and his son.

FATHER [*bowing deeply*]: Please, Honored Sir, what can I do for you?

OLD GENTLEMAN: Do you have a lad here by the name of Jiya?

FATHER: He lies sleeping in my house.

OLD GENTLEMAN: I wish to see him.

FATHER: Sir, he suffered the loss of his parents when the big wave came. Now sleep heals him.

OLD GENTLEMAN: I will not wake him. I only wish to look at him.

FATHER: Please come in.

Dissolve To: Jiya asleep. The Manservant *holds the lantern so that the light does not fall on Jiya's face directly. Old Gentleman looks at him carefully.*

OLD GENTLEMAN: Tall and strong for his age—intelligent—handsome. Hm—yes. [*He motions to the Manservant to lead him away, and the scene returns to the dooryard.*]

OLD GENTLEMAN [*to Father*]: It is my habit, when the big wave comes, to care for those who are orphaned by it. Thrice in my lifetime I have searched out the orphans, and I have fed them and sheltered them. But I have heard of this boy Jiya and wish to do more for him. If he is as good as he is handsome, I will take him for my own son.

KINO: But Jiya is ours!

FATHER [*sternly*]: Hush. We are only poor people. If Old Gentleman wants Jiya, we cannot say we will not give him up.

OLD GENTLEMAN: Exactly. I will give him fine clothes and send him to a good school, and he may become a great man and an honor to our whole province and even to the nation.

KINO: But if he lives in the castle we can't be brothers!

FATHER: We must think of Jiya's good. [*He turns to* Old Gentleman.] Sir, it is very kind of you to propose this for Jiya. I had planned to take him for my own son, now that he has lost both his parents; but I am only a poor farmer, and I cannot pretend that my house is as good as yours or that I can afford to send Jiya to a fine school. Tomorrow when he wakes I will tell him of your fine offer. He will decide.

OLD GENTLEMAN: Very well. But let him come and tell me himself.

FATHER [*proudly*]: Certainly. Jiya must speak for himself.

Old Gentleman *bows slightly and prepares to depart.* Father *bows deeply and taps* Kino *on the head to make him bow.* Old Gentleman *and his Manservant return down the mountain.*

KINO: If Jiya goes away, I shall never have a brother.

FATHER: Kino, don't be selfish. You must allow Jiya to make his own choice. It would be wrong to persuade him. I forbid you to speak to him of this matter. When he wakes, I will tell him myself.

KINO [*pleading*]: Don't tell him today, Father.

FATHER: I must tell him as soon as he wakes. It would not be fair to Jiya to let him grow used to thinking of this house as his home. He must make the choice today, before he has time to put down his new roots. Go now, Kino, and weed the lower terrace.

Dissolve To: Kino *working in the terrace, weeding. It is evident that he has worked for some time. He looks hot and dusty, and he has quite a pile of weeds. He stops to look up at the farmhouse, but sees no one and resigns himself again to his work. Suddenly his name is called.*

FATHER: Kino!

KINO: Shall I come?

FATHER: No, I'm coming—with Jiya.

Kino *stands waiting.* Father *and* Jiya *come down the terraces.* Jiya *is very sad. When he sees* Kino *he tries not to cry.*

FATHER [*putting his arm about Jiya's shoulder*]: Jiya, you must not mind that you cry easily. Until now you couldn't cry because you weren't fully alive. You had been hurt too much. But today you are beginning to live, and so your tears flow. It is good for you. Let your tears come—don't stop them. [*He turns to* Kino.] I have told Jiya that he must not decide where he will live until he has seen the inside of the castle. He must see all that Old Gentleman can give him. Jiya, you know how our house is—four small rooms, and the kitchen, this farm, upon which we have to work hard for our food. We have only what our hands earn for us. [*He holds out his two workworn hands.*] If you live in the castle, you need never have hands like this.

JIYA: I don't want to live in the castle.

FATHER: You don't know whether you do or not; you have never seen the castle inside. [*He turns to Kino.*] Kino, you are to go with Jiya, and when you reach the castle you must persuade him to stay there for his own sake.

KINO: I will go and wash myself—and put on my good clothes.

FATHER: No—go as you are. You are a farmer's son.

Kino *and* Jiya *go, reluctantly, and* Father *stands looking after them.*

Dissolve To: The mountainside and the two boys nearing the gate of the castle. The gate is open, and inside old Gardener *is sweeping moss under pine trees. He sees them.*

GARDENER: What do you want, boys?

KINO: My father sent us to see the honored Old Gentleman.

GARDENER: Are you the Uchiyama boy?

KINO: Yes, please, and this is Jiya, whom Old Gentleman wishes to come and live here.

GARDENER [*bowing to* Jiya]: Follow me, young sir.

They follow over a pebbled path under the leaning pine trees. In the distance the sun falls upon a flowering garden and a pool with a waterfall.

KINO [*sadly*]: How beautiful it is—of course you will want to live here. Who could blame you?

Jiya *does not answer. He walks with his head held high. They come to a great door where a* Manservant *bids them to take off their shoes. The* Gardener *leaves them.*

MANSERVANT: Follow me.

They follow through passageways into a great room decorated in the finest Japanese fashion. In the distance at the end of the room, they see Old Gentleman, *sitting beside a small table. Behind him the open panels reveal the garden.* Old Gentleman *is writing. He holds his brush upright in his hand, and he is carefully painting letters on a scroll, his silver rimmed glasses sliding down his nose. When the two boys approach, the* Manservant *announces them.*

MANSERVANT: Master, the two boys are here.

OLD GENTLEMAN [*to boys*]: Would you like to know what I have been writing?

Jiya *looks at* Kino, *who is too awed to speak.*

JIYA: Yes, Honored Sir, if you please.

OLD GENTLEMAN [*taking up the scroll*]: It is not my own poem. It is the saying of a wise man of India, but I like it so much that

I have painted it on this scroll to hang it there in the alcove where I can see it every day. [*He reads clearly and slowly.*] "The children of God are very dear,
But very odd—
Very nice, but very narrow." [*He looks up over his spectacles.*] What do you think of it?

JIYA [*looking at Kino who is too shy to speak*]: We do not understand it, Sir.

OLD GENTLEMAN [*shaking his head and laughing softly*]: Ah, we are all children of God! [*He takes off his spectacles and looks hard at Jiya*]. Well? Will you be my son? [Jiya, *too embarrassed to speak, bites his lip and looks away, etc.*]

OLD GENTLEMAN: Say yes or no.

Either word is not hard to speak.

JIYA: I will say—no. [*He feels this is too harsh, and he smiles apologetically.*] I thank you, sir, but I have a home—on a farm.

KINO [*trying to repress his joy and speaking very solemnly as a consequence*]: Jiya, remember how poor we are.

OLD GENTLEMAN [*smiling, half sad*]: They are certainly very poor and here, you know, you would have everything. You can invite this farmboy to come and play, sometimes, if you like. And I am quite willing to give the family some money. It would be suitable as my son for you to help the poor.

JIYA [*suddenly, as though he had not heard*]: Where are the others who were saved from the big wave?

OLD GENTLEMAN: Some wanted to go away, the ones who wanted to stay are out in the back yard with my servants.

JIYA: Why do you not invite them to come into the castle and be your sons and daughters?

OLD GENTLEMAN [*somewhat outraged by this*]: Because I don't want them for my sons and daughters. You are a bright, handsome boy. They told me you were the best boy in the village.

JIYA: I am not better than the others. My father was a fisherman.

OLD GENTLEMAN [*taking up his spectacles and brush*]: Very well—I will do without a son.

The Manservant motions to the boys to come away, and they follow.

MANSERVANT [*to* Jiya]: How foolish you are! Our Old Gentleman is very kind. You would have everything here.

JIYA: Not everything. . . .

KINO: Let's hurry home—let's hurry—hurry—

They run down the mountainside and up the hill to the farmhouse. Setsu sees them and comes flying down to meet them, the sleeves of her bright kimono like wings, and her feet clattering in their wooden sandals.

SETSU: Jiya has come home—Jiya, Jiya—

Jiya *sees her happy face and opens his arms and gives her a great hug.*

Act 5

NARRATOR: Now happiness began to live in Jiya, though secretly and hidden inside him, in ways he did not understand. The good food warmed him, and his body welcomed it. Around him the love of four people who received him for their own glowed like a warm and welcoming fire upon his heart.

Time passed. Eight years. Jiya grew up in the farmhouse to be a tall young man, and Kino grew at his side, solid and strong, but never as tall as Jiya. Setsu grew too, from a mischievous child, into a happy, willful, pretty girl. But time, however long, was split in two parts, the time before and the time after the big wave. The big wave had changed everybody's life.

In all those years no one returned to live on the empty beach. The tides rose and fell, sweeping the sands clear every day. Storms came and went, but there was never such a wave as the big one. At last people began to think that never again would there be such a big wave. The few fishermen who had listened to the tolling bell from the castle, and were saved with their wives and children, went to other shores to fish and they made new fishing boats. Then, as time passed, they told themselves that no beach was quite as good as the old one. There, they said, the water was deep and great fish came close to shore. They did not need to go far out to sea to find booty.

Jiya and Kino had not often gone to the beach, either. At first they had walked along the empty sands where once the street had been, and Jiya searched for some keepsake from his home that the sea might have washed back to the shore. But nothing was ever found. So the two boys, as they grew to be young men, did not visit the deserted beach. When they went to swim in the sea, they walked across the farm and over another fold of the mountains to the shore.

Yet Jiya had never fogotten his father and mother. He thought of them every day, their faces, their voices, the way his father talked, his mother's smile. The big wave had changed him forever. He did not laugh easily or speak carelessly. In school he had earnestly learned all he could, and now he worked hard on the farm. Now, as a man, he valued deeply everything that was good. Since the big wave had been so cruel, he was never cruel, and he grew kind and gentle. Jiya never spoke of his loneliness. He did not want others to be sad because of his sadness. When he laughed at some mischief of Setsu's when she teased him, his laughter was wonderful to hear because it was whole and real. And, sometimes, in the morning, he went to the door of the farmhouse and looked at the empty beach below, searching with his eyes as though something might one day come back. One day he did see something. . . .

JIYA: Kino, come here! [Kino *comes out, his shoes in his hand.*]

JIYA: Look—is someone building a house on the beach?

KINO: Two men—pounding posts into the sand—

JIYA: And a woman—yes, and even a child.

KINO: They can't be building a house.

JIYA: Let's go and see.

Dissolve To: The beach. The two Men, Jiya and Kino, Woman and Child.

JIYA [*out of breath*]: Are you building a house?

FIRST MAN [*wiping sweat from his face*]: Our father used to live here, and we with him. We are two brothers. During these years we have lived in the houses of the castle, and we have fished from other shores. Now we are tired of having no homes of our own. Besides, this is still the best beach for fishing.

KINO: What if the big wave comes again?

SECOND MAN [*shrugging his shoulders*]: There was a big wave, too, in our great-grandfather's time. All the houses were swept away. But our grandfather came back. In our father's time there was again the big wave. Now we return.

KINO [*soberly*]: What of your children?

The Men begin to dig again. The Woman takes the Child into her arms and gazes out to the sea. Suddenly there is a sound of a voice calling. All look up the mountain.

FIRST MAN: Here comes our Old Gentleman.

SECOND MAN: He's very angry or he wouldn't have left the castle.

[*Both throw down their shovels and stand waiting. The Woman sinks to a kneeling position on the sand, still holding the Child. Old Gentleman shouts as he comes near; his voice is high and thin. He is very old now, and is supported by two Manservants. His beard flies in the wind.*]

OLD GENTLEMAN: You foolish children! You leave the safety of my walls and come back to this dangerous shore, as your father did before you! The big wave will return and sweep you into the sea.

FIRST MAN: It may not, Ancient Sir.

OLD GENTLEMAN: It will come, I have spent my whole life trying to save foolish people from the big wave. But you will not be saved.

JIYA [*stepping forward*]: Sir, here is our home. Dangerous as it is, threatened by the volcano and the sea, it is here we were born.

OLD GENTLEMAN [*looking at him*]: Don't I know you?

JIYA: Sir, I was once in your castle.

OLD GENTLEMAN [*nodding*]: I remember you. I wanted you for my son. Ah, you made a great mistake, young man. You could have lived safely in my castle all your life, and your children would have been safe there. The big wave never reaches me.

KINO: Sir, your castle is not safe,

either. If the earth shakes hard enough, even your castle will crumble. There is no refuge for us who live on these islands. We are brave because we must be.

SECOND MAN: Ha—you are right.

The two men return to their building.

OLD GENTLEMAN [*rolling his eyes and wagging his beard*]: Don't ask me to save you the next time the big wave comes!

JIYA [*gently*]: But you will save us, because you are so good.

OLD GENTLEMAN [*looking at him and then smiling sadly*]: What a pity you would not be my son! [*He turns and, leaning on his Man-servants, climbs the mountain.*]

Fade To: His arrival at the castle gate. He enters, and the gates clang shut.

Dissolve To: The field where Father *and* Jiya *and* Kino *are working.*

FATHER [*to* Jiya]: Did you soak the seeds for the rice?

JIYA [*aghast*]: I forgot.

KINO: I did it.

JIYA [*throwing down his hoe*]: I forget everything these days.

FATHER: I know you are too good a son to be forgetful on purpose. Tell me what is on your mind.

JIYA: I want a boat. I want to go back to fishing.

Father *does not pause in his hoeing; but* Kino *flings down his hoe.*

KINO: You, too, are foolish!

JIYA [*stubbornly*]: When I have a boat, I shall build my own house on the beach.

KINO: Oh, fool, fool!

FATHER: Be quiet! Jiya is a man. You are both men. I shall pay you wages from this day.

JIYA: Wages! [*He falls to hoeing vigorously.*]

Dissolve To: The beach, where the two young men are inspecting a boat.

JIYA: I knew all the time that I had to come back to the sea.

KINO: With this boat, you'll soon earn enough to build a house. But I'm glad I live on the mountain. [*They continue inspecting the boat, fitting the oars, etc., as they talk.*]

JIYA [*abruptly*]: Do you think Setsu would be afraid to live on the beach?

KINO [*surprised*]: Why should Setsu live on the beach?

JIYA [*embarrassed but determined*]: Because when I have my house built, I want Setsu to be my wife.

KINO [*astonished*]: Setsu? You would be foolish to marry her.

JIYA [*smiling*]: I don't agree with you.

KINO [*seriously*]: But why—why do you want her?

JIYA: Because she makes me laugh. It is she who made me forget the big wave. For me, she is life.

KINO: But she is not a good cook. Think how she burns the rice when she runs outside to look at something.

JIYA: I don't mind burned rice, and I will run out with her to see what she sees.

KINO [*with all the gestures of astonishment and disbelief*]: I can't understand. . . .

Dissolve To: The farmhouse, and Father who is looking over his seeds.

KINO [*coming in stealthily*]: Do you know that Jiya wants to marry Setsu?

FATHER: I have seen some looks pass between them.

KINO: But Jiya is too good for Setsu.

FATHER: Setsu is very pretty.

KINO: With that silly nose?

FATHER [*calmly*]: I believe that Jiya admires her nose.

KINO: Besides, she is such a tease.

FATHER: What makes you miserable will make him happy.

KINO: I don't understand that, either.

FATHER [*laughing*]: Someday you will understand.

Dissolve To: Narrator.

NARRATOR: One day, one early summer, Jiya and Setsu were married. Kino still did not understand, for up to the last, Setsu was naughty and mischievous. Indeed on the very day of her wedding she hid Kino's hairbrush under his bed. "You are too silly to be married," Kino said when he had found it. "I feel sorry for Jiya," he said. Setsu's big brown eyes laughed at him, and she stuck out her red tongue. "I shall always be nice to Jiya," she said. But when the wedding was over and the family had taken the newly married pair down the hill to the new house on the beach, Kino felt sad. The farmhouse was very quiet without Setsu. Already he missed her. Every day he could go to see Jiya, and many times he would be fishing with him. But Setsu would not be in the farmhouse kitchen, in the rooms, in the garden. He would miss even her teasing. And then he grew very grave indeed. What if the big wave came again?

Dissolve To: The new house. Kino turns to Jiya.

KINO: Jiya, it is all very pretty—very nice. But Setsu—what if the big wave comes again?

JIYA: I have prepared for that. Come—all of you. [*He calls the family in.*] This is where we will sleep at night, and where we will live by day. But look—

The family stands watching, and Jiya pushes back a long panel in the wall. Before their eyes is the sea, swelling and stirring under the evening wind. The sun is sinking into the water.

JIYA: I have opened my house to the sea. If ever the big wave comes back, I shall be ready. I face it, night and day. I am not afraid.

KINO: Tomorrow I'll go fishing with you, Jiya—shall I?

JIYA [*laughing*]: Not tomorrow,
   brother!
Setsu *comes to his side and leans*
   against him, and he puts his arm
   around her.
FATHER: Yes, life is stronger than
   death. [*He turns to his family.*]
   Come, let us go home.

Father *and* Mother *and* Kino *bow*
   and leave. Jiya *and* Setsu *stand*
   looking out to the sea.
JIYA: Life is stronger than
   death—do you hear that, Setsu?
SETSU: Yes. I hear.

Curtain

What Do You Think?

1. Why did Kino's father believe that it was important to understand death?
2. Describe Jiya's behavior after his parents died. How did he deal with his sorrow?
3. How did Jiya's understanding of life change after the big wave?
4. Why do you think Jiya returned to the life of a fisher?
5. The word "cycle" is used to describe things that happen again and again. Describe one of the many cycles in the story.

Taking a Closer Look

1. How did Kino's family support itself? How did Jiya's family support itself?
2. Before the big wave, what did Kino fear and respect most? What did Jiya fear and respect most?
3. How do the sea and earth work together?
4. Why did Old Gentleman put up a red flag?
5. What happened to the people in the village?
6. Kino's father said, " . . . our people never fear death." How did he explain this to Kino?
7. Why was Old Gentleman upset when the people began to build houses on the beach again?
8. How was Jiya's house different from the others on the beach?

Putting Ideas to Work

Imagine that Jiya had decided to become the son of Old Gentleman. Write a description of Jiya's life as an adult. Be sure to emphasize the differences between his life and that of a fisher's.

Some days seem to have magic in the air. In remembering those days one might feel that it was all imagined. But in sharing the memory it becomes real.

The Day We Flew Kites

Frances Fowler

"String!" shouted Brother, bursting into the kitchen, "we need lots more string."

Outside, Father and Mr. Patrick next door were doing chores about their large yards. March was a busy time.

Indoors Mother and Mrs. Patrick were running around in a spring-cleaning marathon. Such a windy day was ideal for "turning out" clothes closets, and already woolens flapped on clotheslines that snaked across the adjoining backyards.

Somehow the boys had slipped away to the back lot with their kites, but now, even at the risk of having Brother impounded to beat carpets or wash windows, they had sent him for more string. Apparently there was no limit to the heights to which kites would soar today.

My mother looked out the window. The sky was piercingly blue, the breeze fresh and exciting, and up in all that blueness sailed great puffy billows of clouds. It had been a long, hard winter, but today was spring. Mother looked from the pie-baking clutter on the kitchen table to the disordered sitting room, its furniture all moved out of line for a Spartan sweeping. Again her eyes wavered toward the window. "Come on, girls." She fumbled in the kitchen drawer for a new roll of twine. "Let's take string to the boys and watch them fly the kites a minute."

On the way we met Mrs. Patrick, laughing guiltily, escorted by her girls.

There never was such a day for flying kites! God doesn't make two such days in a century. We played all our fresh twine into the boys' kites and still they soared until we could hardly distinguish the tiny, orange-colored specks. Now and then we slowly reeled one in, finally bringing it dipping and tugging to earth, for the sheer joy of sending it up again. What a thrill to run with them, to the right, to the left, and see our poor, earthbound movements reflected minutes later in their majestic sky-dance! We wrote wishes on slips of paper, punched holes in them, and slipped them over the string. Slowly, irresistibly, they climbed up until they reached the kites.

Even our fathers dropped hoe and hammer and joined us. Our mothers took their turns, laughing like schoolgirls, their hair blowing out of their pompadours and curling loose about their cheeks; their gingham aprons whipping about their legs. Mingled with our puppyish delight was a feeling akin to awe. These adults were playing with us, really playing! Once I looked at Mother and thought she looked actually pretty—and her over forty!

We never knew where the hours went on that hilltop day. There were no hours, just a golden, breezy Now. I think we were all a little beyond ourselves. Parents forgot their duty and their dignity; children forgot their combativeness and small spites. Perhaps it's like this in the kingdom of heaven, I thought.

It was growing dark before we all stumbled sleepily back to the houses. I suppose we had some sort of supper; I suppose there was a surface tidying up, or do I remember?

The strange thing was, we didn't mention that day afterward. I felt a little embarrassed. Surely none of those other sensible, balanced people had thrilled to it as deeply as I had. I locked the memory up in that deepest part of me where we keep the "things that cannot be and yet are."

The years went on; and then one day I was scurrying about my own kitchen in a city apartment, trying to get some work out of the way, while my three-year-old insistently cried her desire to "go park and see ducks."

"I *can't* go!" I said. "I have this and this to do, and when I'm through I'll be too tired to walk that far."

My mother, who was visiting us, looked up from the peas she was shelling. "It's a wonderful day," she offered, "really warm, yet there's a fine, fresh breeze. It reminds me of that day we flew the kites."

I stopped in my dash between stove and sink. So she remembered! The locked door flew open, and released a gush of memories. I pulled off my apron. "Come on," I told my little girl, "it's too good a day to miss."

Another decade passed and we were in the uneasy aftermath of a great war. All evening we had been asking our returned soldier, the youngest Patrick boy, about his experiences as a prisoner of war. He had talked freely, but now for a long time he had been silent. What was he going to tell us? The silence seemed suddenly to throb. What was he thinking of—what dark and dreadful things?

"Say!" A smile twitched his lips. He looked like the little boy he used to be, the very little boy always tagging behind. "Do you remember . . . no, of course you wouldn't. It probably didn't make the impression on you it did on me."

I hardly dared speak. "Remember what?"

"I used to think of that day a lot in PW camp, when things were bad. Do you remember the day we flew the kites?"

Winter came and the sad duty of a call of condolence on Mrs. Patrick, recently widowed. I dreaded the call. I couldn't imagine how Mrs. Patrick would face life alone.

We talked a little of my family and her grandchildren and the changes in the town. Then she was silent, looking down at her lap. I cleared my throat. Now I must say something about her loss, and she would begin to cry.

When Mrs. Patrick looked up, she was smiling. "I was just sitting here thinking," she said, "Henry had such fun that day. Frances, do you remember the day we flew the kites?"

What Do You Think?

1. Do you think that the author's comparison of this experience to the kingdom of heaven is a valid one? Why or why not?
2. Why do you think the girl in this story suddenly realized on that day that her mother was pretty?
3. What made the day they flew kites so memorable?
4. Tell what you think the writer of this story learned.

Taking a Closer Look

1. Why was Mrs. Patrick laughing *guiltily* on the way to the field?
2. What incident first reminded the author of the day they flew kites?
3. Name three people other than the author who remembered the day they flew kites. Under what circumstances did each one remember this event?

Putting Ideas to Work

Write a letter to someone describing a happy day of your life or a special tradition in your family. What made it so happy? How did you feel? How did things look to you?

Headings and Subheadings

To preview something is useful in many ways. This look-ahead view gives you a chance to anticipate what will happen next. It is an opportunity to add clues together, to see how things relate, and to predict outcomes.

When reading texts, a look ahead can tell you what to expect in each chapter. This is helpful when reading information-type texts, such as special-topic, science, and social studies books. These books use headings and subheadings. Headings (major titles) and subheadings (minor titles) tell about the topic, its main idea, and specific details. They assist you in locating needed information.

Take a first look at the make-believe text page about folktales. Preview the headings and subheadings carefully.

FOLKTALES: FACT OR FAKE?

Not everyone agrees on the answer. Many people who have studied folktales might say that they contain scads of fakery and a pinch of fact.

What Is a Folktale?

Folktales are stories that are told orally. The word folktale literally means "tale of the folk." Most are short tales that are told simply to entertain. If the teller is gifted, however, the tale could last for days. Folktales are considered fictitious. Sometimes, they have a moral.

Beginnings

Almost as soon as there were people, storytelling began. All cultures have folktales. The original tellers of these tales, however, are anonymous. Sometimes, the same folktale is told throughout the world. The title and the character names may be different, but the theme is the same. So, where each tale originated is not really known.

Folktale Themes

Folktales tell of heroic deeds and brave creatures—some human, some animal, some both, some neither. The themes are universal—things that concern people everywhere.

Are Folktales Important?

Folktales tell about history, tradition, and culture. Some tell how groups of people survived and of the courage and sacrifice that was needed. This is true of cultures all over the world, including our own. Folktales show another way to see how people have changed, or stayed the same, throughout the ages. Folktales also tell how people are alike, or how and why they differ.

Story Saving

If folktales are word-of-mouth stories, how come there are so many folktale books? People have become interested in "saving" folktales. Folktale scholars have carefully collected and recorded tales, to prevent the tales from being lost forever. Sometimes, this has involved traveling to remote corners of the earth. Other times, talking with a grandparent has brought forth marvelous stories.

Folktale scholars may not agree with all the facts on this make-believe text page. But most would agree that folktales are valuable.

1. Which paragraph would you read to find an answer to the title? Which paragraph might give more detailed information about the title?

2. Which subheading—"What Is a Folktale?" or "Beginnings"— defines the word *folktale?*

3. Which subheading explains what folktales mean to people? Is there another subheading that gives more details about folktale significance?

4. Where would you find information about saving folktales?

5. What paragraph gives a summary of the topic? Is there more than one paragraph that summarizes? If so, tell where they are located.

VISIONS OF BROTHERHOOD

While Peter slept on the roof he had a dream. When Martin Luther King, Jr., stood before a crowd of people he told them, "I have a dream." The dream for equality is a very old one. It is an imagining that can become real.

A Vision for Change

About noon the following day as they were approaching the city, Peter went up on the roof to pray. He became hungry and wanted something to eat, and while the meal was being prepared, he fell into a trance. He saw heaven opened and something like a large sheet being let down to earth by its four corners. It contained all kinds of four-footed animals, as well as reptiles of the earth and birds of the air. Then a voice told him, "Get up, Peter. Kill and eat."

"Surely no, Lord!" Peter replied. "I have never eaten anything impure or unclean."

The voice spoke to him a second time, "Do not call anything impure that God has made clean."

This happened three times, and immediately the sheet was taken back to heaven.

While Peter was wondering about the meaning of the vision, the men sent by Cornelius found out where Simon's house was and stopped at the gate. They called out, asking if Simon who was known as Peter was staying there.

While Peter was still thinking about the vision, the Spirit said to him, "Simon, three men are looking for you. So get up and go downstairs. Do not hesitate to go with them, for I have sent them."

Peter went down and said to the men, "I'm the one you're looking for. Why have you come?"

The men replied, "We have come from Cornelius the centurion. He is a righteous and God-fearing man, who is respected by all the Jewish people. A holy angel told him to have you come to his house so that he could hear what you have to say." Then Peter invited the men into the house to be his guests.

The next day Peter started out with them, and some of the brothers from Joppa went along. The following day he arrived in Caesarea. Cornelius was expecting them and had called together his relatives and close friends. As Peter entered the house, Cornelius met him and fell at his feet in reverence. But Peter made him get up. "Stand up," he said, "I am only a man myself."

Talking with him, Peter went inside and found a large gathering of people. He said to them: "You are well aware that it is against our law for a Jew to associate with a Gentile or visit him. But God has shown me that I should not call any man impure or unclean. So when I was sent for, I came without raising any objection. May I ask why you sent for me?"

Cornelius answered: "Four days ago I was in my house praying at this hour, at three in the afternoon. Suddenly a man in shining clothes stood before me and said, 'Cornelius, God has heard your prayer and remembered your gifts to the poor. Send to Joppa for Simon who is called Peter. He is a guest in the home of Simon the tanner, who lives by the sea.' So I sent for you immediately, and it was good of you to come. Now we are all here in the presence of God to listen to everything the Lord has commanded you to tell us."

Then Peter began to speak: "I now realize how true it is that God does not show favoritism but accepts men from every nation who fear him and do what is right. This is the message God sent to the people of Israel, telling the good news of peace through Jesus Christ, who is Lord of all. You know what has happened throughout Judea, beginning in Galilee after the baptism that John preached—how God anointed Jesus of Nazareth with the Holy Spirit and power, and how he went around doing good and healing all who were under the power of the devil, because God was with him.

"We are witnesses of everything he did in the country of the Jews and in Jerusalem. They killed him by hanging him on a tree, but God raised him from the dead on the third day and caused him to be seen. He was not seen by all the people, but by witnesses whom God had already chosen—by us who ate and drank with him after he rose from the dead. He commanded us to preach to the people and to testify that he is the one whom God appointed as judge of the living and the dead. All the prophets testify about him that everyone who believes in him receives forgiveness of sins through his name."

While Peter was still speaking these words, the Holy Spirit came on all who heard the message. The circumcised believers who had come with Peter were astonished that the gift of the Holy Spirit had been poured out even on the Gentiles. For they heard them speaking in tongues and praising God.

Then Peter said, "Can anyone keep these people from being baptized with water? They have received the Holy Spirit just as we have." So he ordered that they be baptized in the name of Jesus Christ. Then they asked Peter to stay with them for a few days.

—Acts 10:9-48 NIV

I Have a Dream

Martin Luther King, Jr.

. . . Five score years ago a great American, in whose symbolic shadow we stand, signed the Emancipation Proclamation. This momentous decree came as a great beacon light of hope to millions of Negro slaves who had been seared in the flames of withering injustice. It came as a joyous daybreak to end the long night of captivity.

But one hundred years later, we must face the tragic fact that the Negro still is not free. One hundred years later, the life of the Negro is still sadly crippled by the manacles of segregation and the chains of discrimination. One hundred years later, the Negro lives on a lonely island of poverty in the midst of a vast ocean of material prosperity. One hundred years later, the Negro is still languished in the corners of American society and finds himself in exile in his own land. So we have come here today to dramatize an appalling condition.

In a sense we have come to our nation's capital to cash a check. When the architects of our republic wrote the magnificent words of the Constitution and the Declaration of Independence, they were signing a promissory note to which every American was to fall heir. This note was a promise that all men would be granted the unalienable rights of life, liberty, and the pursuit of happiness.

It is obvious today that America has defaulted on this promissory note insofar as her citizens of color are concerned. Instead of honoring this sacred obligation, America has given the Negro people a bad check; a check which has come back marked "insufficient funds." But we refuse to believe that the bank of justice is bankrupt. We refuse to

Martin Luther King, Jr., delivering his "I Have a Dream" speech. ➤
UPI PHOTOGRAPH

believe that there are insufficient funds in the great vaults of opportunity of this nation. So we have come to cash this check—a check that will give us upon demand the riches of freedom and the security of justice. We have also come to this hallowed spot to remind America of the fierce urgency of *now*. This is no time to engage in the luxury of cooling off or to take the tranquilizing drug of gradualism. *Now* is the time to make real the promises of democracy. *Now* is the time to rise from the dark and desolate valley of segregation to the sunlit path of racial justice. *Now* is the time to open the doors of opportunity to all of God's children. *Now* is the time to lift our nation from the quicksands of racial injustice to the solid rock of brotherhood.

It would be fatal for the nation to overlook the urgency of the moment and to underestimate the determination of the Negro. This sweltering summer of the Negro's legitimate discontent will not pass until there is an invigorating autumn of freedom and equality. Nineteen sixty-three is not an end but a beginning. Those who hope that the Negro needed to blow off steam and will now be content will have a rude awakening if the nation returns to business as usual. There will be neither rest nor tranquility in America until the Negro is granted his citizenship rights. The whirlwinds of revolt will continue to shake the foundations of our nation until the bright day of justice emerges.

But there is something that I must say to my people who stand on the warm threshold which leads into the palace of justice. In the process of gaining our rightful place we must not be guilty of wrongful deeds. Let us not seek to satisfy our thirst for freedom by drinking from the cup of bitterness and hatred. We must forever conduct our struggle on the high plane of dignity and discipline. We must not allow our creative protest to degenerate into physical violence. Again and again we must rise to the majestic heights of meeting physical force with soul force. The marvelous new militancy which has engulfed the Negro community must not lead us to a distrust of all white people, for many of our white brothers, as evidenced by their presence here today, have come to realize that their destiny is tied up with our destiny and their freedom is inextricably bound to our freedom. We cannot walk alone. . . .

I say to you today, my friends, that in spite of the difficulties and frustrations of the moment, I still have a dream. It is a dream deeply rooted in the American dream.

I have a dream that one day this nation will rise up and live out the true meaning of its creed: "We hold these truths to be self-evident; that all men are created equal."

I have a dream that one day on the red hills of Georgia, the sons of former slaves and the sons of former slave owners will be able to sit down together at the table of brotherhood.

I have a dream that one day, even the State of Mississippi, . . . will be transformed into an oasis of freedom and justice.

I have a dream that my four little children will one day live in a nation where they will not be judged by the color of their skin but by the content of their character.

I have a dream today!

I have a dream that one day, . . . down in Alabama, . . . little black boys and black girls will be able to join hands with little white boys and white girls . . . as sisters and brothers.

I have a dream today!

I have a dream that one day every valley shall be exalted, every hill and mountain shall be made low, the rough places will be made plains, and the crooked places will be made straight and the glory of the Lord shall be revealed and all flesh shall see it together.

This is our hope. This is the faith with which I return to the South. With this faith we will be able to hew out of the mountain of despair a stone of hope. With this faith we will be able to transform the jangling discords of our nation into a beautiful symphony of brotherhood. With this faith we will be able to work together, to pray together, to struggle together, to go to jail together, to stand up for freedom together, knowing that we will be free one day.

This will be the day when all of God's children will be able to sing with new meaning.

My country 'tis of thee,
Sweet land of liberty,
Of thee I sing;
Land where my fathers died,
Land of the pilgrim's pride;
From every mountain side,
Let freedom ring.

And if America is to be a great nation, this must become true. So let freedom ring from the prodigious hilltops of New Hampshire. Let freedom ring from the mighty mountains of New York.

Let freedom ring from the heightening Alleghenies of Pennsylvania!

Let freedom ring from the snow-capped Rockies of Colorado.

Let freedom ring from the curvaceous peaks of California!

But not only that; Let freedom ring from Stone Mountain of Georgia!

Let freedom ring from Lookout Mountain of Tennessee!

Let freedom ring from every hill and molehill of Mississippi. From every mountainside, let freedom ring.

When we let freedom ring, when we let it ring from every village and every hamlet, from every state and every city, we will be able to speed up that day when all of God's children, black men and white men, Jews and Gentiles, Protestants and Catholics, will be able to join hands and sing in the words of the old Negro spiritual, "Free at last! Free at last! Thank God Almighty, we are free at last!"

What Do You Think?

1. In what way is Martin Luther King, Jr.'s message the same as Peter's? In what way is it different?
2. What did Dr. King mean when he said, "We have come to our nation's capital to cash a check"?
3. What did the voice mean when it said, "Do not call anything impure that God has made clean"?
4. Why did Dr. King use such terms as "chains of discrimination," "mountain of despair," and "symphony of brotherhood"? Find other examples of such figurative language.
5. Summarize in your own words Dr. King's dream.
6. Do you think God gave Dr. King his dream? Explain your answer.
7. Do you think Dr. King's dream will ever be completely fulfilled on this earth? Explain your answer.

Taking a Closer Look

1. What occurred after the dream to show Peter that "God does not show favoritism but accepts men from every nation"?
2. For what reason had Peter gone up on the roof?
3. To what American President does Dr. King refer in the first paragraph of "I Have a Dream"?

Putting Ideas to Work

Write a short speech about your own dreams for the future of mankind. Share it with the class.

Martin Luther King, Jr.

Gwendolyn Brooks

A man went forth with gifts.

His was a prose poem.
He was a tragic grace.
He was a warm music.

He tried to heal the vivid volcanoes.
His ashes are
    reading the world.

His Dream still wishes to anoint
    the barricades of faith and of control.

His word still burns the center of the sun,
    above the thousands and the
    hundred thousands.

The word was justice. It was spoken.

So it shall be spoken.

Martin Luther King, Jr. UPI PHOTOGRAPH

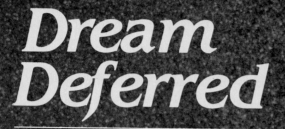

Dream Deferred

Langston Hughes

What happens to a dream deferred?

Does it dry up
like a raisin in the sun?

Or fester like a sore—
And then run?

Does it stink like rotten meat?
Or crust and sugar over—
like a syrupy sweet?

Maybe it just sags
like a heavy load.

Or does it explode?

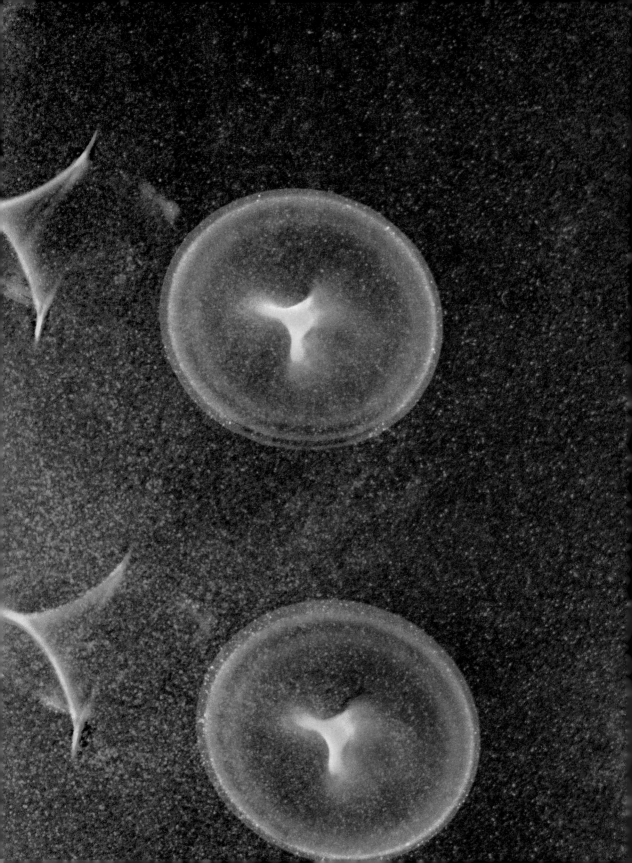

A Thought Went up My Mind Today

Emily Dickinson

A Thought went up my mind today—
That I have had before—
But did not finish—some way back—
I could not fix the Year—

Nor where it went—nor why it came
The second time to me—
Nor definitely, what it was—
Have I the Art to say—

But somewhere—in my Soul—I know—
I've met the Thing before—
It just reminded me—'twas all—
And came my way no more—

Managing Time

Time. Do you control it, or does it control you? Most people operate on a time schedule. Some of the schedule seems automatic. We eat, sleep, play, and work without wasting time analyzing each move. Once in a while, however, it's a good idea to watch how well your clock operates.

Make a copy of the "Clock Watch" table. Pick a busy day that would be interesting to watch. Under "Imagined Time," record how long you *think* each activity will take. (If you wish, divide your time into 30-minute segments from the moment you wake up until you go to sleep.) Under "Activities," briefly state how you usually use or plan to use your time. Note where you have "Free Time." Do not write anything under "Real Time" yet.

When you have your imagined, or predicted, time schedule charted, check it against the real day's happenings. On the day you picked to watch, time your activities. Under "Real Time," record how long each activity actually took. Then compare your "Real Time" with your "Imagined Time." Did you really have time to do everything you had scheduled? Did you really do as much as you thought you would? And what happened to your "Free Time"?

You can control your time. Think about ways to improve your time management. Look again at your Clock Watch—even if your "timing" was good. Ask yourself:

a) When is my best time of day to get things done?

b) Do I use my best time to get the most done?

c) Would I have time to do something "spur of the moment"?

d) Do I plan ahead, or just let things "happen"?

e) When is the worst time of day for me to get things done?

You can use the Clock Watch to help you take charge of your time. (Reviewing the Clock Watch once in a while is time well spent.) As you go over your daily routine, think about the "Ask yourself" questions. Find out where you could reschedule—either yourself or an activity—to make time work better for you.

334

CLOCK WATCH

NAME: _____ DATE: _____

	IMAGINED TIME	REAL TIME	ACTIVITIES (REAL AND IMAGINED)	FREE TIME	DID YOU BEAT THE CLOCK?
WAKE UP!					
BEFORE LEAVING FOR SCHOOL					
GOING TO SCHOOL					
SCHOOL MORNING					
LUNCH BREAK					
SCHOOL AFTERNOON					
AFTER SCHOOL					
DINNER TIME					
AFTER DINNER					
GOING TO BED					
ASLEEP!					

Look again at your filled-in Clock Watch. Where could you find time to do the following activities? Use a colored pencil to show where on your Clock Watch.

1. Doing forty-five minutes of exercise, without skipping anything else.

2. Taking a paying job two afternoons a week (three hours each afternoon).

3. Hosting a new student for two weeks, after school and weekends.

4. Joining a school team or club that requires meeting and practice time. (Would you have to give up something else?)

5. Taking part in family events—special guests, pet care, babysitting, family talks, etc.

6. Making time for yourself alone.

IN SPACE AND TIME

Technology has brought about many changes in your own space and time. In this unit read about the effects and sometimes strange results of technology. Whose technology is it? And how is time involved?

World's Biggest Moving Job— Icebergs!

E. D. Fales, Jr.

Iceberg science! This new branch of research may produce some answers to future needs.

Will people soon be drinking icebergs? Don't laugh. The idea of using icebergs as a water supply for an increasingly overcrowded world has long been under speculation. Now it is under serious study. The drought-parched regions of the western United States and the arid, untillable lands of other nations no longer make the prospect a laughing matter.

Contrary to some beliefs, icebergs do not consist of frozen seawater. They are, instead, huge drifting chunks of frozen fresh water that *calve*, or break off, from northern glaciers or Antarctic ice masses. They thus produce clean, salt-free water that can be used for drinking, agricultural irrigation, and other freshwater uses. Icebergs are also much colder and denser than other forms of ice. This means that they melt more slowly even when brought into warmer regions of the world.

In October 1977 a meeting of iceberg experts was held at Iowa State University in Ames, Iowa. The convention drew more than two hundred scientists from eighteen nations, including a prince from a Middle Eastern country. To prove that sizable chunks of frozen water can be moved from one place in the world to another, the scientists had had a 4785-pound iceberg partly airlifted and partly trucked from Anchorage, Alaska, to Ames. The results of this meeting and others held recently are that exciting things are beginning to happen in the world of iceberg science.

Already, plans are underway to tow mile-long ice slabs called *tabular*, or flattop, bergs from the frozen wastes of Antarctica to the shores of California. There, the slowly melting ice could provide billions of gallons of fresh, pure water in a continuous flow for years. Engineers propose using helicopters to wrap the icebergs in sheets of plastic to reduce melting during the 8000-mile tow from Antarctica.

The prince who attended the meeting in Iowa dreams of hauling icebergs up from Antarctica to irrigate the dusty deserts of the Middle East. His ambitious plan has two stages. The first berg or bergs will be brought to islands in the Indian Ocean and allowed to melt in the hot sun. Surging streams of rushing water from the melting bergs will generate hydroelectric power in the course of the runoff. Then the water will be pumped into tankers and shipped to the Middle East. Eventually billion-ton bergs will be towed directly there and moored offshore. It could take as long as three years for a large berg to melt away. During that time, hundreds of thousands of gallons of fresh water could be drawn off daily. It would pour new life into once barren, waterless wastelands.

And there would be an important extra. Such a "captive" berg could serve as a massive floating freezer to preserve perishable foods. The prince says that, for most of its three-year life, this natural refrigerator could store his country's entire food supply. Then another billion-ton berg would be brought up from Antarctica.

There is even talk that properly placed weatherbergs might ultimately help control our weather patterns. Specifically, in hot, storm-prone tropical areas the icy chill of an iceberg could cool down a raging hurricane or typhoon by reducing the heat of the surrounding atmosphere.

All this might sound a bit fanciful if it were not that some of it has already started. In northern waters ships are actually towing icebergs that may weigh two to four million tons or more. The tow ships pull the mighty mountains of ice away from offshore oil rigs that would otherwise be destroyed.

"Iceberg Alley"

For some time, drillers have been probing deep undersea off the Newfoundland-Labrador coast. Platforms have been built, gas has been found, and one of the world's richest oil deposits has been discovered. But the trouble is that all this drilling and eventual pumping lie smack in the middle of "Iceberg Alley." This famous ice chute is a 1000-mile stretch of sea where the big bergs drift south from Greenland glaciers. In 1974, 3000 bergs plowed down the Labrador Current in a terrifying parade. The next year there were 2000. If even a little 50,000-ton growler should hit an oil rig, it would be a disaster.

In 1970, with the new oil field in sight, it suddenly dawned on two top oceanographic engineers that science knew too little about icebergs. Dr. Angus Bruneau and Robert Dempster both worked for Newfoundland's great "Iceberg University." From its campus on the windy hills at St. John's, the scientists could see icebergs streaming down the "alley." Dr. Bruneau and Dempster worried about all those drillers out there: sitting ducks. They were also concerned about protecting Newfoundland's new oil industry. So they took their worries to the university and then to the government. All agreed that something should be done—fast.

To do the job a think-tank group was formed, headed by engineers and oceanographers. The group quickly chartered the husky arctic supply ship *Percy M. Crosbie* of London.

The ship was ready to sail on June 1, 1971. Aboard were Bruneau, Dempster, a university crew, and an oceanographer named Colin Langford, former shipmaster. He was the project boss, a job that would soon prove to be a headache.

Sailing north from St. John's, the scientists had secret orders to try to grab hold of a berg and to pull it, if they could. The plan was to move dangerously close to a berg, drop a steel net overboard with buoys to hold it up, and gradually pay out the net while the ship steamed around the berg. Once the net was around the berg, the *Crosbie* would snatch up the floating ends of the net and tie them to a rope bridle.

This in turn would be tied to a 1000-foot towrope.

Told by the International Ice Patrol about where to find bergs, the crew of the *Crosbie* poked cautiously through fog. The next day, on radar, a big iceberg was spotted drifting south. It was an 80,000-tonner about 400 feet long and 200 feet high.

The *Crosbie*, a tough little ship of 2800 horsepower, cut to dead slow. When the crew felt the sudden chill of ice, the engines were stopped. In eerie silence the ship drifted until a cry came down from the crow's nest: "Ice ahead!" Slowly the ominous shape of an iceberg emerged from the fog.

There were now two dangers. Unlike Antarctica's flattop bergs, arctic bergs are rollers. They keep tipping upside down. A berg that tips toward a ship can smash it. But seven-eighths of an iceberg is underwater. So if the berg tips away from a ship, great reefs of ice come up to spear the ship or even lift it out of the sea. The other danger, of course, was calving. When towering ice pinnacles split off northern bergs, they crash down to become smaller bergs, or calves.

To test for possible calves, the *Crosbie*, at close range, cut loose with long whistle blasts that might loosen cracked masses of ice. Then the ship moved back to wait. No ice fell.

However, the crew was still worried. This iceberg had a huge tower of ice, estimated to weigh 7000 tons, that might split off and smash down on the *Crosbie* at any moment.

When the *Crosbie* moved in again, the fog had lifted. All eyes were now on the mass of ice above. All ears were alert for the booming thunderlike roar that would mean an icefall.

Close up there were weird sounds: constant small popping and cracking noises, occasional echoing bursts like distant thunder, more cracking noises, and the curious effervescent sizzling of the water. (Melting bergs release billions of cells of compressed gases.) Always there was the crash and boom of waves breaking on the berg's ice beaches. Meanwhile, the ship danced in the backwash chop.

Carefully the *Crosbie* ventured into the very shadow of the berg and circled it, slowly streaming out the ropes and net. This took an hour. Nothing happened. The towrope was attached, and the engine went slow-ahead to pick up the strain.

All hands watched the cable tighten. The ropes and net could be seen adjusting themselves evenly around the berg's waist near the waterline. A snapping towrope is a terrible thing and is capable of killing or maiming anyone within reach. And so a careful watch was kept. Periodically a few more inches of rope were payed out to change the wear point on the towrope as it came through a steel guide on the stern.

A meter that measured the strain on the rope now held all eyes. Slowly the strain rose to 10,000 pounds, then 20,000. When it topped off at 30,000 pounds, the engines were full ahead.

Surging high on the seas, the *Crosbie* fought to move the load. The first berg was not large; even so, 80,000 tons is a terrible weight to be pitted against a little 2000-ton ship.

To check on its headway, the *Crosbie* relied on radar. By constantly reading the radar echoes, the crew could fix position and see how fast they were moving the berg. They weren't moving it at all!

Then, without warning, came the icefall. The ship surged. The captain ran for the bridge. His ship had been jerked backward. High on the berg the 7000-ton tower had toppled, falling on the net and the ropes. Incredibly they held. But this in itself was a danger. The ice had fallen on the far side of the berg and the berg now rocked toward the ship. If the berg capsized forward, it could pull the towrope under and possibly sink the ship.

Two crew members with axes stood ready to chop the towrope. Then the berg stabilized and, fortunately, the emergency release was not needed.

A new radar bearing showed the berg still had not moved. It soon became apparent what was happening. While the berg appeared to remain stationary, it was drifting south on the Labrador Current at one-third-knot speed, while the ship was pulling it north at the same speed.

"So we knew that even though the berg stayed there," Langford said, "we were holding it against the current. In

effect, we were towing it at one-third knot."

The berg was cut adrift and thus ended the first towing test, not dramatic but still significant. It had shown that little ships really can tow huge icebergs.

After a few more experiences, the crew of the *Crosbie* found they could forget about the steel net. On another tow they simply tied a rope lasso around a berg and pulled. Suddenly a chunk fell off. The berg rolled dangerously away. Under the ship the water turned a weird, bright green. As the berg fell away, its vast underwater ice reefs were coming up to smash the ship. Just then the berg rolled back. The bright light in the sea went out. The ice reefs were sinking out of sight again.

All this time the single rope held.

In three weary weeks the *Crosbie* towed and released seven

bergs, the largest weighing four million tons. The crew sailed home—exhausted and awed, but triumphant.

In the official report the days on board the *Crosbie* were described as "thrilling, but harrowing." One time, for example, a berg twenty stories high rolled upside down as the crew was getting ready to lasso it. Another time the crew nearly got washed off the ship while trying to tie a rope to a berg.

The scientists thus found out that icebergs can be tricky and treacherous. Bergs frequently don't want to go where a tow ship wants them to go. They can flip over on top of a ship without warning. And often it's a question of which is towing which—the ship towing the berg or the berg towing the ship.

Such is the curious new world of iceberg science. More than one hundred northern icebergs have been towed so far. Have there been any close calls? Yes, but despite the dangers involved, the need for towing icebergs continues.

In some years only a hundred or so icebergs have come down "Iceberg Alley." This year, or next, may see thousands of icebergs appear. When they do, it will be a big test for the iceberg movers of the north. And, whenever the iceberg movers of the south tow icebergs up from Antarctica, people *will* be drinking icebergs.

What Do You Think?

1. Compare the icebergs from Antarctica with the arctic icebergs. Which do you think man will harness first? Which is the most valuable to man?
2. Do you think icebergs will ever be used very much in the future? Explain your answer.
3. If you were in charge of selecting the crew for the *Crosbie*, what characteristics would you look for in the people you interviewed?
4. Why do you think the families of the crew may have been concerned about the safety of their loved ones aboard the *Crosbie?*

Taking a Closer Look

1. How many uses have been suggested for icebergs?
2. Describe what is meant by "Iceberg Alley."
3. Explain in your own words the Middle Eastern prince's idea for using icebergs to help his country.
4. As used in this article, what are "calves"?
5. What dangers are there in towing icebergs?

"ONE PERCENT INSPIRATION..."

Thomas A. Edison, the inventor of many devices we take for granted every day, once said, "Genius is one percent inspiration and ninety-nine percent perspiration." In the following three selections, you will get a chance to see how the minds of inventors work.

Young Inventors

Westinghouse

It is a curious fact that a remarkable number of the world's most important inventions and discoveries have been made in kitchens and barns and tiny workshops by the ordinary variety of tinkerer and putterer. Even more remarkable is the fact that many of those tinkerers have been simply bright boys and girls of high school age.

For instance, late in the nineteenth century, a frail, blue-eyed, brown-haired English boy named Will Perkin had chemistry as his hobby. In an attic room under the gable of his home he had a little chemical laboratory. Shelves and workbenches contained bottles of acids, brilliant yellow salts of chromium, blue and green crystals of copper. One day,

347

having heard his chemistry teacher at school remark what a wonderful thing it would be if some scientist could learn how to manufacture synthetic quinine, seventeen-year-old Will Perkin set to work.

The boy mixed up everything in his laboratory. Of course, every experiment that he tried had been tried before by famous adult chemists for half a century. Each of the boy's attempts failed to produce a bit of quinine. Finally he tried mixing two new chemicals that had been produced from coal tar—that too had been tried by others.

Instead of quinine, the bottom of the test tube filled with a thick purple sludge. Disappointed, the boy went over to the wastebasket to chuck the stuff out. That, too, was exactly what everyone before him had done.

But this time there was one difference. As he started to dump out the mixture, it ran back on his fingers, staining them purple. No matter how he washed and scrubbed his hands, the stain would not come off. Then suddenly he forgot all about making quinine. "Why!" he cried, "I have discovered the most beautiful new dye in the world!"

And he had. It was aniline purple, the first of the thousands of brilliant, permanent aniline dyes that we have today; the dyes upon which nearly the entire dye industry depends—discovered by a seventeen-year-old English schoolboy whose hobby was chemistry!

Fifty years ago in Bologna, Italy, another schoolboy—a wealthy, handsome, olive-skinned Italian youngster—had a different hobby, electricity. Ever since he was eleven or twelve years old, the toys of this child had been batteries and static machines and condensers. When he was nineteen or twenty, he studied physics in school under Professor Righi.

Professor Righi would take two coils of insulated wire and lay them on the workbench about a foot apart. Then he would connect the first coil to an electric condenser, which shot a spark of electricity through the wire. Each time the professor did this, he showed the class how the needle of a delicate electrical meter connected to the second coil would jump across the dial, thus proving that an electric current formed in that second coil also, although there was no connection between them. It was caused, the professor explained, by invisible electromagnetic waves that passed through the air. Every teacher in the world knew about that experiment, which was a common one. But it took a twenty-one-year-old to place the first coil in England and the second one across the Atlantic Ocean, and thereby send the world's first long-distance wireless message. That youngster's name was Guglielmo[1] Marconi.

There are dozens of cases like this. William Siemens, at twenty, invented the steam governor. Bessemer, at twenty-one, invented electroplating. Edison, at twenty-four, the stock ticker; Colt, at twenty-one, the revolver. George Westinghouse was only twenty-one when he invented the air brake. A few years ago a New York youngster named Jordan Bierman became the youngest person ever to receive a patent from the United States Patent Office; he was eight years old! And two famous schoolboys named Wright, playing with kites, invented the world's first flyable airplane!

Yet these inventors were not child prodigies. They were simply bright, healthy young people whose love of science made it the most fascinating adventure they could ever know.

---

[1] Guglielmo (gül yel'mō)

Marconi's wireless

Homework in the Dark

Ruth Rosenbaum

Becky never planned to be an inventor.
She just wanted to find a way to
do her homework in the dark.

NASA has been keeping tabs on Becky Schroeder for some time now. When the first official inquiry came to Becky's home in Toledo, Ohio, she was only ten. Her parents wrote back: "No, Becky has never worked for NASA."

It seems that NASA had heard about an invention of Becky's and thought it could be useful on future space flights. That first invention was a luminescent backing sheet. It makes the top page of a stack of papers visible in the dark. Becky's four following patents also involve seeing in the dark. NASA has been in touch again.

"I never thought I'd be an inventor," Becky says in a quiet voice. Neither did her parents. Her father, a patent attorney, handles the practical side of his daughter's creations. He still wonders "how a ten-year-old could have known that the luminescent backing sheet needed to be activated by a ten-second exposure to real light." He doesn't know "how she got the idea to make black visible in the dark."

In this case, mother necessitated invention.

"I was waiting in the car for my mother outside a shopping center," Becky recalls. "She was taking a long time, so I started my homework. When it got dark, I was really mad because I couldn't keep writing."

Mr. Schroeder didn't take Becky's idea of glowing paper very seriously. But he did buy her some luminescent paint to play around with. A few weeks later he was contacting the patent office.

Soon after her intuitive breakthrough, Becky began studying the science of light and improved on her first brilliant invention with two more. Her fourth and fifth inventions both use a battery to trigger phosphorescence. One is a night strip that can glow for eight hours; the other is a flashy memo pad—"great for writing in the dark." Becky is now working on something new and totally unrelated to light, but she is not ready to talk about it.

"I don't really have to think about inventing," she says. "Things come to me just right out of my head. I'll notice how something can be improved, something that's missing. Like when we go to a restaurant, sometimes it's so dark I can't even read the menu. So I thought of a way of making menu letters glow in the dark. Lots of times, I don't talk about my ideas because I don't think they're important enough."

Already Becky's ideas are important not only to NASA, but also to some large companies that have shown interest in marketing her inventions. "They're a little expensive for the current market," Mr. Schroeder says, "but one large corporation indicated that it won't matter because there's nothing else out yet that's like them."

Though Becky turned out five patentable inventions between the ages of ten and fourteen, she's not a driving, ambitious person. "She moves at her pace," her father says. "You can't make her move faster. She just doesn't feel the pressure of time."

Besides finding time for inventing, schoolwork, guitar, tennis, swimming, and volunteering at a nearby wildlife preserve, Becky has also begun research on how light affects the biological activity of animals and people.

"It won't be patentable, of course," said her father, "but it could be very significant work."

Inventor for Safety

Robert C. Hayden

Garrett Morgan was thinking all the time. And his imagination turned into inventions that have saved thousands of lives.

Garrett A. Morgan

On July 25, 1916, a violent explosion ripped through Tunnel No. 5 of the Cleveland Waterworks, 250 feet below the surface of Lake Erie. Deadly gases, thick smoke, dust, and debris quickly filled the underground space, and thirty men were trapped inside.

Firefighters, doctors, nurses, police officers, and waterworks employees gathered at the tunnel's entrance. Relatives and friends of the trapped men stood by grimly. No one knew the fate of the trapped workers. It was unlikely that they could stay alive for more than a few hours. If the men were to be found and rescued, someone would have to enter the tunnel. But the heavy smoke and poisonous gases made this impossible. The workers had little hope of being saved.

353

Morgan's gas mask

Then someone at the scene suddenly remembered the name Garrett Morgan. Morgan had recently demonstrated a gas mask hoping to interest manufacturers in it. In 1914 he had received a patent for the mask. In the same year he had received the Grand Prize at an international safety exposition. But he had not been too successful in selling his invention.

Rescue officials contacted Morgan immediately and asked him to come to the tunnel with several of his gas masks. Morgan arrived at the Lake Erie tunnel with his brother. Quickly they and two volunteers donned Morgan's masks and descended into the tunnel to search for the trapped men. They were the only ones able to reach the bodies of the unconscious and dead men. The rescuers breathed clean air carried in a pouch in the mask. Morgan led the rescue team in and out of the tunnel many times. Together they saved the lives of thirty people.

This heroic act thrust Morgan before the public. He received a gold medal from the City of Cleveland. But more important, his heroism also helped to prove the value of his invention.

Orders for the mask poured into Cleveland from fire companies all over the United States. Morgan explained and demonstrated his invention in many cities and towns. During World War I, American soldiers used his improved mask in battle to protect them from deadly chlorine fumes, and Morgan's invention saved many lives.

Garrett Morgan was born on March 4, 1877, in Paris, Kentucky. His mother had been a slave who was freed by Lincoln's Emancipation Proclamation in 1863. He grew up on a farm with his brothers and sisters and was able to attend school only through the sixth grade.

When Morgan was fourteen, he left home to look for a job in Cincinnati. There he worked for four years as a handyman for a wealthy landowner. During this time he hired a tutor to help him with his English grammar. In 1895 Morgan moved to Cleveland, Ohio, which was to be his home for the rest of his life.

His first job in Cleveland was that of a sewing-machine adjuster for a clothing manufacturer. Morgan loved to tinker with machinery, and his skill provided jobs for him with several different firms.

In 1907 Morgan decided to start a business of his own. He opened a shop for the repair and sale of sewing machines. He did well, and two years later started a tailoring business. He hired thirty-two workers and began making coats, suits, and dresses with the various sewing devices that he had built.

Morgan was always trying new ideas. In 1923 his tinkering paid off when he was awarded a patent for inventing a three-way traffic signal.

The "Go-Stop" signals in use before Morgan's invention were not practical because there was no neutral position. The signal indicated either *stop* or *go*. There was no yellow caution signal as there is today. Without a traffic officer present, the signals could be ignored completely. Morgan's traffic signal solved the problem by creating a half-way position between *stop* and *go*. As drivers approached Morgan's signal and found it in the half-way position, they would do the same as today's drivers do when approaching a

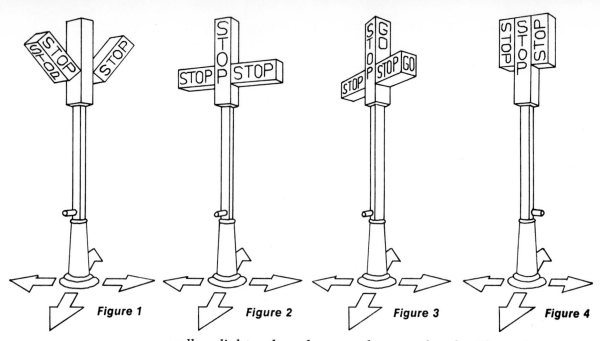

Figure 1   Figure 2   Figure 3   Figure 4

Traffic signal

yellow light—slow down and move ahead with caution.

Morgan's idea also solved another problem. When the officers became tired, they often failed to change the signal quickly. The delays usually confused both drivers and pedestrians.

Morgan's traffic signal eliminated the need for a traffic officer. The *stop* and *go* signs could be left in a position (Figure 1) that enabled traffic to move carefully in all directions.

Figure 2 shows traffic moving east and west while the north/south traffic is stopped. To stop the traffic moving east and west, the signal post was rotated so that *go* faced north and south—as shown in Figure 3. Figure 4 shows the position of the signal that stopped traffic in all directions to allow pedestrians to cross the street in safety.

Morgan sold the rights to his invention to the General Electric Corporation for $40,000 and it became the forerunner of the overhead and sidewalk lights that you see every day.

It would be difficult to estimate how many lives have been saved as a result of Morgan's inventions. Many veterans of World War I certainly owed their lives to the gas masks they wore on the battlefield. The electric-light signal system has been responsible for protecting lives on our streets, highways, and railways.

What Do You Think?

1. Will Perkin discovered something that he wasn't looking for. Did this make his discovery any less important? Why or why not?
2. Do you agree with the author that the young inventors were not prodigies? Do you think any of your friends, or even you, could ever be a young inventor? Give reasons for your answer.
3. How do hobbies sometimes lead to important discoveries?
4. Becky's study of how light affects animals and people will not be patentable. Does this make it any less important?
5. Explain the sentence: "In this case, mother necessitated invention." There is a common saying that necessity is the mother of invention. Do you think that this is an appropriate turn of the phrase? Why or why not?
6. Which do you think was Garrett Morgan's most important invention: the gas mask or the traffic light? Why?

Taking a Closer Look

1. In your own words describe the experiment that led Marconi to make his "wireless."
2. How were Will Perkin and Guglielmo Marconi alike? How were they different?
3. How many patents did Becky apply for while she was between the ages of ten and fourteen?
4. Why did NASA think Becky's invention might be useful on space flights?
5. Explain why someone on the scene of the waterworks accident should think of the name Garrett Morgan.

Putting Ideas to Work

Imagine yourself a Cleveland newspaper reporter. Write a news story about Garrett Morgan's rescue of thirty-two workmen. Write a headline to go with it.

An inventor is:
A man with wheels in his head.
A man who knows how to borrow from his experiences.
A whirlwind of activity.

Understanding a Diagram

Space exploration has produced drama, discoveries, and heroes. One special achievement came during the Apollo 9 mission. Using a portable life-support system (PLSS), astronaut Russell Schweickart became the first human satellite. During a 40-minute space walk, he tested a two-million-dollar spacesuit and backpack that would be used on the moon.

To understand how the PLSS works, use both the article below and the diagram on the next page. Each has different information. For example, the diagram shows that the hose from the emergency oxygen pack was attached to the right-hand side of the astronaut's suit. This information is not given in the article. On the other hand, you cannot learn from the diagram how much the PLSS weighed. You learn this in the article.

The diagram contains four important parts. The *caption* tells what the diagram is about. The *picture* shows the parts of the PLSS and how each part works. The *labels* tell the names and locations of the parts. The *key* explains the symbols in the picture.

APOLLO 9 PORTABLE LIFE-SUPPORT SYSTEM

The PLSS backpack weighed 84 pounds. It measured 26 inches high, 18 inches wide, and 10 inches deep. Power for the system was produced by a battery the size of a pocket transistor radio. The PLSS contained three separate systems (oxygen, air conditioning, communications):

1. The *oxygen-supply system* provided oxygen for breathing and controlled air pressure in the suit. Oxygen was forced through the suit to remove harmful gases and to cool the astronaut. The astronaut also carried a second backpack called the oxygen-purge system. If the PLSS failed, the second system would provide enough oxygen for 30 minutes.

2. A water-transport loop was used to provide *air conditioning*. Water was driven through a series of tubes by a pump. The loop supplied water to cool the system. The water, once heated, was forced outside the unit.

3. Two radios, medical transmitters, and various warning systems were parts of the *communications system*.

359

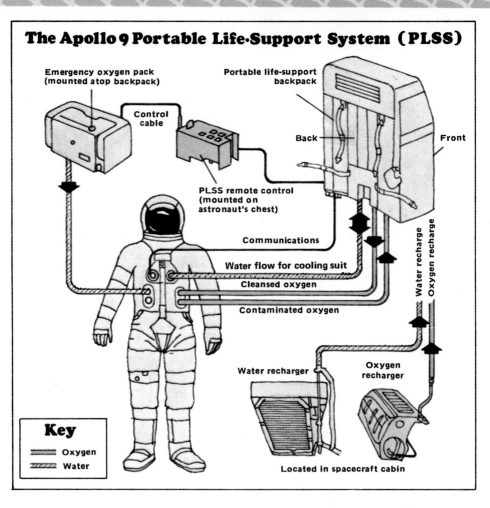

The Apollo 9 Portable Life·Support System (PLSS)

Emergency oxygen pack
(mounted atop backpack)

Portable life-support
backpack

Control
cable

Back

Front

PLSS remote control
(mounted on
astronaut's chest)

Communications

Water flow for cooling suit

Cleansed oxygen

Contaminated oxygen

Water recharge

Oxygen recharge

Water recharger

Oxygen
recharger

Key
═══ Oxygen
▨▨▨ Water

Located in spacecraft cabin

Answer each of the following questions. Tell whether your answer came by looking at the diagram or by reading the article.

1. Where are the oxygen and water rechargers located?

2. What were the measurements of the PLSS?

3. Where was the emergency oxygen pack located?

4. If the PLSS failed, how long could the astronaut survive outside the spacecraft?

5. Name the parts of the communications system.

6. To what was the PLSS remote control attached?

7. Which PLSS system used the water-transport loop?

8. What information does the key give?

Houston, We've Got a Problem

Anne G. Jones

Perhaps the most awesome technological achievement of all time was the landing of people on the moon. Yet, technology can fail as well as succeed, and it's back to human resourcefulness to solve the problems.

On April 13, 1970, while speeding through space toward the moon, the Apollo 13 spacecraft ran into serious problems. The astronauts of Apollo 13 never got to walk on the moon. They had enough trouble just getting back to Earth.

The Apollo 13 mission was part of the program that first put a human being on the moon. Less than a year before Apollo 13, the Apollo 11 mission had sent three astronauts to the moon. Neil Armstrong of Apollo 11 had stepped from the lunar-landing vehicle and made the first human footprints in the moon's dust. The Apollo 12 mission soon followed, and more astronauts walked on the moon. Apollo 13 was the third attempt.

Even before takeoff, the mission developed a problem. The astronauts for a flight are trained as a crew, so that they can work together well. Scheduled for Apollo 13 were astronauts Jim Lovell, Fred Haise, and Ken Mattingly. Shortly before the flight, however, the three men were exposed to German measles. Lovell and Haise had had the disease before, but Mattingly hadn't. An astronaut who becomes sick in space is a danger to the mission. The risk was too great. Therefore, Mattingly was replaced by Jack Swigert. Lovell and Haise had not worked with Swigert before, so the new crew went through intensive last-minute training. This sudden, unforeseen problem was almost a forewarning of the mission's later crisis.

The launching of Apollo 13 took place on Saturday, April 11. A three-stage system of rockets first propelled the spacecraft into Earth's orbit, then on its journey toward the moon. Once on the moon-bound course, the astronauts released the last rocket stage from the spacecraft. Now Apollo 13 consisted of three parts—the command module, the service module, and the lunar module.

The astronauts were in the command module (CM), nicknamed "Odyssey." The CM held most of the equipment for directing the spacecraft's operation. The service module (SM) contained the spacecraft's electrical and oxygen systems. It was

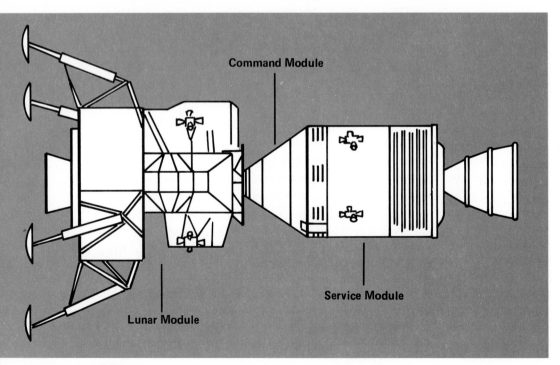

Command Module

Lunar Module

Service Module

Astronauts Fred W. Haise, Jr., John L. Swigert, Jr., James A. Lovell, Jr.

located at the rear of the CM. The final part was the lunar module (LM). It was designed to land two astronauts on the surface of the moon. The astronauts had named the LM "Aquarius." It was attached to the front of the CM in a nose-to-nose manner.

During the early part of the flight, all went well. On Earth, scientists and technicians of the National Aeronautics and Space Administration (NASA) guided the flight. They tracked it from NASA's Mission Control Center in Houston, Texas. The astronauts checked the spacecraft often to make sure everything was working as it should. Things were going smoothly.

Then came the first warning of trouble—the astronauts heard a loud bang. At the same time, the electric power in the command module dropped to an alarmingly low level. The astronauts noticed that the pressure in the service module's two oxygen tanks had fallen. One tank already read zero, and the other was dropping rapidly. Swigert radioed Mission Control: "Houston, we've got a problem."

The astronauts, looking out the windows of the CM, noticed that a gas of some sort was escaping from the service module. It soon became apparent that there had been an explosion. Oxygen from the SM's tanks was leaking into space.

This oxygen was needed for breathing. It was also necessary for the spacecraft's fuel cells to operate. Without the oxygen, the command module's main source of electricity was gone. There was a second, battery-powered electrical supply. However, this would last only 10 hours. At this time, the spacecraft was almost a quarter of a million miles from Earth. It would take at least 87 hours for it to return.

The astronauts and NASA gave up any idea of going to the moon. The mission's goal now became the survival of the three crew members. Because of the power loss, the command and service modules could not, by themselves, get the crew back to Earth. The lunar module became the crew's only hope.

CAPSULE COMMUNICATOR (CAPCOM): We're starting to think about the LM lifeboat.

SPACECRAFT: Yes, that's something we're thinking about, too.

The lunar module had been designed to carry two astronauts from the main spacecraft to the moon. After the moon landing, the astronauts were to have used the LM to return to Odyssey. The LM had its own guidance system and power. But this system was much simpler than that of the command module. Aquarius was never meant to be used on long trips through space, and certainly not to travel all the way back to Earth. Also, though the LM would hold two people comfortably, a third person would have to squeeze in.

The astronauts really had no choice. They had to use the lunar module as best they could. Lovell, Haise, and Swigert shut down all the power in the command module. Then they crawled through a connecting tunnel into Aquarius.

There was no time to relax after moving into the LM. The crew had to perform some critical tasks. The first of these was to change the trajectory of the spacecraft. The path they were presently on would take them close to the moon, and would have been ideal for a lunar landing. However, though the spacecraft would head back toward Earth after looping around the moon, it would miss Earth by about 250 miles. Unless they changed course, the astronauts would be lost in space.

To change the LM's trajectory, they would need to fire the vehicle's rockets. NASA decided it would be best to fire them twice. The first "burn" would head the spacecraft safely

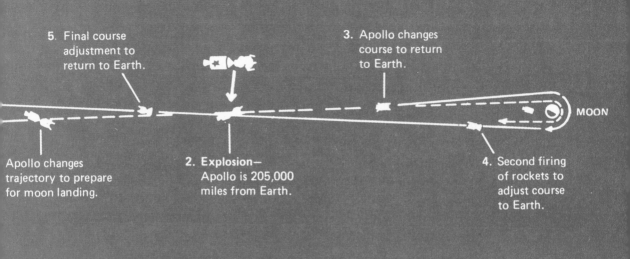

5. Final course adjustment to return to Earth.

3. Apollo changes course to return to Earth.

Apollo changes trajectory to prepare for moon landing.

2. Explosion— Apollo is 205,000 miles from Earth.

4. Second firing of rockets to adjust course to Earth.

MOON

toward Earth, with a splashdown in the Indian Ocean. But a rescue at that site would be difficult, because there were no ships nearby. Firing the rockets a second time would not only shorten the flight by ten hours, it would also change the place of splashdown to the mid-Pacific Ocean. Here there were several recovery ships waiting.

Six hours after the accident, the astronauts tried the first course change. They had to make sure two things were just right—the time length of the burn, and the position of the spacecraft when the rockets were fired. When the astronauts fired Aquarius' rockets, the people at Mission Control kept their fingers crossed. The LM rockets had been designed to move only the LM—not the whole three-module spacecraft. But the burn went well; the LM's small rockets changed the spacecraft's trajectory. Hours later, when the spacecraft passed behind the moon, the second course adjustment took place. The first big hurdles had been passed. The astronauts were on their way home.

By now, people everywhere knew of Apollo 13's accident. Newspaper headlines and television broadcasts all over the world were focused on the plight of the small, crippled spacecraft speeding back toward Earth. Many countries offered to help rescue the astronauts. Russian ships in the Pacific headed for the place where the spacecraft was supposed to splash down.

Lovell, Swigert, and Haise were heartened by the world's concern. But there was one thing they couldn't forget. From now on, the lunar module had to function perfectly. If it were to be damaged as the service module had been, they would not make it back home.

They were not reassured by the next news from Mission Control. Because of a faulty guidance system, the trajectory changes had not been completely successful. On its present path, the spacecraft would still miss Earth by almost a hundred miles. This meant a third course correction. And the spacecraft's guidance equipment couldn't be relied on.

Mission Control suggested that the astronauts use the stars to determine the spacecraft's position, much as sailors have done for ships since ancient times. But the spacecraft was surrounded by glittering debris from the explosion. The astronauts couldn't make out the stars.

They could, however, see the sun and Earth. They decided to find the spaceship's position by taking a sighting on the sun and on Earth. This procedure had been done only once before, during a previous Apollo mission. It had been an experiment then. Would it work now? Haise and Lovell adjusted the spacecraft's position. Swigert timed the firing. The course adjustment was perfect!

The crew now worked to preserve the limited supplies of electricity, oxygen, and water inside Aquarius. The LM had been designed to support two people for about 50 hours. Now three people would be in it for over 80 hours. The crew determined that there would be enough oxygen; they moved food and water in from Odyssey. Using cardboard, plastic bags, and tape, they adapted a device from the CM to purify the LM's air. As a way of saving power, they let the temperature in the LM's cabin drop far below normal. Lovell and Haise kept warm by wearing their heavy moon boots. Swigert pulled on an extra suit of long underwear.

The spacecraft fast approached Earth. As the planet loomed larger and larger, the three men inside Aquarius welcomed the sight.

SPACECRAFT: That Earth is whistling in like a freight train.

But they couldn't relax yet. Before the spacecraft entered Earth's atmosphere, they had to get rid of the damaged service module. While the SM was still joined to the rest of the spacecraft, it had been out of the astronauts' line of sight. When they released the SM, and it floated away into space, they were finally able to see what the explosion had done. They took photographs to help NASA figure out what had gone wrong.

SPACECRAFT: Man, that's unbelievable. Looks like a lot of debris is just hanging out the side. . . .

Now the astronauts had to leave Aquarius, for the LM would burn to a crisp as it fell through the atmosphere. They had to return to the command module, which was equipped with a protective heat shield, and then separate the CM from the LM.

After so many hours in Aquarius, the three men crawled back through the connecting tunnel into Odyssey. Swigert pushed the button that released Aquarius from the command module.

CAPCOM: Farewell, Aquarius, and we thank you.

SPACECRAFT: She was a great ship.

Odyssey, with the three astronauts aboard, fell with increasing speed through the atmosphere. The parachutes opened. The spaceship that had been through so much splashed down safely in the Pacific Ocean. Lovell, Haise, and Swigert were welcomed by the U.S. aircraft carrier *Iwo Jima*.

Some have said that astronauts have it easy—that all the real work on space flights is done by computers and machines. But the Apollo 13 mission showed what a fallacy such a statement is. When the machinery failed, it was human judgment and intelligence that adapted the spacecraft and saved the lives of the crew of Apollo 13. Lovell, Haise, Swigert, and several people at NASA were awarded medals for heroism.

What Do You Think?

1. Why would a sick astronaut be dangerous for the mission?
2. Who was CAPCOM? What was CAPCOM's function?
3. Suppose the explosion had occurred in the LM instead of the SM. Would its effect have been as serious? Why?
4. Why did CAPCOM call the LM a "lifeboat"?
5. The Earth-sun sighting procedure for finding a spaceship's position had been done only once before. Why had it not been used more often?
6. Why didn't the LM have a heat shield?
7. The author says that without human judgment and intelligence, the astronauts wouldn't have survived. Describe one incident that shows this.

Taking a Closer Look

1. What was the goal of the Apollo program?
2. How did Swigert happen to join the crew of Apollo 13?
3. For what specific purpose was the lunar module designed and built?
4. What important supply did the explosion destroy? Give two reasons why this substance was so important.
5. Why weren't the first course corrections perfectly accurate?
6. Why did the astronauts have to return to the CM before splashdown?

Putting Ideas to Work

Imagine that you are Ken Mattingly, who trained with Lovell and Haise but didn't get to go on Apollo 13. Write an account of how you felt when you heard about the spacecraft's accident.

Lillian M. Gilbreth

USA 40c

U.S. postage stamp commemorating Lillian Gilbreth

Lillian Gilbreth, Engineer

Eleanor Clymer and Lillian Erlich

What is an engineer? Someone who runs a locomotive, someone who controls sanitation problems, or someone who builds engines?

Long before her gifted children made her known to the general public as the mother in *Cheaper by the Dozen,* Dr. Lillian Moller Gilbreth was famous among engineers all over the world.

Some called Dr. Gilbreth an efficiency engineer. She preferred to say that she worked with management—the science of planning better ways of doing work, and thus getting better production as well as better lives for the workers.

Has your home a modern kitchen? The chances are that its design was based on her work. Have you visited a modern factory and seen the smooth dovetailing of work processes? That is the result of *motion study,* a term invented by Frank Bunker Gilbreth, her husband, teacher, and partner. For Lillian Gilbreth's career started as a partnership.

No one could have been more surprised than Lillian Moller if you had told her in 1900 that one day she would be honored as the country's foremost woman engineer.

She grew up in Oakland, California, the oldest of nine children. The family was a very close and affectionate one. In fact, the tendency was toward overprotectiveness. Lillian expected to spend much of her life helping to care for her younger brothers and sisters, and then, when she was no longer needed at home, to be a teacher. So she majored in English and psychology at college.

369

She did not think she would ever marry. She was attractive, slim and blonde, but shy and reserved. In fact, she had been known to walk around the block so as not to have to speak to boys!

And then, during a stop in Boston on the way to Europe, she met Frank Gilbreth.

He had grown up in Boston, where his widowed mother had worked hard to give her children a good education. Frank's sisters went to college but he had decided he wanted to take care of his mother. So right after high school he started out to learn the construction business. He began at the bottom, as an apprentice bricklayer. Almost at once, his quick and original mind sensed that much effort was being wasted by the haphazard work methods the men were using. Soon he began to make a name for himself as the originator of new and better ways of building. He arranged the bricks and mortar so the men would not have to stoop. He studied the motions they made and picked out the best ones for them to use. This was the beginning of his lifelong search for the One Best Way of doing things.

Within a few years Frank Gilbreth had his own business, and more contracts than he could handle. He was a man to whom nothing seemed impossible. Perhaps that boundless confidence and energy were what attracted Lillian Moller to him. He was like a fresh breeze blowing.

They were married in 1904. From the start Frank said that their marriage was to be a partnership. He wanted her to share his work if she found she liked it. If not, he would try to share hers.

Soon Lillian was following him up ladders and learning how buildings were constructed. However, she was less interested in that than in what she thought was Frank's real talent—the ability to find the best way of working and to teach others these principles. The principles of motion study were not all new. Many of them had always been used by "motion minded" people. For instance, there have always been people who placed their tools and materials conveniently in front of them, who stored tools near the work place, who cut out unnecessary motions, and made their chairs and tables a comfortable height to reduce fatigue.

Frank Gilbreth's great contribution was to systematize these ideas and apply them to different kinds of work. He began to show factory owners that they could get better results if they improved the layout of their plants and used well-designed tools and safety devices, and if they allowed rest periods, since a tired worker does not produce as much as a rested one. Soon he was being asked to visit factories as a consultant.

His wife encouraged him to put his findings into writing. Here her college training in English helped. But even more important was her knowledge of psychology. Where he saw work processes, she saw first human beings at work. She saw that workmen often resisted change because they did not understand the reasons for it. When the reasons were explained, or when they were asked to help make plans, they accepted more readily. She saw that it was a good idea to find the right person for the job, and to see that workers got along well together.

She went with her husband to meetings of engineers and at one such meeting, in 1908, she spoke a few words. She said that the human being was the most important element in industry, and that he had not been receiving enough attention. Many employers at that time were interested more in the machines than in the employees. Here was a woman recommending that psychology be used as a major tool not only to keep people happy, but to measure skills so that workers would be put into jobs they could handle.

Nowadays every big company has its personnel department, and many give aptitude tests before hiring. But in 1908 these ideas were very new.

Lillian Gilbreth did not appear in public as much as Frank. She had a growing family to care for. Three little girls had been born. Frank's mother helped with the children, and Lillian had her office and laboratory at home, so that she could spend part of her time studying and working, and the rest with her children.

In 1912 they moved to Providence, where Frank had a job as consultant for a factory. Lillian worked for her doctor's degree at Brown University. In 1915 she received her Ph.D. in the psychology of management. Frank retired from the construction business, and together they founded the firm of Frank Gilbreth, Inc., Consulting Engineers. There were more children now, and they took a house big enough to hold the family, the helpers and guests, and their offices and laboratories.

When the United States entered the First World War, Frank offered his services. He planned ways to train soldiers by use of films. He also developed courses to train teachers for crippled soldiers, and devised ways in which handicapped persons could do useful work. Lillian was to take charge of the work at home while he was away. She had the staff to direct, new jobs to superintend, and a large family to see to.

More and more jobs were coming their way. There were contracts with Remington, the U.S. Rubber Company, and many more. There was work with the Red Cross, devising ways to help the blind and epileptic.

In 1919 they moved to a big roomy house in Montclair. There were nine children now. With such a large family, there was much work to do. The Gilbreths applied their principles of motion study in the family group. Everyone helped, even the smallest child, for the parents believed that

The Gilbreth Family. Copyright by Underwood and Underwood, N.Y.

the happiest life came from a planned sharing of work and responsibility. The boys helped with the outdoor work, the girls shared the housework. Dad invented new ways of teaching them typing, French, the Morse code, astronomy. Life was never dull. The children never knew what fascinating project would come next. General problems were solved in family council. And Mother, with her talent of seeing people as individuals, made each of her children feel as precious as an only child.

Jane, their twelfth child, was born in 1922. In June 1924, Frank and Lillian were getting ready to sail for Europe, where he was to deliver a paper before the First International Management Congress at Prague. He had been working at top speed, and was very tired. Suddenly, in the middle of a telephone call, his heart stopped.

Lillian Gilbreth had known this might happen. They had been warned that his heart had been strained. When it happened, she showed the heroic stuff she was made of. The children were gathered in from wherever they were, and told that their father had died. They had to be helped to accept the fact of death. Then they in turn helped their mother. After the simple funeral, she sailed alone and read her husband's paper before the congress. Then she came home and set about earning a living for her family.

Lillian Gilbreth was forty-six when she had to assume the whole burden of earning a living and keeping a firm hand on eleven lively children. (One child had died at the age of five.) It was a difficult time.

She had to plan carefully. She would have little time for research and would have to hand that work over to others. She herself gave courses in her home, to train younger people in motion study techniques. She took consulting jobs which demanded as little time away from home as possible. More companies were using the new engineering methods to eliminate fatigue for their workers. Macy's, Dennison, Sears Roebuck were among her clients. In 1926 she went to Europe to preside at a summer school to study human relations and conditions in industry.

And now the colleges were opening motion study laboratories. Dr. Gilbreth was asked to speak at Yale, Harvard, Purdue, California. In 1935 she was offered a position on the faculty at Purdue. She was glad to accept it.

She felt at home in the college atmosphere. It was exciting to find that people in other fields besides industry were eager to use motion study. Students in the School of Agriculture began to learn how fatigue could be lessened on farms by better placing of animal pens and feed bins and tool sheds. Home economics students began to do studies of dishwashing, bedmaking, ironing. They were amazed to find that a housewife sometimes walked as much as five miles a day as she did her daily work. By rearranging her sink, stove, work counters, and storage places, much of the walking could be cut out. It was not long before makers of kitchen equipment began to take notice of the value of good design. Dr. Gilbreth designed a model kitchen for the Brooklyn Gas Company and worked for the *New York Herald Tribune* Homemaking Institute.

She was sixty-five when the United States entered the Second World War. Five of her sons were in the armed services. It was a good time for her to be as busy as possible. Dr. Gilbreth found herself in such demand that she stepped up her activities. She took a job as industrial consultant in a plant that filled Navy contracts.

In the national crisis, efficiency was more important than ever. There were labor shortages. There were bound to be conflicts. Dr. Gilbreth was invaluable as an arbitrator. Labor and management found she could sit down at a conference table with them and help iron out differences, so that they could all work together toward their common goal.

She began to help in the Navy's program for rehabilitation. She traveled from coast to coast, helping industries to make places for the physically handicapped. Wherever she went, she found younger men and women she had helped to train, doing important jobs.

Her children were all grown up now. She was free to rest on her laurels and enjoy her leisure, or to go on working. She chose the latter. She loved work for its own sake.

In a job for the American Heart Association, she helped to plan a kitchen for the homemaker with a heart condition. The "Heart Kitchen" is a marvel of simplicity and common sense which can be enjoyed by any housewife, rugged or delicate.

She went on with her writing. Her books are as clear and easy to read as her model kitchen is easy to work in. They all express her deep philosophy: that life is, or should be an exciting adventure which can be made more meaningful by the planned sharing of work and responsibility.

The "Heart Kitchen" as designed by Lillian Gilbreth.

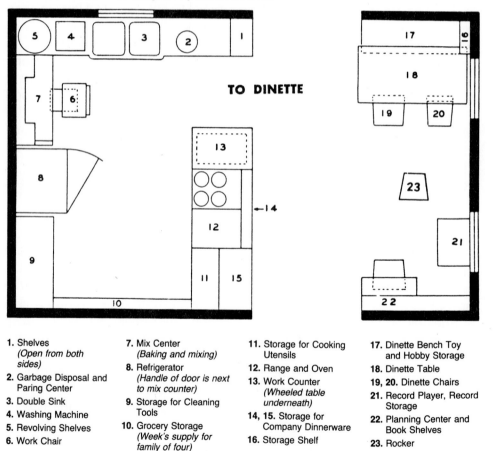

1. Shelves
   (Open from both sides)
2. Garbage Disposal and Paring Center
3. Double Sink
4. Washing Machine
5. Revolving Shelves
6. Work Chair

7. Mix Center
   (Baking and mixing)
8. Refrigerator
   (Handle of door is next to mix counter)
9. Storage for Cleaning Tools
10. Grocery Storage
    (Week's supply for family of four)

11. Storage for Cooking Utensils
12. Range and Oven
13. Work Counter
    (Wheeled table underneath)
14, 15. Storage for Company Dinnerware
16. Storage Shelf

17. Dinette Bench Toy and Hobby Storage
18. Dinette Table
19, 20. Dinette Chairs
21. Record Player, Record Storage
22. Planning Center and Book Shelves
23. Rocker

What Do You Think?

1. Mrs. Gilbreth saw that workers resisted change when they didn't understand the reasons for the changes. For what other reasons do people resist change? Do you feel uncomfortable with new situations? Why or why not?
2. In what ways could a mother of twelve children make each one feel like an only child? Think of specific things that she might do.
3. How do you think Mrs. Gilbreth felt when she read her husband's paper at the meeting in Prague? Write a paragraph describing those feelings.

Taking a Closer Look

1. Give evidence from the story to show that Lillian Moller was shy as a young girl.
2. In your own words, explain Frank Gilbreth's contribution to the construction business.
3. How did Lillian Gilbreth's training in English and psychology contribute to her partnership with her husband?
4. Explain how motion study can help a housewife.

Putting Ideas to Work

How could motion study help you? For one hour be very observant of the things that you do. Do you open your desk once to get out a pencil, again to get your books, and a third time for your paper? After you have analyzed an hour of your time, plan ways to cut down unnecessary motions. Write a few paragraphs describing your wasted motions and your plans for eliminating the waste.

Fueled

Marcie Hans

Fueled
by a million
man-made
wings of fire—
the rocket tore a tunnel
through the sky—
and everybody cheered.
Fueled
only by a thought from God—
the seedling
urged its way
through the thicknesses of black—
and as it pierced
the heavy ceiling of the soil—
and launched itself
up into outer space—
no
one
even
clapped.

Thomas Jefferson's Dream House

Johanna Johnston

Thomas Jefferson, by Rembrandt Peale. Courtesy of the New York Historical Society, New York City.

Among his many accomplishments, Thomas Jefferson designed his own home. No detail of his dream house was too small for his attention.

The west front of Monticello

Every part of Thomas Jefferson's dream house, Monticello,[1] reflected the mind of its designer and builder, the man who saw everything as though it were brand-new, and asked himself how it worked, and if it could be made to work better.

The house consisted of a central pavilion, fronted by a portico, and extended on either side in two long ells. When it was finally completed, it looked only one story high from the

---

[1] Monticello (mon tə chel'ō)

377

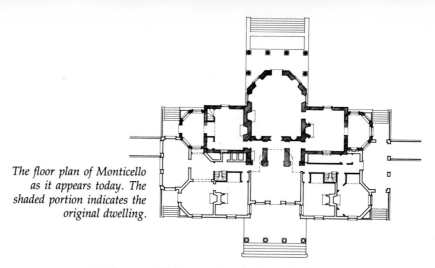

The floor plan of Monticello as it appears today. The shaded portion indicates the original dwelling.

outside, and this was by design. Jefferson had never wanted a towering house on his hill, but a house that looked as though it clung to the land, growing up from it like another long, low crest. Still, when one entered the main doors, the central hall rose in spacious two-story height.

The look of uncluttered space in this hall was no accident either. Jefferson had thought a long time about the problems of this main hall, asking himself first of all what its chief purpose was, then the other ways in which it would be used and how it could best be designed to serve those ends.

It was, of course, the room visitors would enter to gain their first impression of the house. It was also the room from which one went right and left to all the other rooms in the house, the room from which, most usually, a stairway would ascend to the rooms on the floor above.

But before Jefferson built his stairway, he remembered one of the chief uses of every central stairway he had ever seen. The occupants of the house used it. But even more than they, the servants were forced to use it in an unending parade of activity. Firewood had to be carried to the fireplaces on the second story, ashes brought down again. Hot water for bathing, cold water for drinking, food and dishes had to be carried up; jugs of water and dishes had to be brought down again.

Surely all the beauty of a wide, sweeping stairway was lost in the confusion of such traffic. In addition, heat rising up the stairway was wasted in the level above.

378

How, Jefferson wondered, could he banish all that needful, but distracting, activity out of sight and keep the heat from rising up the stairways?

The answer he worked out was two small, sharply turning stairways hidden away on either side of the main hall, which prevented a rapid, upward flow of air, and left the hall itself free, open, and beautiful.

He looked at other housekeeping problems and studied them as if no one had ever attempted to solve them before. The kitchen, for a large house like Monticello, was almost always in a small separate building near the main house. As a matter of fact, all the workshops of a large plantation were usually clustered about the main building in a random, haphazard fashion.

Jefferson had already decided to banish these unsightly shops, offices, and sheds, and hide them along the rear of the house, under a terrace. The kitchen would be there too. Even so, the food would have to be carried to a warming kitchen and serving pantry inside the house.

Surely there was something that could be improved on here. Hot food lost its heat on this journey, and the servants were exposed to all sorts of weather. Jefferson decided to build an underground passage from the kitchen to the main house.

Winding staircases at Monticello were only 24 inches wide.

But this decision brought new problems. A tunnel would be damp. In the dampness, would the usual mortar hold the stones, or would it soon crumble away?

He began to experiment with mortar, using various proportions of lime and ash. Finally, after a dozen or more experiments, he hit upon a formula which seemed to solve the problem perfectly. He jotted down the proportions in his notebook: "1 bushel each of lime, wood ashes, and pulverized brick, brought to the proper consistency will harden in water."

Actually, what he had arrived at, in those homely experiments on the hilltop, was an almost exact chemical foreshadowing of our modern formula for cement. And so the underground passage was built and it is solid and dry to this day.

The underground passage was not the only innovation he thought of to make the serving of food more convenient. Before Monticello was finally completed, he had designed and built a service door to hang between the serving pantry and dining room. The door had shelves on the side turned to the pantry, which could be loaded with dishes and food. Then the door swung on a central pivot to bring the shelves into the dining room where they could be unloaded by the servants there. Naturally, it worked just as well in reverse, when it was time to clear the table.

Still another convenience was a small dumbwaiter, concealed in the fireplace in the dining room. This dumbwaiter went down to the cellar below, so that things could be placed on it, and then drawn up into the dining room when needed. And, of course, the used items could be returned the same way.

Other rooms in the house received his attention. There were large double glass doors between the main hall and the drawing room, and Jefferson worked out an intricate mechanism, concealed in the paneling, which caused one panel to open or shut automatically in harmony with the other as it was opened or closed.

He gave some thought to his own room, and how it might best be arranged for his own habits and needs. He liked to rise early in the morning and, after a cold bath, get to work at once on his notebooks or accounts. He liked to read at night, or answer letters before he went to bed. His room, in other words, was as much a study and a workroom as it was a bedroom. Was it necessary to have a bed, used only at night, taking up space all day in a room that was really a study?

He decided it was not, and designed a sort of double room with an alcove between the two halves. In this alcove, he placed his bed. Since the alcove was open on both sides, Jefferson could enter either his study or his dressing room from his bed. Both rooms seemed large and airy because of a skylight and large mirrors that increased the amount of light and the sense of spaciousness in the rooms.

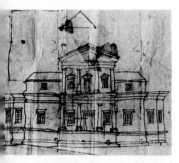

Thomas Jefferson's sketch of the exterior of Monticello

And still he thought of more ways to make his house functional.

Years before real plumbing systems were invented, he evolved a plumbing system for Monticello, a way by which indoor privies could be emptied and the waste carried away from the house, and deposited underground in a central tank out on the grounds.

He achieved this by means of buckets, placed under the privy seats, which could be removed by a manually operated pulley, carried along an underground tunnel to the spot for emptying, and then returned, by pulley, the way they had come.

How does it work? How—if it has never been done before—can it be made to work? Asking himself these questions, there seemed no end to the improvements Thomas Jefferson could make in his home.

And there was always another question too. How may it all be made as beautiful as possible, worthy of the hilltop?

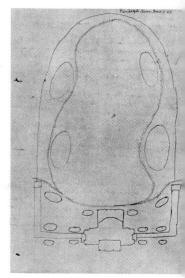

Thomas Jefferson's sketch of the gardens and lawns

Tall, graceful windows opened every downstairs room to the lovely views on every side, and opened the whole house to the cool airiness of hilltop breezes. Cornices, moldings, and fireplaces were carved in simple, classic designs, and none was too hidden to be worked with meticulous care.

The doors were made of pine but treated with a method known as painted graining to make them look like more expensive mahogany. The double doors between the entrance hall and parlor were equipped with a mechanism that caused both doors to move when one was opened or closed.

He had wonderful plans for the grounds surrounding the house—plans for informal gardens and a small garden pavilion, plans for wildlife.

Oh yes, Thomas Jefferson had hundreds of plans, and as the years went on, he kept thinking of new plans.

Jefferson's dream house still stands on its hillside near Charlottesville, Virginia, and every year thousands of people tour Monticello, a living monument to the genius who designed it.

Gutenberg's Big Idea

Gary B. Swanson

Gutenberg did more
than save the world
from writer's cramp.
Before his day, of course,
a book was made by hand—
a hapless scribe sat hunched
over a candle-lit desk
and lettered out whole books.
He didn't have to read, you know,
only copy what he saw—
a sort of paint-by-number printing process
that took a year or more
to make a single copy
of the Old Testament.
And when he'd finished,
he'd take a long, deep, weary sigh
and stretch his poor, aching hand
and start again:
"In the beginning, God . . . ."

And then, too,
each scribe included
fresh errors of his own
to those passed on to him
by scribes whose hands
had given out long before.
Scribes were human, after all;
even at their best
they must have misspelled
there or *their*, or is it *thier?*
Even the best of us
drops a comma or mistakes
an *e* for an *i.*
If you've ever played "Rumors,"
you may have an idea
of the problems they had:

send a whispered message
through twenty people
and "Don't fire till
you see the whites of their eyes"
becomes
"Don't you admire
all the lights in the skies?"
Just try to send
the whole Old Testament
through three centuries
and several hundred
bleary-eyed scribes.

And the product of a scribe's
year of effort
would cost much more than
a blacksmith's wages.
For a time—
far too long a time—
only the big shots—
dukes and princes and guys like that—
could afford to buy books of their own.

If you wanted to read a book,
you often had to walk
a hundred miles
and beg its owner
to let you look at it—
pretty hard to imagine
when today you can disappear
for months at a time
into the darkest science alcoves
of the county library
or choose among six biographies
of Gutenberg himself—
two with color plates,
and one with large type.

Read any of those
six biographies,
and you'll find out
that he changed his name
from Gensfleish—gooseflesh.
I think I would
have changed my name too.

Anyway, one day Gutenberg
was standing in his shop
with his hands in his pockets
whistling quietly to himself
and thinking.
People with great ideas
often do a lot of that—
thinking, not whistling.
He looked at a woodcut
and wondered why letters
couldn't be carved in reverse
like woodcut pictures
and then used over and over again.
The Chinese had tried it,
but they had a couple thousand
characters in their alphabet—
imagine trying to keep
that mess organized.
German was better—only 26 letters.

So Gutenberg took
a whole bunch of letters,
all facing upward and backward,
spread a nice coat of ink on them
and then covered them
with a piece of paper.
That's all it took.
When the page was all printed,
he rearranged the letters
to print the next page,

and no matter how many copies
of each page he made,
they looked exactly the same.

Meanwhile, back at the Reformation,
people were trying to think of a way
to make the Bible available
to everybody who wanted one,
and with Gutenberg's process
everyone—the cobbler, the wheelwright, the baker—
could buy and read
a Bible of his own.
He didn't have to borrow
or try to understand the priest
reading in Latin from the Bible.
He could take it home
and sit by the fire at night
and read until he fell asleep—
they didn't have TV in those days.

Not many people
knew how to read at first,
but before long everybody
was working at it.
I guess you could say
Gutenberg was partly responsible
for the need for schools.
But don't hold it against him.
People always have a way
of ruining someone else's great idea.

And when you consider
that one little press
can make thousands of copies
of the Bible,
it's a little difficult to imagine
that God didn't have
a hand in it all.

What Do You Think?

1. What kind of man would you say Thomas Jefferson was? Think of at least five adjectives to describe him.
2. Compare Gutenberg and Jefferson. In what ways were they alike? In what ways were they different?
3. Why should Thomas Jefferson be considered an inventor?
4. Why did the author include such seemingly insignificant details as Gutenberg's changing of his name?

Taking a Closer Look

1. Find evidence in this story to support the idea that Thomas Jefferson was a scientist.
2. What did Jefferson design so that he could avoid the confusing traffic on a central stairway?
3. According to the poem, "Gutenberg's Big Idea," how did Gutenberg help spread the Word of God?
4. How did the use of scribes to copy the Bible seem to cause errors?

Putting Ideas to Work

Jefferson designed his house around practicality and serviceability. If you could design your room to fit your own personal needs, what changes would you make? Make drawings of the room as you would plan it and tell how the design meets your personal needs.

The City Stood Still

On November 9, 1965, about 5:30 P.M. the lights went out and
millions of people stumbled in the dark.

Power Failure Darkens Northeast

NEW YORK (AP) — A massive electric power failure plunged New York City, Boston, and a vast area of the northeast back into the days of candlelight Tuesday, choking traffic and disrupting communications.

The blackout extended into parts of Canada and was estimated to have hit cities, towns, and countryside in which at least 20 million people live.

Countless commuters were stranded in subways and elevators and in electric trains. Airliners were diverted from New York's blacked-out airports to Newark and Philadelphia airports.

President Johnson was informed that the blackout, which first closed in about 5:30 P.M. EST, would be over by 10 P.M., as harried power experts strove to remedy the break or breaks.

The cause was reported to be a disruption near Niagara Falls, N.Y., in a vital point in a vast grid system carrying electricity to far-flung areas.

Johnson commissioned Secretary of Defense Robert S. McNamara and other officials to extend all needed federal aid to the affected communities in New York State, Connecticut, Maine, New Hampshire, Vermont, Pennsylvania, and elsewhere.

An official of Consolidated Edison, which supplies power to New York, said the blackout in the metropolitan area occurred when its system suddenly found part of its power supply being drained out toward Niagara Falls, rather than flowing from that area.

This caused power plants in the metropolitan area to shut off automatically, he said.

The result was a spreading power blackout through the area.

In order to restore power in most areas, it became necessary to disengage the individual systems, then resume service as soon as possible.

Electric clocks in the vast metropolis of New York stopped at 5:28 P.M. and in Boston at 5:21 P.M. Traffic signals also went dead, producing monumental traffic jams.

The light of candles and matches gleamed from skyscraper windows, as well as from the more familiar setting atop dining tables.

Many New York stores, including those selling suddenly needed flashlights, put up shutters and closed down too.

In New York City thousands of persons made their way to Grand Central Station, only to learn that no trains were moving to suburban areas. Snack bars began doing a brisk business.

Associated Press
November 10, 1965

Large Ontario Section Plunged in Darkness

TORONTO (CP)—A massive power failure—worst in North American history—plunged a large section of Ontario and the northeastern United States into darkness Tuesday night, snarling communications and disrupting industry.

Ontario Hydro officials said the failure in upstate New York near the Canadian border collapsed the entire system which supplies power to industrial Quebec province, Ontario, and the northeastern U.S. Quebec province was isolated from the system at the time and not affected.

In a series of power interruptions lasting from five minutes to two hours, thousands of homebound commuters were stranded as Toronto subways halted, auto assembly plants outside Toronto sent their men home, oil refineries shut down, and a London, Ont., bakery lost 4500 loaves of bread when ovens cooled.

Hydro officials said the initial breakdown occurred at 5:16 P.M. EST, affecting most of southern Ontario east of Peterborough. There were disruptions in Trenton, Belleville, Smiths Falls, and Brockville, where the darkness was lighted by a $2,000,000 fire burning since morning.

Ontario officials, busy restoring their own system to normal, were unable to pinpoint the cause. But they said an "unprecedented power surge" along lines carrying hundreds of thousands of volts flashed into the Ontario system at Cornwall west to Niagara Falls and back into New York State.

Engineers pulled switches, isolating Ontario from the northeastern U.S. power exchange grid, and called all generating resources in the province into full operation. By 8:30 P.M. service was almost completely restored.

Sent Workers Home

Meanwhile, this happened in Ontario's industrial heartland:

—Ford Motor Co. of Canada lost an entire production shift at its Oakville assembly plant and sent home 2000 workers.

—At Brampton another 500 to 600 workers went home.

—Shell Oil at Oakville fell 10,000 barrels behind in production.

—Workers at Wolverine Tube Co. in London watched furnaces cool and molten copper begin to solidify before power was restored.

—Canada Bread Co. bakers at London saw a batch of bread ruined and out-of-town deliveries were delayed.

—Blackouts were reported in Smiths Falls, Perth, Prescott, and areas around Cornwall; and in Ottawa and Kingston lights flickered and faded.

—Newspapers and radio and TV stations had their news wire services disrupted.

—Hospitals were on auxiliary power. There were no reports of deaths.

Need Detailed Probe

Robert Hillery, Ontario Hydro director of operations, said a "serious and detailed investigation" would be conducted.

"We never thought this was possible," he said. "The entire system is geared so that when a power line is broken—by falling trees or drunken drivers—the excessive current back-up actuates relays, which isolate the trouble spot and reroutes the electricity.

"We will play a large role in the investigation, which will be a full-scale study by computers.

"It could never reach disaster proportions—even in winter. Ontario Hydro has enough different stations and split systems to interconnect and give power to every community."

But Tuesday night's failure—worst since a six-hour interruption at the Niagara Falls generating station before the First World War—was more serious than a tipsy motorist or a falling tree could cause. President Johnson ordered an investigation by the United States Federal Power Commission into the trouble which affected an estimated 30 million people.

—Canadian Press
November 10, 1965

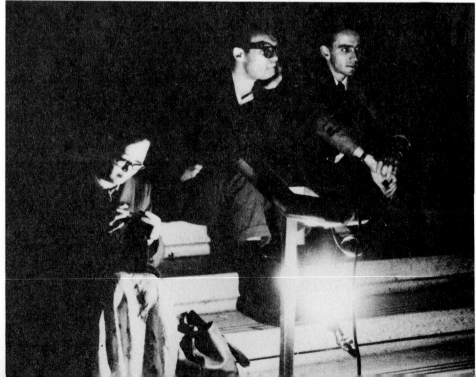

The Buses Run in Eerie Dark at Two Miles Per

At first the street lights flickered and the city seemed a bit dimmer, but you didn't notice anything was wrong until you started to enter the subway at Grand Central and saw the masses of people pouring out, their faces expressionless. When you asked what was wrong, there was no response. No one seemed to know.

There was still some light in the IRT station, but once outside again you saw no light—in any direction. The first thing that hit you was the crisscross of traffic in the middle of the street, and you realized that the signals were no longer switching from red to green.

For a moment the city stood still.

Policeman Puzzled

At the corner of 42nd and Lexington at 5:30 P.M. yesterday, a policeman standing next to an emergency call box was as bewildered as anyone. Only when several people asked him what was happening, did he pick up his phone and ask: "What's cooking?"

"Nothing here, either," he said after a few moments, and when people asked him where to go, he said, "Try the BMT or the IND. Maybe they're working."

At least, someone said, the buses were running.

The 101 to City Hall, Bus 2299, pulled up at the southwest corner of 42nd and everyone started to scramble aboard a vehicle already too full. A middle-aged woman used her pocketbook as a blocking weapon. A young bearded youth stepped aside to let a gray-haired woman in ahead of him, and once on the bus established himself as a traffic cop, directing passengers in and out.

Somehow everyone managed, actually made it a point, to pay the fare.

It took an hour and five minutes to get to City Hall, a trip that could normally be made in less than half the time. Along the way there was anger and humor, worry and "cool," and an ever-present sense of isolation. It was every man for himself.

Along the way civilians with flashlights had taken upon themselves the job of directing traffic. And they were obeyed.

—Judy Michaelson
New York Post
November 10, 1965

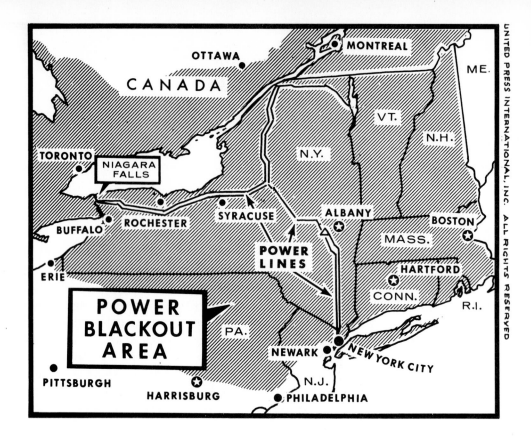

Detroit Supplies Power to Ontario

DETROIT, Nov. 10—The Detroit Edison Co. last night was called upon to furnish emergency power to southern Ontario after power-producing equipment there was knocked out in the massive power failure.

A spokesman said Detroit Edison, which usually operates an interconnection with the Hydroelectric Power Commission of Ontario, had to replace 200,000 kilowatts Ontario was unable to get from New York State.

New York also had an interconnection agreement with Canada.

The spokesman said a power surge caused by the East Coast failure knocked out Ontario equipment about 5:30 P.M. Detroit Edison supplied power until Ontario was able to restore its system about 8 P.M.

They were back to full capacity about 10:20 P.M.

—United Press International
November 10, 1965

City by Moonlight
—the Gallant Spirit

In the cockpit of his TWA airliner coming into Kennedy Airport from Pittsburgh, Capt. William Brown began his approach to runway 4-right. "Captain," said his copilot, "the runway lights are starting to dim."

On an elevator leaving the lobby of the Winslow Hotel on Madison Ave., a 91-year-old woman, Mrs. Edgar Moyes, began to relax for the ride up. Before the car reached the second floor, it rocked to a halt.

In the headquarters of the United Nations, James Roosevelt of the United States delegation, the son of the late President, began arguing with Soviet delegates to the UN's 17-nation economic committee. He never finished his argument.

And in the Independent "D" train, moving southward out of the 50th St. station, Gabriel Rosenthal began to read his evening newspaper. Suddenly, the car lurched to a stop.

Everywhere lights flickered, died, glowed again, and died. Television screens sputtered, then went blank. And electric clocks stood still.

The brightest city in the world had gone dark.

There was, incredibly, almost no panic, no chaos; only at first understandable nervousness, then a remarkable demonstration of self-discipline and cooperation among New Yorkers that only heightened their helplessness and frustration.

30 Million

At first people everywhere suspected that it was only their room or their house or their block or their neighborhood, but then, as they took to the streets and to their transistor radios, they began to realize the enormity of the situation. Quickly most people learned that the whole city—except Staten Island—had gone dark, a weird darkness cut by the headlights of cars cruising unlit streets and the sudden stares of flashlights and the glow of an almost full moon.

Within minutes after the power failed, Times Square was filled with people, remarkably well-mannered, remarkably well-behaved. The traffic in the area moved carefully, but smoothly. Slowly word filtered through the crowd about the power failures elsewhere, in Boston, in Toronto, in Buffalo, spreading over 80,000 square miles, touching at least parts of eight states plus Canada, affecting perhaps 30 million people.

All around the city, there were small, individual dramas. At 6:10 P.M., at St. Vincent's Hospital in Greenwich Village, James J. Walsh, the assistant administrator, received a telephone call from the hospital's new Cronin Building. A patient needed an emergency craniotomy, to treat a possible blood clot on the brain.

Mr. Walsh turned to one of his assistants. "We've got to get a man to the OR," he said. "We have to get a pallet and four strong men to do it." The operating room was nine flights up. But fortunately Mr. Walsh soon learned that the service elevator was running in the Cronin Building. The patient was taken up to Cronin 9, the one operating room in use, and surgeons performed the operation without unusual difficulty.

At 6:20 P.M. Johanna Slavin, an 18-year-old NYU freshman, was making her way home to the Bronx, walking along Broadway in the 80s, when suddenly in front of her, a subway grate swung open and a man popped out. He pushed himself up to the sidewalk, brushed himself off and turned to Miss Slavin.

"Excuse me," he said, "but how do I get to CCNY?"

At 6:30 P.M. Engine Company 65 raced to answer a fire alarm call on the 36th floor of the Pan American Building, a building where three out of 65 elevators remained stuck throughout the blackout. Half a dozen firemen walked and ran all the way up to the 36th floor. They found a fire in a wastepaper basket. They put it out. Then they walked down to the first floor.

By 7 A.M. the streets began to fill again, with people heading toward work—the "GG" subway line resumed operation first—and a cab driver named Fortunato Paladino cruised along Park Ave. picking up multiple passengers.

"The boss said I could double up, it was an emergency," Paladino said. "And I said to him, 'What emergency?'

"Who knew there was a power failure? I went to sleep early last night."

—Dick Schaap
New York Herald-Tribune
November 11, 1965

Nervous City Goes Home

A city frankly frightened that a second mysterious blackout might douse all its lights and stop all its wheels cut back drastically on power consumption yesterday and sent employees home early by the tens of thousands.

After a chaotic 12-hour snarl of stalled subway and commuter trains, diverted planes and crawling surface traffic, transportation facilities were back in service for the early-afternoon rush hour.

Mayor Wagner pleaded with business and individuals to avoid unnecessary use of electricity "until further notice" and directed that all city buildings and agencies set a conservation example.

He released the municipal work force of between 180,000 and 200,000 employees at 4 P.M. The Board of Education canceled all after-school and evening school activities.

Patched-Up Facilities Work

During the day's period of peak demand—from 4:30 to 6 P.M.—Consolidated Edison's patched-up facilities held firm. The utility reported that usage was below normal for the period, indicating that the public was cooperating in conserving electricity.

While again stressing the need for conservation of electricity, Wagner said that all electrical energy had been restored to New York after the blackout that began at 5:28 P.M. Tuesday and continued well into the morning yesterday.

Only One Fatality

Despite the most frightening city emergency in peacetime—an all-night drama in which 800,000 straphangers were trapped for varying periods, countless thousands stranded between floors in elevators, and auto, train, and plane traffic hopelessly snarled—there was only one fatality attributed to the blackout.

The victim was John J. Lynch, 62, of the Bronx, a retired city detective and investigator for the Hanover Insurance Co. Lynch, who had decided to stay all night in his fourth-floor office on William Street, left about 1:30 A.M. to get some coffee.

At 10:15 A.M. Frank Flynn, the building super, found his body at the ground floor of a fire stairwell. He had apparently fallen in the dark and struck his head against a radiator, police said.

13 Policemen Hurt

A noontime casualty roundup at Police Headquarters disclosed that, in addition to a number of injuries in 33 auto accidents, 13 patrolmen were hurt while helping the public.

There were 219 reports of persons stuck in elevators, 720 requests for police assistance and 150 injury cases.

Crime was "lower than normal," Commissioner Broderick said.

The commissioner praised the citizens not only for obeying the law but also for pitching in to help the police, and hailed New York as "one of the safest and greatest cities in the country—and last night proved it."

—William Federici,
Henry Machirella,
and Henry Lee
New York Daily News
November 11, 1965

WIDE WORLD PHOTOS, INC.

What Do You Think?

1. If you had been there during the blackout, what would you have done to pass the time?
2. Do you think people behave well in emergencies? Explain your answer.
3. What is meant by the expression, "The brightest city in the world had gone dark"?
4. What industry, service organization, or group of people do you think was most severely affected by the blackout? Give reasons for your answer.
5. In one newspaper report a sentence reads "It was every man for himself." Then in the next paragraph the report says "Along the way civilians with flashlights had taken upon themselves the job of directing traffic." Do these two reports contradict each other? Explain your answer.
6. What do you think the following slang terms from these articles mean:
   a. straphangers
   b. super
   c. cool

Taking a Closer Look

1. Why do you think the trains were affected?
2. At about what time of day did the power go off?
3. How did the blackout cause the death of one person?
4. How far-ranging was the blackout? Tell what states and provinces were affected.

Putting Ideas to Work

Think about the things that you've done in the last hour. How would things have been different had there been no electricity? Write a paragraph describing how you would be affected right now by a blackout.

Central Park Tourney

Mildred Weston

Cars
In the Park
With long spear lights
Ride at each other
Like armored knights;
Rush,
Miss the mark,
Pierce the dark,
Dash by!
Another two
Try.

Staged
In the Park
From dusk
To dawn,
The tourney goes on:
Rush,
Miss the mark,
Pierce the dark,
Dash by!
Another two
Try.

Line Graphs

A line graph is a way to organize information in picture form. Look at Sunspot Line Graph #1, which shows the frequency of sunspots from 1700 to the present. (Sunspots are dark patches that appear and disappear periodically from the sun's surface.)

The line graph has a vertical (up-and-down) axis and a horizontal (left-to-right) axis. The vertical axis gives the number of sunspots. The horizontal axis gives the years from 1700 to 2000.

See if you can use Sunspot Line Graph #1 to answer some questions. *In what year did the greatest number of sunspots occur?* To find the answer, first locate the highest point on the vertical axis. Next, move your finger from that point straight down to the horizontal axis where the years are marked. The greatest number of sunspots occurred in 1959.

In what years were no sunspots recorded? First, locate "0" on the vertical axis. Now, run your fingers straight across the horizontal axis. The years at which the graphed line *touches* the bottom line (at 0) tell when no sunspots were recorded—in 1711, 1810, 1823, 1879, 1901, and 1912.

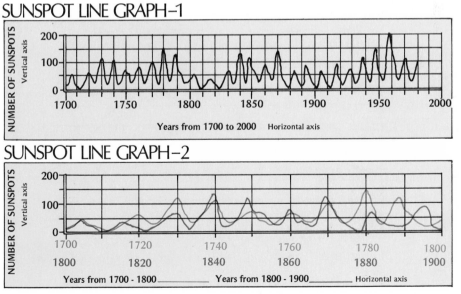

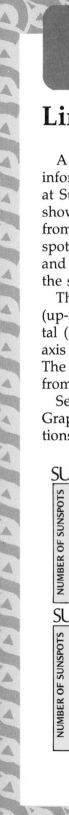

Now look at Sunspot Line Graph #2 (on page 399). It contains two graphed lines. These were drawn to compare sunspot activity in the 18th and 19th centuries. Different colors highlight the lines.

Use Sunspot Line Graph #2 to compare the lines every tenth year. How many times are there more sunspots in the 1700s? Which years in the two centuries had the same number of sunspots?

Now look at the Temperature Line Graph. It compares the average temperatures of four cities for each month of the same year. The marks (circles, triangles, dashes, or dots) are located at each month on the lines. As shown in the Key, each mark represents a different city. Where to place the marks for each city on the vertical axis was determined by averaging daily temperatures.

Use the Temperature Line Graph to answer the following questions.

1. Which line shows the temperature for Goose Bay?
2. Which city had the highest average temperature in January?
3. Was Prince Rupert's February temperature higher or lower than its January temperature?
4. Which city had the lowest average temperature in July? Which city had the highest?
5. In which city would you find the coolest weather in May?
6. Was Fort Nelson cooler in April or September?
7. Was Prince Rupert hotter in July or August?

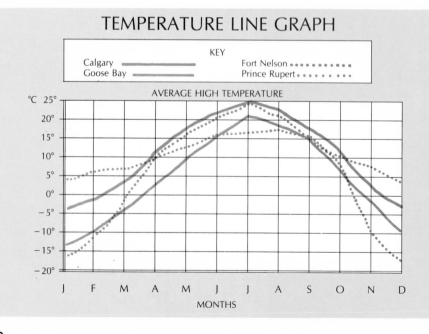

TEMPERATURE LINE GRAPH

Bell's Belles

Paul Aurandt

In this story you'll meet a young speech therapist whose invention was a failure. Or was it?

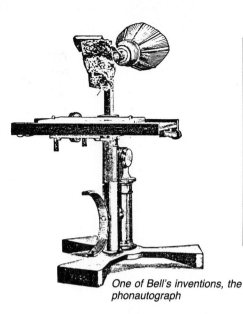

One of Bell's inventions, the phonautograph

Once upon a time there was a speech therapist . . . a schoolteacher speech therapist whose compassion for deaf children was so great that he drew up plans for an invention. This invention, said the therapist, would "hear" for the deaf . . . would render sound waves visible, identifiable, to those who could not perceive them otherwise. If the therapist's machine was a success, his little deaf students would be able to see speech as others heard it.

The machine was a failure. Almost.

Because, in the process of time, that unsuccessful apparatus became the telephone of today. The speech therapist . . . the schoolteacher who started out working with deaf children . . . was Alexander Graham Bell.

But you just *think* you know THE REST OF THE STORY. . . .

Now, if it's true that behind every great man is a woman, then it was doubly true of Alexander. There were two women in Aleck's life . . . two ladies who greatly inspired him: his mother and his wife.

Bell's mother, Eliza, was a teacher. She directed his childhood attention to acoustics and particularly to the study of speech. Whenever Aleck set about on his various youthful enterprises and hobbies, Eliza was always there to encourage him. But she never interfered. She never got in his way. She knew that Aleck would

Alexander Graham Bell as a young man

Mabel Hubbard as a young schoolgirl

Eliza Bell with an ear trumpet

have to find out certain things for himself. And he did.

It wasn't long before Aleck and his brother had invented a machine that could talk. It had lungs and vocal cords and a mouth and a tongue. And what were its first words? "Mama," of course.

Yes, there can be no doubt that the original "Ma Bell" was a marvelous inspiration to young Aleck. In fact, so concerned were Bell's parents that Aleck speak English without an accent, that when the young man finally came to teach school in Boston, no one could tell he had been born in Scotland.

Enter Mabel Hubbard . . . the second belle in Bell's life . . . his future wife.

Mabel's daddy was one of Aleck's earliest acquaintances in Boston. She, the beautiful young daughter, had recently returned from school in Germany.

From there on, the story of Alexander Graham Bell and Mabel Hubbard weaves a romantic tapestry.

She, youthful, lovely, rich.

He, brilliant, ardent, poor.

Together they would encounter the traditionally romantic obstacles of parental objection, despair, ridicule of his genius. And yes, they eventually succeeded. Fame and fortune became theirs. And yes, they lived happily ever after. Mabel's daddy even became first director of the Bell Telephone Company, in 1877.

Of Bell and his wife it was once said: Their story is as thoroughly unspoiled and charming as a story can be.

It was true. Mabel, like Aleck's mother, Eliza, inspired Bell through love and through devotion to him . . . and perhaps, in many ways, through something else.

Alexander Bell's primary interest was speech and speech therapy. His occupation, first and foremost, was his work with those who could not hear. Isn't it ironic, then, that his beloved students could never benefit from his most celebrated invention, the telephone?

Yes, and it is even more ironic when you consider that Bell's belles . . . his mother and his wife . . . the two women who inspired him the most . . . could never fully appreciate it either.

For they also . . . his mother and his wife . . . they too . . . were deaf.

What Do You Think?

1. Irony is the unexpected twist in a story. List two ironies in "Bell's Belles."
2. Explain the meaning of the title of this story, "Bell's Belles."
3. Why did Mabel's father become the director of the Bell Telephone Company if he disapproved of Aleck?

Taking a Closer Look

1. In what ways did Bell's mother influence him?
2. Where was Alexander Graham Bell born?
3. Who was the original "Ma Bell"?
4. In what country was Mabel Hubbard Bell educated?

Putting Ideas to Work

In your local library find the book *The Rest of the Story.* Share some of your favorite selections from it with the rest of the class.

MEDICAL MIRACLES

John Sibley knew he must have help soon. He knew what he needed, but he couldn't tell anyone his problem. Besides, who would help a stranger on a New York subway train?

Folk Medicine on the BMT *John Sibley*

The danger signals were clear as I descended the twisting stairway to the BMT subway station at Canal Street. Though it was near noon on a day in late July, New York's summer heat couldn't account for the sweat that had soaked through my shirt and was starting to dampen my jacket. My footing was uncertain. I reeled dizzily and grabbed the handrail firmly, taking each step with careful deliberation.

After twenty-three years as a diabetic, I knew all too well what was happening. The sugar level in my blood had fallen dangerously low. It was still falling fast. I was on the verge of insulin shock. Unless I got sugar into my system quickly, I would fall into unconsciousness. It had happened too many times before. I would wake up in a hospital emergency room with a sugar solution being pumped through a needle in my arm vein. What I needed now was to gulp down something sweet, a couple of candy bars or a soft drink. Normally I carried a package or two of chocolate-covered candies. But when dressing this morning, I had switched to a clean suit and had forgotten to transfer the candies.

Suddenly I found myself experiencing another common symptom of insulin shock: I could no longer think clearly. With great effort I forced myself to size up my situation.

I reached the uptown BMT express platform at Canal Street. The vending machines here dispensed only gum—no candy or soda. I thought about returning to the street. A candy store stood at the station entrance. But the climb was long, and the effort could easily burn up what little sugar remained in my system. I might collapse on the stairs.

The platform was becoming crowded. A train would be pulling in soon. If I could only hold out a while longer, I could take the train to Fourteenth Street, where I knew there were candy machines on the platform. Or I could walk along the platform, explain my problem to the other riders, and ask if anyone could feed me something sweet.

But the thought of asking for a handout was objectionable to me. I felt it would make me a target of ridicule and scorn. So instead of seeking help, I foolishly tried to hide my distress. I braced myself against a steel column and made a conscious effort to feel confident. Finally, a train rolled into the station, and I made my decision. As I stepped into the train, my phony confidence became genuine. I was sure I could keep myself under control until we reached Fourteenth Street. But no sooner had the train left Canal and headed north under Broadway, than it screeched suddenly to a halt.

My emergency loomed larger. The sweat no longer merely oozed from my skin; it poured down my back. I gripped the center pole with one hand, and clumsily removed my jacket. It slipped to the floor. I didn't try to pick it up. I was too busy trying to keep *myself* from falling to the floor.

And then I learned the truth about New Yorkers.

A tall woman rose from her seat and walked toward me. A burly laborer bounced to his feet right behind her. They took hold of my arms and guided me back to the bench. Two other passengers gave up their places so I could ease myself down to a half-reclining position.

Throughout the entire car, the riders, usually withdrawn and aloof, had become neighborly because of the long delay. Now their attention and their conversation focused on me. Burly Laborer loosened my tie and, firmly but gently, stretched my body into a fully reclining position. Tall Woman asked anxiously: Did I have heart trouble? Was I

carrying some medication I should be swallowing? The last of my strength was draining fast. The urge to let myself lapse into sleep was tremendous. I sighed deeply but made no reply to Tall Woman's questions. Then Burly Laborer dealt me two stinging open-handed blows to the face. This forced my eyes open, and in thick-tongued fashion I explained that I was diabetic, that I would pass out unless someone fed me sweets.

Word immediately spread through the car. Hands reached into pockets and purses, searching for candy. A youthful parish priest from Brooklyn, herding a dozen active ten-year-olds on a Central Park outing, directed the youngsters to move through the car and gather up whatever sweets the passengers had to offer. Suddenly, the priest realized that each child's lunch bag held a can of orange soda. He moved quickly to my side and asked if maybe a sweet soft drink would help. "That's perfect," I gasped. Instantly, the metal tabs on three cans popped open.

At this point the train conductor walked through the car announcing definite delay due to a signal-system failure. He paused long enough to size up my situation, strode forward to the motorman's compartment, and told him to radio ahead for an ambulance to stand by at Fourteenth Street.

But as it turned out, the ambulance wasn't necessary. Long before the train began to roll again, the urban folk medicine administered by my companions was taking effect. For my final dose, I gratefully accepted a cellophane-wrapped chocolate cake from a shy woman across the aisle.

I left the train at Times Square without learning the names of Tall Woman or Burly Laborer or Shy Woman. Parish Priest and I had introduced ourselves, but in my haste to gather myself together, I forgot both his name and that of his church. However, I have not forgotten what he said when I tried to give the children enough money to replace the soda I had drunk.

"They learned something," Parish Priest told me as he refused payment. "And they'll feel good about what they did for the rest of the day."

An Affair of the Heart

Herbert Ford

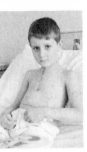

Paschalis after surgery

The Loma Linda University Heart Surgery Team has become well known throughout the world. A group of Seventh-day Adventist nurses and doctors has performed hundreds of heart surgeries in many countries where such delicate surgery is not normally available. While doing so they train doctors and nurses in that country to carry on after the Loma Linda team leaves. In this story a reporter who traveled with the Adventist surgery team on a follow-up visit tells about Paschalis, a Greek boy who was especially happy that the team came to his country.

The Olympic Airways DC-7 bored its way up into the hot, brassy-colored morning sky. The plane banked left, and the deep blue of the Aegean Sea appeared through the windows. A bank to the right, and the white of the city of Athens, bathed in early morning sunlight, stretched to distant Mount Pentelikon.

Far off on the left wing, the snowy 9500-foot peak of Mount

Athens as it looks today

Olympus looked down on the Greek countryside. The plane began its glide path down toward Thessaloniki, the seaport city where the Apostle Paul trod the streets and preached his sermons and to which he wrote epistles to the Thessalonians. Thessaloniki is the busy, modern-day home of some 350,000 people—and of Paschalis Nikoltsis.

Paschalis Nikoltsis lives in a Thessaloniki tenement. From the waterfront his home is a five-minute taxi ride through the clanging street of the coppersmiths, past the Roman Arch of Falerius, and finally two turns up dreary streets to 81 Olymbou.

"Eh-La-teh MEH-sa (Come in)," a grinning boy standing in front of the tall building said. "KHEH-ro po-LEE (I am happy to know you)."

The elevator, which can hold only three persons, creaked its way up the dingy interior of the building. With a grinding of gears and a loud bang it came to a halt. The youngster operating the mechanism, still grinning broadly in the faltering light, yanked the wire-mesh door open with a flourish.

And there in the hall, all eight years of him, stood Paschalis. A quiet smile played across his face as his stocky mother reached her weathered arms out in greeting. "Ka-lee-MEH-ra (Good morning)," she beamed. "POHSS ESS-THEH (How are you)?"

The one-sided conversation proceeded in Greek as we moved down the narrow hall and into the three or four simple rooms that made up the Nikoltsis home. We could do little else but gesture and smile.

A half hour later an uncle who spoke English arrived. "I learned the English when I shipped to America in the merchant marine," he explained. "Three times I was in New York—very big city!" Then he began to translate our questions about Paschalis, who played with toy logs on the floor.

"Paschalis was born in the Ligda Hospital here in Thessaloniki." The uncle translated the answers the boy's mother gave. "Even when he was very tiny, his mother—Elpis here—could tell that something was wrong. He didn't seem to have much strength.

"After three months his mother took him to the doctor for a checkup. He told her that the baby had a problem in his heart.

410

The doctor didn't know exactly what it was, but he was sure there *was* a problem—the heart just didn't sound right.

"As the child grew older, his mother noticed other signs that he was not entirely normal. He didn't move around and play like his brother Kenofan had at the same age. He did not play and run with the others when he grew older. From time to time his mother took Paschalis to different doctors here in Thessaloniki. Each one of them told her the boy had trouble with his heart."

The man paused in his translating to greet Paschalis's grandmother, who came to pay her respects to the visitors from America.

"Each new year brought more trouble for Paschalis," the boy's uncle continued. "He began school, but he could not run with the others. He was just not part of the school life.

"Then in October 1967, Paschalis's father, George, was reading the newspaper *Makedonia* one evening. He saw a story about a Seventh-day Adventist medical team from the United States. It was coming to Athens to do surgery and to teach Greek doctors to perform heart surgery in our country.

"The family became excited. They thought that maybe the American surgeons could help Paschalis. The doctors here in the city had already told them that the boy probably needed an operation on his heart. The parents asked the doctors who had examined the child for advice. The doctors said to go to Athens; they would send their findings to the American doctors there. And they encouraged the family to take the boy there early so he would have the best chance of seeing the Americans.

"People told us that the Adventist doctors would not charge for their surgical work. This made it possible for the boy's family to think of surgery for him. His father, George, makes about $165 a month in wages as a truck driver. It is not nearly enough for such a costly thing. So it was a godsend that the doctors did not charge for their services.

"Paschalis's family took him to Athens in November," he continued. "The Adventist doctors examined him carefully at the Evangelismos Hospital. They found that he had a heart defect that needed surgery.

"On the 18th of November Paschalis had his eighth

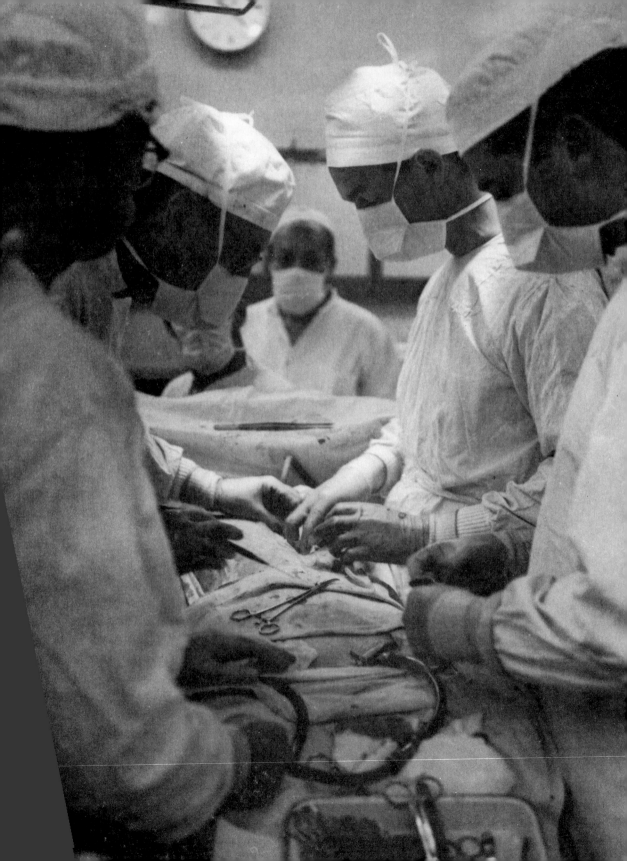

birthday—in the hospital. Two days later the surgeons operated on him, their twelfth patient.

"At the hospital while they were operating on Paschalis, we learned of the American lady—Mrs. Weiler, I believe they called her—to whom we owe so much for getting the heart team to come to Greece. About her I do not know too much—" The words trailed off.

That the families of the patients should associate the name Weiler with the Loma Linda University heart team was only natural. The woman had been with the group in Greece. Indeed, the surgeons would not have come to this southern European country if it had not been for Rebecca Weiler.

Mrs. Weiler did not have Greece on her mind the day she stopped by the physical therapy office of Mr. and Mrs. Karl Olsen in West Los Angeles, California. She was there for treatment to ease the lingering pain of an auto accident. But in a copy of the *Signs of the Times* magazine Mrs. Olsen had given her, Mrs. Weiler noticed a story about the Loma Linda University heart surgery team. The team had traveled to Pakistan and other southeast Asian countries. Its doctors had examined more than four hundred patients there, operated on fifty-five, and demonstrated their surgical techniques to scores of physicians in Pakistan, Thailand, and Taiwan. The Adventist heart team had made its visit, the article said, as a voluntary gesture of goodwill, with the surgeons refusing any payment. The United States government had arranged for transportation.

The story had gripped Rebecca Weiler. In the back of her mind an idea began to stir. Mrs. Weiler was a volunteer worker at the University of California's Medical Center in Los Angeles. She had seen scores of foreign patients come to the health center for help. Only a short time before, she had given help to two young patients from Greece who had traveled to America for open-heart surgery. Unfortunately, both of the children had died.

Such youngsters had to come thousands of miles from home to a completely unfamiliar country for major surgery. The sorrow of their deaths ran through her thoughts as she read the magazine article about the work of the medical unit in Asia.

◄ *The Loma Linda University Heart Team in action*

Could it be possible, she wondered, to get the group to go to Greece, to take heart surgery to those in need, rather than having the Greek people come thousands of miles to America and spend the life savings of their families in the process?

Excited by the thought, Rebecca Weiler picked up the telephone a short time later and dialed the number of Father Peter M. Kalellis, pastor of St. Sophia's Greek Orthodox Cathedral in Los Angeles. Only a few days before she had seen Father Kalellis conduct the funeral of the two Greek youngsters who had not survived the heart surgery.

"Father Kalellis, I believe I have found a way we can help some Greek people who might need open-heart surgery," she said. "There's a heart surgery team at Loma Linda University,

From left to right Dr. Wareham, Dr. Coggin, Rebecca Weiler, and Father Kalellis. Mrs. Weiler is being presented a leaf from the island of Kos, where Greek medicine originated.

near San Bernardino. They recently went to Asia and donated their services there as an international goodwill gesture. Do you think it might be possible to persuade them to go to Greece also?"

Youthful-looking, darkly handsome Peter Kalellis bubbled over with enthusiasm. To Rebecca Weiler's query he had an immediate answer. "Let's get them on the phone and ask them if they will go to Greece!"

Dr. Ellsworth Wareham took the call from the two, and a new chapter opened in the history of the Loma Linda University heart team. "If the Greek people want us to help, and you can find a way for us to travel to their country, the team will go," he assured the priest and Mrs. Weiler.

Father Kalellis and Mrs. Weiler went to work on the thousand details they had to handle before the medical team could leave for Greece. They had to find funds for supplies and airline tickets. They had to contact a hospital where the surgeons could work. Mrs. Weiler and Father Kalellis found themselves jumping from one problem to the next in the days of October 1967. But they solved them. The team left for Greece at the end of the month.

Elpis Nikoltsis beamed broadly as she spoke. Her brother translated the story of Paschalis's open-heart surgery.

"The operation was very successful," she reported. "Paschalis was a good little patient. He did not have any problems after the American doctors fixed his heart. We stayed six weeks at the Evangelismos Hospital while he got better. It cost fifteen thousand drachmas for the care, but nothing for the services of the wonderful Adventist doctors.

"Now my boy is much better." The mother smiled as she looked at Paschalis playing on the floor of the small room. "He is like a new boy. He eats well now. Before he would not eat much at all. Now he plays with the children all the time. He has just finished at the top of his class.

"Every day we look at the boy. We are so happy he is well. When we look at him and see how strong he is now, we thank God that the Adventist doctors came to Greece. Every day we think of them, and we will always be thankful that they came."

The Miracle That Blew in the Window

It was an important discovery, but it took a long time to convince others. For fourteen years Dr. Alexander Fleming knew he had something the world desperately needed.

The fall of 1928 was damp—damp even for London. Through the open window in the basement laboratory of St. Mary's Hospital drifted leaves, dust, and other things.

The hospital's bacteriologist was Dr. Alexander Fleming. He was washing some culture plates that had been spoiled by molds from the air. He had been studying the plates for an article he was writing on staphylococci—those tough little germs that cause everything from boils to blood poisoning.

Culture plates of staphylococci bacteria were often being ruined by molds. But such accidents did not bother Dr. Fleming. He expected them. As he had done so many times before, he turned on the faucet, glancing at one of the ruined plates. Then he took a closer look.

"That's funny," he said, staring at the plate. The culture plate was indeed a strange sight. Groups of staphylococci were still alive on the outer edges. Around the mold the bacteria had disappeared.

"If my mind had not been in a reasonably perceptive state, I would not have paid any attention to it," Fleming wrote later, in remembering that day. But he had paid attention. Instead of washing the plate with the mold, he looked further.

Dr. Fleming simmered part of the mold in a broth for two weeks. He made a small amount of fluid which he named "penicillin." Then he began to put penicillin to the test.

For years Alexander Fleming had been looking for something able to destroy deadly germs. During World War I, he had learned that the strong chemicals then used to fight bacteria were dangerous.

He had already discovered—in human tears—a substance called lysosome[1], which showed great powers against certain bacteria. He knew as much about the subject as anyone alive.

---

[1] lysosome (lī'sə som)

Yet nothing he had seen could do what the mold that blew in through his window had done.

Staphylococci, he soon found, were not the only germs that penicillin attacked. It could also stop the growth of streptococci and pneumococci, two of the most common causes of death. Even the tough germs that caused diphtheria were powerless against it.

Was penicillin dangerous? That, of course, was the big question. Certain chemicals also killed bacteria in a test tube. But they were not healthy for the human body. Dr. Fleming took two healthy rabbits. Into one he injected penicillin broth and into the other ordinary broth. He found that penicillin was easily endured—at least by rabbits.

Now he faced a grave problem that would frustrate penicillin researchers for the next fourteen years. His supply of the mold was small. He consulted a biologist, Dr. Harold Raistrick. Together the two friends began to grow penicillin. When they had a store of it on hand, they were ready to tackle the biggest question of all. Penicillin killed germs in a test tube and in rabbits. Would it do the same to germs in the human body?

"We tried a little in clinical work," Fleming says, "but not much. The reports were favorable but there was nothing miraculous. We went to the wards and asked the surgeons if they had any surgical cases we could try it on. They always said that they had none."

In one way the surgeons were right in not wanting to use penicillin. Fleming made no secret of the fact that he had barely enough on hand to treat one case.

"We were bacteriologists, not chemists," Dr. Fleming explained later. "And in view of the difficulties the chemists have had in concentrating penicillin, it is not surprising that our amateur efforts at concentration were not successful."

Fleming wished that he could interest biologists and mold experts in penicillin. Then someone would discover how penicillin could be grown easily. He wrote a report on his laboratory experiments and presented it at a medical meeting. The report was overlooked.

Ten years passed. Alexander Fleming kept a small amount of penicillin in a corner of the lab and a vast love for it in his heart.

During that time, the sulfa drugs were discovered. They caused a great stir in the world of medicine. Years later a friend remembered a conversation he had had with Fleming.

"You know," Fleming had said, "I have something much better, but no one will listen to me. I can't even get a chemist who will extract it for me."

"What's the name of it?"

"I named it penicillin."

"I never heard of it."

Few people outside Fleming's laboratory had ever heard of penicillin. However, in Oxford, Dr. Howard Florey and Dr. Ernst Chain were plowing through hundreds of old magazine articles. They were looking for an idea for a research project. One of the articles that seemed promising was Fleming's original paper on penicillin. They decided that Fleming's mold broth should be looked into.

This was in 1937. By the next year it had become clear that England, and perhaps the whole world, would soon be at war. Before long, hospitals would be filled with the wounded. Medical researchers had to find a way to check infection.

Florey and Chain soon realized that Alexander Fleming's penicillin was the answer to this problem. A young chemist named Norman Heatley joined the team. The three men finally were able to get more penicillin than had yet been possible. From this they made the first penicillin salt.

In 1940 England was already under heavy attack. Then they made their first experiment. Florey shot 50 mice full of the most deadly streptococci he could get his hands on. He left 25 untreated. The first 25 were given shots of penicillin every three hours for forty-five hours. Of the mice that did not get penicillin, all 25 died within sixteen hours. Of the penicillin-treated mice, 24 of the 25 lived.

These results were written in the medical magazine *The Lancet* on August 24, 1940. Alexander Fleming glanced through the magazine each week to see what was new in medicine. It is hard to imagine what he felt while reading the report from Oxford.

Within a short time he was knocking on the door of Florey and Chain's laboratory. He was Alexander Fleming, he explained to the scientists. He had come to see what penicillin looked like in a pure state. The two men were barely able to speak. They had thought that Alexander Fleming was dead.

Fleming sent Florey some mold that had been made from his first colony. The Oxford scientists now began preparing mold for their first tests of penicillin on human beings.

Florey began the experiments with a heavy heart. He and Chain had seen from their first experiments with animals that penicillin did not stay in their bodies. It was thrown out almost as quickly as it could be forced in. "Like pouring water down a basin with the plug out," Florey said.

The amount necessary to keep twenty-five mice alive had almost used up the laboratory supply. Could they make enough to treat one person? What, for that matter, did they hope to prove by being able to treat one person? In that year people were dying by the thousands and being wounded by the tens of thousands.

In February 1941 a London police officer cut his face while shaving. It was a common enough accident. But two weeks later, the man was dying. His body had been invaded by staphylococci. The sulfa drugs had no effect. The case seemed made to order for the penicillin researchers.

Every bit of penicillin in the laboratory was taken to the hospital at Oxford. Every three hours the dying man was given a dose of penicillin. Five days passed. Within two days the patient seemed slightly improved. On the third day there were fewer swellings on his face. By the fifth day he was almost well. But the last of the penicillin was gone.

In the laboratory desperate efforts were made to scrape some more together. The efforts came too late. The infection flared up. The police officer died.

Some thought the penicillin had failed, since the patient

died. But those following the case were now even more sure the drug could work.

Early one morning in the Oxford laboratory, the telephone rang. "Florey? Fletcher here. I have a case that I think you might want to look at. Fifteen-year-old boy. I don't give him another forty-eight hours to live. Unless—"

This time it worked. The boy who should have been dead within forty-eight hours lived. The supply of penicillin held out just long enough. "Now," Florey thought grimly, "we have to make more of the stuff."

Penicillin research had reached the point at which it demanded large-scale experiments in hospitals all over the world. So far, enough penicillin had been made to treat two patients, one unsuccessfully. Unless the drug was grown by the ton, not the teaspoon, widespread experiments would never be made.

Yet no drug company would say, "Certainly, Doctor. I'll spend a few million to make this unknown drug which has failed in fifty percent of the two cases you've tried it on." Florey had to have better figures. He needed figures that would appeal to the sales manager of a drug company as well as to the company's laboratory director.

He asked the help of his wife, Ethel, who was a doctor. Dr. Ethel Florey took charge of the clinical research. By the end of the following year, the Floreys had 187 recorded cases proving penicillin's worth to medicine.

In 1941 Howard Florey and Norman Heatley were flown to the United States by the Rockefeller Foundation. They were put on a train and taken to Peoria, Illinois. There the scientists of the Northern Regional Research Laboratory faced up to the problem at once. "Either we find some new way to grow this stuff, or we forget all about it." They began to look for a better way to grow it.

Then it happened. A scientist was making a routine check of his penicillin cultures. He found that one of them was making much more penicillin than had ever been made in the Oxford laboratory. How was the penicillin being grown? In home-brewed, corn-steeped liquor.

The bottleneck was broken. Production was up two hundred times almost overnight. Those drug manufacturers who had said, "Sorry, not interested," were now eager to talk business.

During the first five months, the drug companies produced 400,000,000 units. By the end of the year the figure was 9,194,000,000 units a month.

Sir Alexander Fleming—knighthood was only one of the many honors that came to him—wrote: "There are thousands of different molds, and there are thousands of different bacteria; and that chance put the mold in the right spot at the right time was like winning the Irish sweepstakes."

422

Alexander Fleming

What Do You Think?

1. Why did the writer of "Folk Medicine on the BMT" choose to use names like Tall Man and Burly Laborer?
2. Parish Priest said, "They learned something." What do you think the ten-year-olds learned?
3. How might the Loma Linda University heart team be able to show the love of God to others?
4. What kinds of details would the heart team have to take care of before they could go to a country like Greece?
5. If you were Paschalis, what would you be thinking on the morning after the surgery?
6. Do you think Dr. Fleming's discovery of the mold was just luck? Explain your answer.
7. How did Fleming feel when he read Florey's article?

Taking a Closer Look

1. In the story "Folk Medicine on the BMT," why was the writer reluctant to ask other passengers for help?
2. Explain in your own words what each of the passengers did to help the diabetic man.
3. The author says, "And then I learned the truth about New Yorkers." What was that truth?
4. How did Paschalis's family find out about the Seventh-day Adventist medical team?
5. According to the story "The Miracle That Blew in the Window," what big problem plagued penicillin researchers?
6. Why did World War II make the discovery of penicillin more important?

Putting Ideas to Work

There have been many breakthroughs in medicine since World War II. Use reference materials or library books to learn about one of these "medical miracles."

Understanding Ads and Order Forms

Someday, you might consider joining a book club. There are many book clubs from which to choose. Some offer books of general interest. Others offer books on specific topics (photography, sports, science, home economics, psychology, and so forth). Usually, book-club advertisements can be found in magazines and in Sunday newspapers. They may look something like the advertisement shown on the next page.

Read the advertisement on page 425 carefully. Notice that there are both advantages and disadvantages when you join a book club. For example, you might save money on the books you want, but you must buy four more books within the next year—whether or not you want them.

To answer the following questions, you need to analyze the information in the ad, and to do a little reading "between the lines."

1. Will you be able to order from The Bookworm Club any book you see in a bookstore? What books will you be able to order?

2. What fee will you pay in addition to the price of the book? How much will that fee be?

3. Suppose the bookstore price of a book is $10, and The Bookworm Club price is $9.50 plus postage and handling. Could you accuse the club of "false advertising"? Explain your answer.

4. Suppose you join the club, and you receive the next month's brochure and order form. You decide you don't want the feature book, but you forget to mail the form back within the ten days allowed. What will happen?

5. Copy and fill in the application form. In the boxes, write the numbers of the four books that you might choose. On the name line, circle your title (Ms., Mr., Mrs., or Miss). Then, *print* your name, address, city, state or province, and zip code. Be sure to sign your name where indicated. (If this were a real application for membership, it would be considered a legal contract with the book club. You would be responsible for payment.)

There is a wise Latin saying: *caveat emptor* (ka'vē ät emp' tər). It means "let the buyer beware." Always read advertisements and order forms carefully. You might decide the public library is better for you.

GREAT READING FROM THE BOOKWORM CLUB

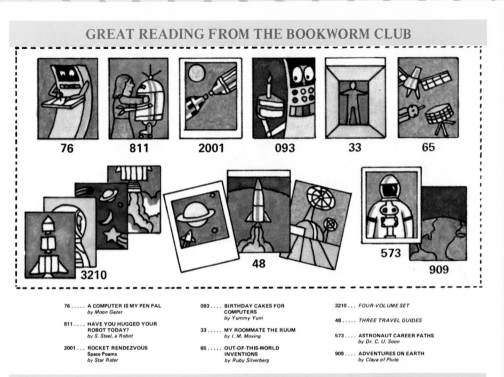

76 ..... A COMPUTER IS MY PEN PAL
by Moon Gazer

811 .... HAVE YOU HUGGED YOUR
ROBOT TODAY?
by S. Steel, a Robot

2001 ... ROCKET RENDEZVOUS
Space Poems
by Star Rider

093 .... BIRTHDAY CAKES FOR
COMPUTERS
by Yummy Yum

33 ..... MY ROOMMATE THE RUUM
by I. M. Moving

65 ..... OUT-OF-THIS-WORLD
INVENTIONS
by Ruby Silverberg

3210 ... FOUR-VOLUME SET

48 ..... THREE TRAVEL GUIDES

573 .... ASTRONAUT CAREER PATHS
by Dr. C. U. Soon

909 .... ADVENTURES ON EARTH
by Claya of Pluto

SAVE MONEY! Join The Bookworm Club, and get any 4 books shown here for $1, plus postage and handling. Once your membership is accepted, you'll save even more. Our prices are up to 30% lower than bookstore prices.

SHOP AT HOME! Every four weeks, you'll receive The Bookworm Club Brochure, showing dozens of popular books that you can order without ever leaving your home. These books have been selected by our editors—who have chosen one book to feature each month.

YOUR ORDER IS PLACED AUTOMATICALLY! If you want the feature book selected for you by our editors, do nothing. It will be shipped to your home automatically. If you want another book, or no book at all, return the order form within 10 days. If you ever receive a book you do not want because you had less than 10 days to order, return it at our expense. A shipping-and-handling charge will be added to your invoice for every book sent to you. Your only membership obligation is to order 4 additional books, at the club's regular low prices, within the next year.

NO-RISK OFFER! Join today. If you are not completely satisfied with your 4 introductory books, just return them within 10 days. Your membership will be canceled, and you will owe nothing.

ANY 4 BOOKS FOR $1 WHEN YOU JOIN

THE BOOKWORM CLUB, Box XYZ, Denver, CO 80202

Please accept my application for membership in The Bookworm Club. Send me the four books or sets of books I have listed below. Bill me $1 plus shipping and handling. I agree to the membership plan described in this advertisement. I understand that I must buy only 4 more books during the next year.

MS./MRS./MISS/MR.:_____
ADDRESS:_____
CITY:_____ STATE:_____ ZIP:_____
SIGNATURE:_____

NOT VALID UNLESS SIGNED

Members accepted in U.S. and Canada only. Offer slightly different in Canada.

VISION AND VOICE

It takes a special vision to see the ordinary in an extraordinary way. Artists give voice to their visions when they create—pictures, pottery, or music.

427

How Artists Look at the World

Manuel Milan

The following works of art show some of the ways in which people have looked at nature through the years. They are all different. Yet they all have something in common. Works of art can tell us about their makers, the time in which the artists lived, and the artists' beliefs about the world around them.

Cranes and Serpents. The Cleveland Museum of Art. Purchase from the J. H. Wade Fund.

This lacquered wood stand, *Cranes and Serpents*, was made in China over 2000 years ago. You can see that the cranes made by this artist do not look exactly like real cranes. Artists then used animals to represent different forces in nature, such as storms, good fortune, and love. Realism—showing things exactly as they are—was not important to the ancient Chinese artists.

Soaring, by Andrew Wyeth. Courtesy Shelburne Museum, Shelburne, Vermont.

Look now at *Soaring,* a painting by Andrew Wyeth, who is a famous present-day American painter. Do you think that realism is important to this artist? Notice how carefully every detail of his buzzard is painted. To Wyeth, every detail is important, and to leave out even the smallest feather would destroy the beauty of the bird.

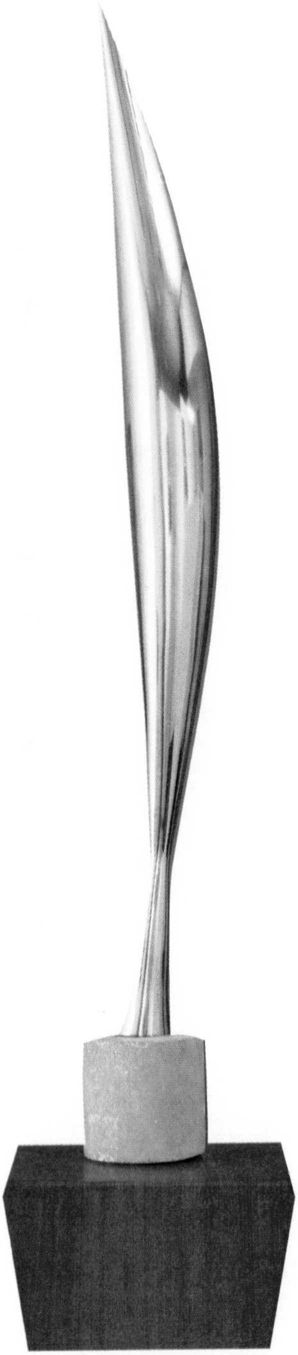

The bronze sculpture, *Bird in Space*, shown at the left, was done by Constantin Brancusi (brän'küsh), one of the greatest sculptors of all time. Unlike Andrew Wyeth, Brancusi is not concerned with detail. To him, the most important thing about a bird is its ability to fly. As you look at his sculpture, can you "see" a bird in space? Would feathers make this bird more like a bird, or is the shape of the sculpture and the gleam of its polished bronze enough to remind you of a bird soaring through the sky?

Through the ages the horse has been important to people. Before cars were invented, horses pulled wagons through the streets of the city. *The City Rises* was painted in 1910 before many people had cars. Does it help you feel what the city must have been like when the streets were full of horses? Do you think the artist was more interested in painting a horse as it really looks or in giving a feeling about the city? On the other hand, the horses in the painting at the right are real racehorses. Edgar Degas (də gä') was a constant visitor to the racetrack, and this artist's eye did not miss a single important detail.

◄ Constantin Brancusi, *Bird in Space* (1928?). Bronze (unique cast), 54" high. Collection, The Museum of Modern Art, New York.

Umberto Boccioni, *The City Rises* (1910). Oil on canvas, 6′6½″ x 9′10½″. Collection, The Museum of Modern Art, New York. Mrs. Simon Guggenheim Fund.

Edgar Degas, *Race Horses*. Oil on canvas, 30.5 cm. x 40 cm. Courtesy, Museum of Fine Arts, Boston. S. A. Denio Collection.

431

Franz Marc, *The Large Blue Horses*. Collection, Walker Art Center, Minneapolis. Gift of the Gilbert M. Walker Fund.

Franz Marc painted very colorful horses, like the ones you see above. Why do you think he used such bright colors? Do you see that the shape of the horses is the same as the hills behind them? Most painters around 1900 decided that the job of artists was not to imitate nature, but to create a special nature of their own with shape and color.

The sea is important to all people, but for many different reasons. To the *Toilers of the Sea* in the painting by Albert Ryder, the sea is very important because they make their living from it. What do you think is the major force in this painting? This artist has strong feelings about the sea and a fisherman's way of life, so he has attempted to show the fisherman's life on the sea as it really is.

Albert P. Ryder, *Toilers of the Sea*. Addison Gallery of American Art. Phillips Academy, Andover, Massachusetts.

Anonymous (American). *The Plantation*. The Metropolitan Museum of Art. Gift of Edgar William and Bernice Chrysler Gabisch, 1963.

Now look at the anonymous painting *The Plantation*. The painting also shows the sea and a boat. Does the sea seem very important in this painting? Which do you think was more important to the artist—the land or the sea? Do you think this picture shows as strong a feeling or understanding of the sea as does the work by Ryder?

If art is just something you look at in a museum on a rainy day, if it is something that seems cold and lifeless to you, then there is much that you are missing. If you remember that works of art reflect the artists and the world in which they lived, art can be a most meaningful experience.

What Do You Think?

1. Of the three representations of birds, the Chinese wood stand, the Wyeth painting, and Brancusi's *Bird in Space*, which do you prefer? Why?
2. Do you agree with the painters of the early 1900s that the job of artists is not to imitate nature, but to create a special nature with shape and color? Why or why not?
3. Compare *The Plantation* and the *Toilers of the Sea*. What are the differences between the two paintings? In what ways are they alike?
4. Think of another name for *Cranes and Serpents*. Explain why you think the name you selected is appropriate.

Taking a Closer Look

1. What is the basic difference between Wyeth's *Soaring* and Brancusi's *Bird in Space*?
2. What is meant by the term *realism?*

Putting Ideas to Work

Use an encyclopedia to find out more about one of the artists mentioned in this article. Tell the class about the artist's life and work.

Tapestry displayed in the lobby of Florida Hospital in Orlando, Florida.

I Saw ThreeAngels

Sometimes an artist decides to interpret something in the Bible. Which of these artistic interpretations of the Three Angels' Messages do you like best?

And I saw another angel fly in the midst of heaven, having the everlasting gospel to preach unto them that dwell on the earth, and to every nation, and kindred, and tongue, and people.

Saying with a loud voice, Fear God, and give glory to him; for the hour of his judgment is come: and worship him that made heaven, and earth, the sea, and the fountains of waters.

436

Sculpture of the Three Angels, *by Alan Collins*

437

The Three Angels *as depicted in the South Window of the College View Seventh-day Adventist Church in Lincoln, Nebraska*

And there followed another angel, saying, Babylon is fallen, is fallen, that great city, because she made all nations drink of the wine of the wrath of her fornication.

And the third angel followed them, saying with a loud voice, If any man worship the beast and his image, and receive his mark in his forehead, or in his hand,

Wood carving of the Three Angels *by an African wood carver*

The same shall drink of the wine of the wrath of God, which is poured out without mixture into the cup of his indignation; and he shall be tormented with fire and brimstone in the presence of the holy angels, and in the presence of the Lamb:

And the smoke of their torment ascendeth up for ever and ever: and they have no rest day nor night, who worship the beast and his image, and whosoever receiveth the mark of his name.

Here is the patience of the saints: here are they that keep the commandments of God, and the faith of Jesus.

—Revelation 14:6-12 KJV

What Do You Think?

Which of the pieces of art in this article do you prefer? Explain why you chose it.

Taking a Closer Look

There are many symbols in this selection from the book of Revelation. What do you think the following symbols represent:
a. Babylon
b. the Lamb
c. the beast

Putting Ideas to Work

Show your interpretation of the Three Angels' Messages. Will you work with clay, with paints, or with some other medium? You decide.

A Prairie Boy's Summer

William Kurelek

William Kurelek,[1] a distinguished artist, grew up on the Canadian prairie. In these selections from his book, *A Prairie Boy's Summer*, Kurelek portrays scenes from his childhood.

School Lunch under the Woodpile

In winter the children had to eat their sometimes-frozen lunch sandwiches at their school desks, but in warm weather they had a bigger choice of places to eat. One of the boys' favorite spots was under the school woodpile. It offered just the right amount of shade if it was hot, and it cut down the wind that tugged at their lunch wrapping.

William was a rather fussy eater and wasn't always excited about the contents of his lunch box. He always seemed to be getting peanut butter or corn syrup stuck to the roof of his mouth. Or else hard-boiled eggs that choked him. Real British Columbian apples, brought by his father from town once in a long while, were a treat.

William was fond of dessert, probably because it wasn't often to be found in his lunch box. When he was smaller and his mother baked a cake, she'd let him scrape out the mixing bowl.

At lunch time, a thermos of milk helped the sandwiches to go down. The thermos was brought in the black, worker's type lunch box that John and he had to share. They envied some of the fancy sandwiches—like brown sugar on butter —of their poorer neighbors. And sometimes they even persuaded them to swap.

Catching Baby Killdeer

One milking time when William and John were helping their mother in the garden, she sent them to fetch the herd.

---

[1] Kurelek (kûr el'ik)

School Lunch Under the Wood Pile

The boys loved birds so they made sure the herd wouldn't step on a killdeer's nest they knew of near the barn road. A killdeer's nest lies flat, naked, and exposed on the ground, but this one was so cleverly camouflaged that William was only able to find it by outsmarting the mother bird. One time, when he happened to be passing by, she'd flown up and fallen to the ground some yards away, crying and fluttering, pretending her wing was broken. He knew that the more fuss she made, the closer he must be to her nest.

This evening William was delighted to see that the eggs had hatched! Darling fluffy little bits of life standing high on legs thinner than toothpicks were scattering in all directions. Not yet able to fly, they tripped on blades of grass and were easily caught. In his hand William could feel the teeny heart going pit-a-pat. He knelt there trying to soothe it by stroking and talking, "Please, please, believe me! I'm not going to hurt you. I just want to hold you for a minute because I love you." How he wished he could tell the frantic mother in bird language that he wouldn't dream of harming her lovable babies.

William was interrupted by his mother's shout from the garden—"Hey, get those cows in!" William let the bird go, knowing that its family would reunite at the nest when they felt it was safe again.

Catching Baby Killdeer

What Do You Think?

1. Which do you think reveals more about prairie life, Kurelek's paintings or the accompanying descriptions that he wrote? Explain your choice.
2. Which of the two paintings do you like best? Explain why you chose that picture.
3. What does the information in these episodes reveal about William Kurelek's mother?
4. What other kinds of experiences and situations do you think William Kurelek might have included in his book, *A Prairie Boy's Summer?*
5. Think of three situations from your own everyday life that might make good subjects for paintings.

Taking a Closer Look

1. Do you think a person must have formal training in art in order to be called an artist? Support your answer with details from this story.
2. Why did the boys like to eat under the woodpile in warm weather?
3. Explain in your own words how William found the killdeer nest.

Putting Ideas to Work

If you enjoyed reading about William Kurelek and his work, you may want to find a copy of his book, *A Prairie Boy's Summer*. Try your nearest public library.

Using an Encyclopedia

Encyclopedias are valuable reference sources. They reflect the vision and voice of our collected wisdom. These works of factual knowledge can be one or many volumes. They contain articles that summarize all the important things people know about many topics. The articles are arranged in alphabetical order. And related information is usually cross-referenced (with a note that suggests that you *see* another article for more facts).

Early encyclopedias tried to summarize all knowledge; and they did quite a good job of it. As time passed, our knowledge grew and grew. Today, encyclopedias may choose to specialize in a certain branch of knowledge. A very general topic may not be covered at all. An example of this is *clay.* Some encyclopedias may not have an entry for clay. Others may discuss it in detail. The article shown here tells what one modern encyclopedia says about clay.

Skim the article. Visualize the information it contains about clay. Be sure, also, to scan the pictures above the article. To answer the questions on this page, use the key words in the questions to find answers in the article. In fact, see if you can match question key words to article key words. Look for the paragraph that has the main idea. Then you can concentrate your answer search on this paragraph. Keep in mind, however, that facts may be found in more than one place. So, read the article carefully before you answer the questions.

1. What does baking do to clay?
2. What are the main ingredients in pure clay?
3. How is shale formed?
4. Explain how to make clay from shale.
5. Name the type of clay used to make tile, fixtures, and ordinary pottery.
6. How did "ball clay" get its name?
7. Describe China clay. Tell its other name.
8. What products require kaolin?
9. What effect does the lime or iron content of clay have on the final product?
10. Tell what ancient peoples made from clay.
11. Why are refractory bricks used to line furnaces? (Hint: *refractory* means "hard to manage.")
12. Fire clay is used to make refractory bricks. What does fire clay contain?

CLAY. Most children have modeled objects with clay at home or at school and made mud pies of clayey soil. Wet clay is plastic and easy to shape. It will hold its form when dry. When baked, it becomes almost as hard as stone and watertight. In very early times people learned how to mold clay to make pottery and bricks. The ancient Sumerians even wrote on wet clay tablets (*see* Babylonia and Assyria). Today clay is the most common industrial raw material. It is used for a large number of products, from common bricks to fine white porcelain.

Pure clay consists mainly of silica and alumina (*see* Silicon). It is made up of very minute platelike crystals produced by the weathering of certain igneous rocks, chiefly feldspar. The smallest particles are colloidal (*see* Colloids). They can hold a film of water, firmly bound or adsorbed on the surface, by electrical attraction. The water acts as a lubricant and enables the particles to slip easily past one another. Wet clay therefore is plastic. Baking drives off the water and melts the particles, causing them to stick to one another.

Clay is found in all good soil (*see* Soil). During the Ice Age it was spread over the surface by glaciers. Deposits accumulated also in the deeper parts of the sea and in lakes and river beds. Clay is mined much like coal.

When beds of clay have been solidified by pressure beneath other sediments, the flaky minerals tend to lie parallel to the bedding, and the rock called *shale* is formed. Powdered shale thoroughly mixed with water becomes clay again. *Slate* is a variety of rock produced by great compression of shale (*see* Slate).

Most clays contain impurities that give the different kinds their distinctive color and qualities. Those rich in iron burn red or brown. Cream-colored bricks are those which contain a high proportion of lime. Lean clays are low in plasticity. Fat clays are highly plastic.

The purest clay is *China clay,* also called *kaolin.* It is smooth, fine-grained, and almost white. It is used for fine china, porcelain, tile, and electric insulators and in making paper. Because it is low in plasticity, it is mixed with the cheaper *ball clay* for most types of ceramics. Ball clay is so called because it is taken from clay pits in ball-like chunks. It is used in the tiles and sanitary fixtures in our bathrooms. It is also the basis of most ordinary pottery (*see* Pottery and Porcelain).

Fire clay, a mixture of sand and clay, is generally found beneath coal seams. Bricks made of fire clay are called *refractory* because they can withstand high temperatures without shrinking or cracking. They are used to line furnaces, cement and lime kilns, coke ovens, and blast furnaces.

About a dozen states have yearly productions of a million or more tons of *miscellaneous clays,* including shales. These clays are used chiefly for common brick, structural tile, sewer pipe, drain tile, and in portland cement. (*See* Brick; Building Construction; Cement.) *Adobe* is a sandy clay that has been used since ancient times for making sun-dried brick.

Adapted and reprinted by permission of F. E. Compton Company, a division of Encyclopaedia Britannica, Inc.

The Music Maker

Marion Mitchelson Gartler

There's no use trying to make music
when others call you "Squeaky Voice."
Or is there?

Antonio Stradivari stood quietly
in the shadows of the narrow,
deserted street. Once he took a step
forward, toward the sunlit square
beyond. But then he hesitated and
stepped back, allowing the darkness of the alleylike street to swallow him again.

His dark eyes were sad and lonely
as he stared at the colorful carnival
scene spread out before him.
Always, at carnival time, it was like
this! Everyone in the small Italian
town of Cremona seemed to join in
the music and the singing—everyone, that is, except Antonio.

At first he used to go to the village
square along with his friends. But
when the singing started, they
would begin to taunt him, laughing
at him and calling him "Squeaky
Voice."

"Well, hello there, Squeaky Voice!" someone called out behind him now. Antonio whirled about, straining his eyes in the flickering light of the alley.

"Oh, hello," he said, recognizing at last the two boys who had come up behind him.

"We're on our way to the square," the older boy, whose name was Luigi, told Antonio. "Roberto is going to sing, and I shall play my violin. Want to come along?"

Antonio hesitated, looking with longing eyes at the violin the boy was holding. Then he looked down at his own hands. In one he held a knife, and in the other he held a small block of wood upon which he had been whittling.

The younger boy, Roberto, gave Antonio an impatient push. "Come on, if you're going to come!" he cried. "It's the last night of the carnival, and we want to have some fun."

Luigi laughed and flashed the violin tauntingly at Antonio. "Yes, come along, Squeaky Voice," he said. "You can whittle there as well as anywhere."

The two boys led the way. Antonio followed them reluctantly, eyes fastened on the violin in Luigi's hand.

Antonio's love of music had once led him to take up violin lessons. How hard he had practiced! But no matter how hard he tried, his playing had not improved. The neighbors complained so much that at last Antonio's parents forced him to give up trying to play.

All the color and the excitement of the carnival burst upon Antonio as the boys left the alleylike street and came out into the square. Laughter and music were everywhere, as the merrymakers danced and sang.

The sun was just setting on the plains beyond Cremona, leaving the cloudless spring sky bathed in glowing tones of pink and red. The village square seemed to catch the colors from the sky and sprinkle them freely over the bright costumes of the carnival throng.

For a little while, the beauty of the scene made Antonio forget about his loneliness and his longings.

People strolling by paused to listen and clap when Luigi began to play. His tunes were happy and lively, and Roberto's voice, as he sang with the violin, was sweet and clear.

As Antonio watched Luigi's fingers moving swiftly along the strings of the violin, his own fingers were moving busily too. He hardly seemed to watch what they were doing. Yet, already, the crude outline of a little violin was beginning to take shape beneath the careful movements of his knife.

After a while, a man came along. He wore no carnival costume, and he did not seem to be taking part in the merrymaking. He moved up close and watched Luigi as he played. "That was nicely done, lad," he said when the song ended.

As he started to turn away, his eyes rested for a moment on Antonio. "What's that you're carving, boy?" he asked, stepping closer.

"Oh, it is nothing," said Antonio, somewhat embarrassed by the attention of the stranger. Reluctantly he thrust forward the crude little violin so that the man could see it.

"Indeed," said the stranger kindly, taking it in his hand. "It is not bad at all for a beginner." He examined it closely for a moment and then asked, "Do you like wood carving?"

"Oh, yes!" replied Antonio eagerly. Then he added, as if he were slightly ashamed, "It is really the only thing I can do!"

"Is that so?" replied the stranger. "Well, that is nothing to be embarrassed about, my boy. It is the only thing I can do too!" And, handing the little violin back to Antonio, he gave the boy a friendly smile and turned away.

As the stranger was swallowed up in the crowd of people, Luigi pulled at Antonio's arm excitedly. "Did you hear what he said?" exclaimed Luigi happily. "Did you hear the great Amati say how well I played?"

"Who is Amati?" asked Antonio, shoving the unfinished violin into his pocket. "And why do you call him great?"

Luigi stared unbelievingly at Antonio. "What?" he cried. "You have not heard of Amati? How can that be, when he is the most famous man in all Cremona? Amati is a violin maker—the greatest in Italy."

Luigi's words sent strange new ideas whirling through Antonio's mind. So, the man was a violin maker! He could make beautiful music without playing a violin *or* singing! And he had said that Antonio's carving was not bad for a beginner.

If Amati could teach him to make violins, Antonio would be able to make music too!

Excitedly, Antonio turned and plunged into the carnival throng, trying to find Amati. As he pushed his way through the people, his ears no longer heard the music that had filled him with longing a little while before. His only thought now was to find the violin maker.

Hours passed. Antonio sat again on the steps of the church, but now the square before him was nearly empty.

Tired and discouraged, he was about to give up his search and drag himself home, when a new thought occurred to him.

"Of course!" he cried aloud. "I will find out where Amati lives and go to his house. If he is so famous, somebody in Cremona will be able to tell me where he lives!"

It was no trouble at all to find out where Amati lived, and Antonio soon found himself before the house of the master violin maker. The windows were dark, and Antonio

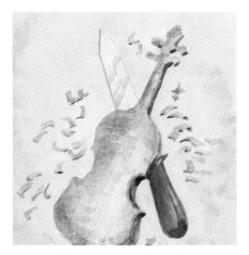

guessed that the people in the house must be asleep already.

He sat down in the doorway to wait for daybreak, and soon he too was fast asleep.

He was awakened very early the next morning by the sunlight shining into his eyes. He listened for sounds from the house, but it was still quiet.

Antonio was too excited to fall asleep again. So he pulled out his knife and began carving on the little violin that was still in his pocket.

"Just think!" he told himself. "With my knife, I have never done anything but whittle a few crude statues. But here, on the other side of this door, lives a man who, with a knife and wood, makes the most wonderful violins in Italy!"

Carving made the time pass quickly, and Antonio did not knock at the door until he had finished the tiny violin.

When he did knock, Amati came to the doorway and stood behind the servant to see who was there. "Look!" exclaimed Antonio. "I have finished it! Tell me, sir, do you think from this that I might learn to make *real* violins?"

Amati smiled, recognizing Antonio from the night before.

"Why do you wish to make violins?" he asked.

"Oh, sir!" cried Antonio. "I love music so much, and yet I cannot even sing! I would give anything to be able to make beautiful music, but all I can do is whittle!"

Amati laid his hand upon Antonio's shoulder. "There are many ways of making music," he said softly. "Making violins is one way; carving statues is another way; painting pictures is another way. Every person in the world has his own way of making music, for the song in the heart is all that matters.

"Come into my house, and you shall have a chance to see if making violins is the way for *you* to make music. If you put your heart in your work, the song you sing by carving will be as beautiful as any other song in the world."

And so Antonio Stradivari became a student of the great Amati. All his life, he tried to make each violin more nearly perfect and more beautiful than any he had ever made before.

Now, whenever people think of violins, they think of Antonio Stradivari. For he became the greatest violin maker that ever lived, not only in Italy, but in all the world.

What Do You Think?

1. Did Antonio need to be ashamed of the fact that carving was one of the few things he felt he could do? Explain your answer.
2. Why do names like "Squeaky Voice" often hurt a person's feelings?
3. What ways can you think of for making music besides those mentioned by Amati?
4. What did Amati mean when he said, "Every person in the world has his own way of making music"?

Taking a Closer Look

1. Why was Antonio sad and lonely at carnival time?
2. Why did Antonio have to quit studying violin?
3. Why did Antonio want to make violins?
4. In a complete sentence, state the main idea of this story.

Putting Ideas to Work

Learn more about the great Amati and the genius Stradivari. Write a paragraph about one of them, giving information that is not included in the story.

A Tree's a Tree, Isn't It?

John Durham

An extraordinary tree brings color to José's ordinary world.

José walked two steps behind Pearl May. He didn't want any of the guys to see him with Pearl May. She was all together. But she wasn't the type for José and the guys. She liked school, for one thing.

"If you think I'm gonna pay any bus fare, you're nuts," he told her.

She smiled, turning her face toward him. "I told you I'd pay."

"Don't even want to go."

Pearl May laughed. "You've made that absolutely clear."

"Wasting a whole day," José said. "That's the thing."

He dragged along behind Pearl May, scraping the metal taps on his heels along the walk.

They got to Fifth and turned up toward the bus stop. A cutting

November wind tugged at their coats. A sheet of newspaper rolled down the sidewalk like an armless, legless being. The paper tumbled into the street. A huge truck crushed it flat.

The two stood at the bus stop, their backs to the gritty wind.

"You picked a great day." José made a face. "Beautiful."

"It's nice and warm in the museum." Pearl May gave him one of those smiles. She had to be the best-looking girl in the neighborhood.

"Where's that bus?" José turned his face into the wind to look downtown, on Fifth.

A sudden pain hit him in the eye like a needle. The one eye hurt so much he had to close the other eye. Tears streamed down his left cheek and dripped from his jaw.

Pearl May touched his wet cheek. "What in the *world?*"

"Something in my eye."

"Well, don't rub it."

José heard the bus grind to a rushing stop near him. The wind from the bus caught at his clothes. The door hissed like a huge snake.

Pearl May took his hand. "The step's right here."

José put his foot on the step.

Pearl May took his elbow. "One more step, now."

José's toe caught on the top step, but he laid a hand against the windshield. He didn't fall.

"Watch it, kid," the bus driver said. "Don't kill yourself on my bus."

"He can't see." Pearl May's voice was angry.

The door hissed shut. The bus thundered into smoky gear and lurched away from the curb. José held onto the glass and metal fare-box.

Pearl May fell against José's back. She righted herself. José heard coins rattle into the box. Pearl May took his hand with her soft fingers.

"Let's go to the back," she said. "It's the only place I can sit next to you. The other seats all have somebody in them."

Pearl May lifted José's hand to the hold-on rail. She steadied him against the swaying of the bus. They walked, swaying, to the back of the bus.

"Poor kid," José heard a woman whisper.

José felt an odd panic rise in him. What if he were blind forever? His eye burned like bursting coals in a furnace.

454

"Here." Pearl May turned to him. "Can you feel where the thing in your eye is?"

"I think it's up under the top lid." José rolled his eye under the closed eyelid. "Sharp as a tack."

Pearl May held his face with both hands. José felt cool metal press against the aching eye.

"Now, wait a minute," he said. "What's goin' on?"

"That's my door key," Pearl May said. "I'm going to lift up your eyelid. Hold still."

José jerked his head back. She carefully took hold of his eyelashes with her fingers.

"Hold *still*."

"*Si, mamacita.*"

"Oh, hush your mouth." But they both laughed.

Pearl May pressed the key against the upper eyelid. She lifted the lid by pulling up on the eyelashes. José saw a blurry line of faces turned toward them.

He was angry with pain and embarrassment. He wanted to tell the other passengers to turn around, to mind their own business.

Pearl May caught the look on his face. "Don't pay any attention to them."

She tilted her head close to his face and looked up at his inner eyelid. "I see it," she said. "It's a little bitty piece of cinder." She sighed. "Now, I need a Kleenex." She had to let the eyelid drop to open her purse.

Then she pressed the key against the eyelid again and pulled the eye open. The piece of Kleenex coming at his eye seemed huge to José.

"Take it easy," he said.

"I'll wait till the bus stops."

At the next stop, she carefully reached for the cinder with the tip of the Kleenex.

"It's still there," José said.

"I *know* that. Hold still." She probed again with the folded Kleenex. It touched José's eyelid, inside.

The pain in José's eye suddenly was gone. It seemed his whole body had hurt. And now the pain was gone. He gave a big sigh.

Pearl May wiped the tears from his face with the Kleenex.

It took a while for his eye to clear. He saw that the bus was just a bus, with posters above the seats and gray-faced people under the posters. The street outside was just a street.

José, however, looked at it all the way a hungry person looks at a bowl of minestrone.

"Man, I'd hate to be blind."

Pearl May reached up and pulled the cord.

The bus pulled up in front of the museum. Pearl May said, "You're here and I'm here. Let's enjoy it."

"You twisted my arm."

"All I said was I'd help you with your math if you went with me."

José groaned. "I'm failing math. That's twisting my arm."

The big, warm building felt good, coming in out of the raw wind. José stared around the huge high-ceilinged lobby.

"You could fly a plane in here," he told Pearl May.

All sorts of people drifted around the lobby. A lot of good-looking college types, mixed in with old men and women. It looked like a big party that hadn't been pulled together.

Pearl May led him left, into a room full of old statues. They all looked dead to José, like just so much rock. They passed the statues and went into a section where pictures hung in rooms.

They'd stop and look at a picture. Pearl May would point out the artist's name and tell José something about the painter. But the paintings all looked dead to him. He couldn't get into it.

"I'll take baseball," he said. "Give me a good baseball game."

"Oh, come *on*. Open your eyes and look at them."

Pearl May and he were staring at a picture. Then José turned and she was gone. He almost panicked. There were so many rooms. José wanted to call her, loud. But everyone spoke in low voices.

José went through room after room of pictures. He had to twist and turn through groups of people, around odd little corners. He felt the way he had felt when he got lost in the mountains, back in Puerto Rico.

Then José came into a room that had in it only one old man with very thick glasses. The old man seemed to look at nothing. He leaned on his cane and looked inside himself.

But José saw the picture of the trees. It caught him the way a magnet catches a piece of scrap steel.

The painter had laid so much paint on the canvas that the trees looked like solid flames. They twisted upward along a country roadside

456

Cypresses

like green flames. The road and the sky above the trees were so bright they almost hurt José's eyes.

He bent to look at the name on the brass plate on the frame. *Van Gogh.*

Someone touched his arm. José jumped.

"You like it?" Pearl May said. "The van Gogh?" She said the name as if it were spelled van Go.

José shrugged.

"Van Gogh went insane," Pearl May said, thoughtful.

"No wonder. Laying out all that cash for paint."

"Now, you tell me you like that picture," Pearl May said. José shrugged. "A tree's a tree, isn't it?"

"You like it," she said. Her voice had a little song in it.

"Maybe," José said.

They left the museum and crossed the street.

José looked around with new eyes. Bricks that had been just bricks before now were a bright mix of brown and red. A passing cab blazed like a yellow flower. A girl in a bright plaid coat looked to José like a dancing pattern of lights—not just another girl.

The whole city clanged with color. José felt the way he had on the bus when the cinder came out of his eye. Everything looked new.

He and Pearl May reached the bus stop and turned their backs to the wind. It was colder now. José hunched up in his jacket.

"I *thought* you'd like that picture," Pearl May said. "I was going to show it to you. But I guess it's better you found it yourself."

José said nothing. He watched the bus swirl green and white toward them. The door whooshed open.

José took Pearl May's elbow to help her up the step.

They took seats near the driver.

"Well, did I waste your day?" Pearl May asked him.

José didn't answer. He was too busy looking at faces. White faces, he saw now, weren't white at all. They were pink, or tanned, or pink with brown spots. In fact, every face had several colors blended in it. Black and brown and white were just words, when it came to people.

"What're you thinking?" Pearl May said.

"I was thinking about that tree picture," José said. "And the French ones with all the little dots of color that make the picture. Those guys were onto something big."

Pearl May laughed softly. "Maybe you're right," she said.

What Do You Think?

1. Why do you think Pearl May wanted to take José to the museum?
2. Why did José almost panic?
3. What changed for José after he saw the picture of the trees?
4. Do you agree with Pearl May that it was better that José found the picture for himself? Why or why not?
5. What important discovery did José make as a result of his visit to the museum?
6. After visiting the museum, José felt as he had when the cinder came out of his eye. Explain the comparison.

Taking a Closer Look

1. What did Pearl May ask José to do? How did she get him to agree?
2. What happened to José just before the bus came?
3. How did Pearl May help José?
4. At first, how did everything in the museum look to José? How did this change?

Putting Ideas to Work

One of the painting techniques that José liked, using little dots of color that are mixed by the eye of the viewer to produce an effect, can be used with words too. Make a list of descriptive words and, like dots of color, put them together into a short poem that creates a picture of a scene, animal, or person.

Study SKILL

Using Information Sources

An English writer (Virginia Woolf, 1882-1941) once asked, "How shall I ever find the grains of truth embedded in all this mass of paper?" One answer is to conduct an organized search. Information sources can provide the answers you are seeking.

When you look for nonfiction information, you are doing research. Factual information can be found in reference sources. The scene of the search can be the library, school, or home. Five nonfiction sources are: (1) almanac, (2) atlas, (3) card catalog, (4) dictionary, and (5) encyclopedia.

1. An *almanac* is a reference book that is published yearly. It contains general information, in summary form, on many subjects. Use this source for facts and figures about astronomy, weather, sports, holidays, and miscellaneous historical notes.

2. An *atlas* is a book of maps. It also contains map-related information. Use this reference source to locate just about anything geographical (highways, population numbers, distances between areas, state maps, maps of countries, world maps).

3. A *card catalog* is a set of drawers in which all entries are arranged in alphabetical order on 3" x 5" file cards. Libraries usually put card catalogs in clearly visible places. To make it easier to locate information, there are three types of card systems:

a. *Author cards:* These are filed under authors' last names. They tell the titles and "call numbers" of books. Look for an author card if you know the name of an author but not the book title.

b. *Subject cards:* On these cards, the subject of a book is printed on the top line. Below that are the title, author's name, and call number of the book. Look for a subject card when you have a topic but need to find the title and author of a book.

c. *Title cards:* These cards are filed according to the first important word in the book title. (Generally, *the, a*, and *an* are not considered "important".) The title is printed on the top line of the card. Below that are the author's name and call number of the book. Look for a title card when you know the book title but not the author's name.

4. A *dictionary* contains the words of a language arranged alphabetically. Use a dictionary to find the meaning, spelling, and pronunciation of a word. Sometimes, dictionaries give other information, such as word histories, word synonyms and antonyms, abbreviations, and parts of speech.

5. An *encyclopedia* is a set of books

or one book that gives detailed information on all branches of knowledge. Encyclopedia volumes are arranged in alphabetical order. Articles within the encyclopedia tend to be arranged alphabetically by subject. There are three ways to locate information in an encyclopedia:

a. *Guide words* are located at the top of each page. They tell the first or last article on each page.
b. *Cross references* are provided at the end of articles. They tell where else to look for topic data.
c. The *index* lists all pages with topic information. Sometimes, the index is located in a separate volume.

Plan your strategy before you begin your search. Define the type of information you need to gather. If you want to learn the meaning or spelling of a word, look in the dictionary. If you want detailed information about earthquakes, look in an encyclopedia. If you want to know the World-Series scores of last year, look in an almanac. If you are looking for detailed map or population data, seek out an atlas. The card catalog can direct you to many information sources as long as you know the subject matter, the author's name, or the book title.

Keep in mind that sometimes more than one source can give you information. For example, both an encyclopedia and an almanac can tell you about the weather.

For each of the following questions, name the source(s) of information that you think would best supply the answer. Find the answers to at least four of the questions.

1. Who wrote "Don Quixote"? Did that author write other books?
2. How many states in the U.S.A. border on Canada?
3. What is a *passport*? Is a *visa* the same thing?
4. Who won the National Diving Championship last year?
5. How many books did Margaret Mead write? What are their titles?
6. How do you pronounce *potpourri*? Is potpourri something to eat?
7. What were the milestones in the development of computers? What is a *milestone*?
8. What is the largest lake in Maine? Where exactly is it located?
9. How many inches of rain fell in Los Angeles last year? Was it more or less rain than San Francisco received?
10. What is the history of the Olympic Games?

Cameras and Courage

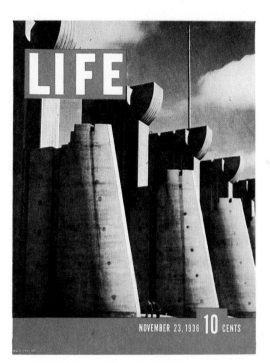

Iris Noble

When *Life* began as a picture news magazine in 1936, Margaret Bourke-White's photograph of the Fort Peck Dam in Montana was used on its first cover. She was one of the four original staff photographers for that history-making magazine. What prompted her to pursue this career?

Margaret had to find work. She had a little money saved, but not enough to see her through the whole senior year. As soon as she arrived at Cornell[1] she applied, through college channels, for a job as a waitress. "Sorry, every job is taken," she was told. "Try the student library."

She hadn't realized that there were so many other students who needed work to get them through. Thoroughly alarmed, she raced over to the student library—only to be told that those jobs, paying forty cents an hour, had been snapped up that first morning. She would be put on the waiting list, but there was little chance of a job falling vacant.

What was she to do? She had come to Cornell full of high resolve, sure that things would turn out well. Now it seemed as if she would not be able to stay beyond the first term.

---

[1]Cornell: a university in Ithaca, New York

It was a beautiful day in the town of Ithaca; the college campus more than lived up to its promises. She wandered about, looking at the lovely library Tower and the other fine buildings and the green lawns, and at last came to a waterfall and sat and looked at it. Suddenly tears welled up. She did not cry, but the tears blurred her eyesight so that the great falling waters were clouded and misty, shimmering with rainbows.

The sight was so beautiful. She dried her eyes and remembered the camera with the cracked lens that her mother had bought her three years ago. At least she could take pictures of this waterfall and Cayuga Lake and the campus buildings, so that even if she had to leave Cornell, she could carry such pictures with her always.

At that moment the idea came to her: why not make and sell such pictures? If *she* wanted to have those scenes on print to treasure always, surely others might also want them. Would they want them enough to buy them?

It was a wild idea, and she knew it. There was no guarantee that she could take artistic pictures, or that anyone would want to buy them if she did. Nevertheless, it was the only idea she had for making any money, and she determined to try it.

All that autumn, while Cornell and the surrounding countryside grew more and more beautiful with each changing month, Margaret took pictures. She wanted them to look much like paintings of the Impressionist School, and so she deliberately made dreamy, soft-focus pictures. The waterfalls gleamed through misty sprays; the sharp outlines of buildings were seen as if in twilight, shot through with the last gleams of sunset.

She remembered what she had learned in that short course at Columbia,[2] but actually she was wholly a beginner. It was not enough, she found, to point the camera at what she saw and hope to get a picture of it. The eye was selective, but the camera lens was not—unless she did the selecting for it. She learned that it was just as important to *leave out* material from a picture as it was to get it in.

---

[2]Columbia: a university in New York City, New York

Suddenly she found herself thrilling to the camera. Classes were unbearable at times, when she could see outside the classroom windows a few white clouds in a blue sky. She wanted those clouds. Any architectural structure, she felt, looked far more interesting against clouds or a partly clouded sky than it did against an empty one.

She began to "compose." Sometimes, she found, a person at the base of a building would show, by comparison, the real height of the building, while a tall structure alone might seem only ordinary. She began to realize that some of her pictures were lopsided or out of balance or too fussy, too crowded. A hill taken from the wrong distance was nothing but a small mound; lights and shadows were tricky things. But when the composition of a picture pleased her, she studied it to find out why. She saw that she had selected out of a broad landscape that portion of it that best expressed the mood, that she had balanced her picture, that she had emphasized one or two things and that her picture had a sharp focal point of interest.

Maddening as many of her mistakes were, and costly as they were, she kept on. The camera began, slowly, to seem to be just an extension of her fingers and her eyes. But it was hard work, just the same.

She could not afford to have experts clean and service her camera, and so she learned to take it apart and do everything herself. She could not afford to have her film processed by others, but she arranged with a Mr. Head, a commercial photographer in Ithaca, to allow her to use his darkroom at nights, to develop and enlarge her prints.

After Mr. Head had finished his own work for the evening, she was free to use his facilities, although she paid for her own developing solutions and other materials. She learned her way around his darkroom. She could remove her own film, wash it and immerse it in developing solution, stir it gently at intervals of a minute, drain the developing solution back into a bottle so as not to waste it and pour in the fixer. Not until later, when the film was being washed in tap water and when it was hung up to dry, could she sit and munch an apple and study for her lessons for the next day.

The hours grew very late, but she had such splendid health and energy that she was rarely tired. It was not easy to concentrate on lessons, but that was only because she was so eager to see how good or bad her picture would turn out to be.

Then came the printing on paper and the enlarging. All of this took time and learning and effort. Her darkroom technique did not yet equal her growing talent with the camera, although she was becoming at ease with acids and various solutions. She made all the usual mistakes, such as opening the door into the darkroom and letting in light to ruin her negatives, but she made that mistake only once. Never again.

Just before Christmas she carefully selected her best enlarged photographs and placed them on a table-booth in front of the dormitory dining room. A hand-lettered price list beside them announced that she would take orders for any prints desired. To her enormous astonishment, the orders came in so fast that she could not write fast enough or rake in the money fast enough.

She telephoned Mr. Head to start printing and she would pay him; then she went back to taking more orders. And every night she helped Mr. Head in the darkroom.

466

The sum she earned was large, and now she made what was nearly a mistake. Since she had done so well in so short a time with the students who had passed her order-table, surely she would do just as well in January and February with all the students she had missed this first time who had not yet seen her samples. What she failed to take into account was that the sale had been a seasonal one and the pictures were bought for Christmas presents.

During January no one would buy. They had spent all their Christmas money. The prints were piled up in stacks in Margaret's room, and much of the money she had earned had gone to pay for the materials for them and for Mr. Head's work.

Still, she could not resist going on to make more and more pictures. It was becoming an excitement she could not forgo. Winter, when the ice formed on the waterfalls and snow covered the campus, blanketing trees and roofs of buildings, brought out an irresistible itch in her to photograph everything she saw.

Winter did something else for her. It cured her of trying for the soft-focus, romantic, blurry film that imitated paintings or made everything "pretty." The stark white of snow and the clean, dark edges of buildings and the sudden relief of black shadow were too beautiful to be disguised.

She was becoming fascinated by what the camera could do, not what it could imitate or pretend to do. She was also finding drama and beauty in objects not ordinarily considered either dramatic or beautiful. Anyone could appreciate a waterfall, but Margaret could make a striking picture of an icicle hanging from the eave above a window.

The day came when she looked about Mr. Head's commercial studio and saw that, while her bad pictures were awful, her best were better than any of his. Also, hers were selling again—so well, in fact, that she hired student salespeople to work for her. The undergraduates wanted to display romantic Cornell to their friends at spring break, and seniors wanted them for keepsakes.

What was even more thrilling was that the *Alumni News*, a

magazine sent all over the world to Cornell alumni, bought a picture of a different campus building from her every single month for the cover, paying her five dollars for each. The five dollars was fine, but those cover pictures gave her an entirely new idea of her camera work.

Cornell graduate architects, working at their professions throughout the country, saw those pictures of buildings and wrote to her. They said that she was an exceptionally talented architectural photographer and there were few good ones around. Was she going to take this up as a career?

Such a thought had never occurred to her. An architectural photographer? She hadn't planned to be any kind of a photographer. It was now close to graduation, and she had been offered a job by the Curator of Herpetology[3] at the Museum of Natural History in New York. For this she had studied and trained. Could she give this up for a career with a camera? Did she want to?

The answer was yes. Margaret had found that photography was becoming a passion with her, superseding her old interests.

The problem was to find out if she could make more than just a living at it. The usual sort of photographer was someone, like Mr. Head who had a small studio in a small town, making a precarious living taking wedding portraits and school class pictures. She wanted more than that. If she was to venture into architectural photography, she needed the opinion of an expert. If the verdict was favorable, then she'd risk the new venture and turn down the museum offer.

She went to New York to the office of Benjamin Moskowitz, of the architectural firm of York and Sawyer, and asked the receptionist to be allowed to see Mr. Moskowitz. No, she had no appointment. All she had was the big portfolio of pictures she was carrying.

The receptionist shrugged and shook her head. It was late. The offices were closing soon. Mr. Moskowitz was just about to

---

[3]herpetology (hèr′pə tol′ə jē): branch of zoology dealing with reptiles and amphibians

468

leave. As a matter of fact, at that moment he came striding past, with his coat on and his briefcase in hand. He was much annoyed to be interrupted on his way home by this young woman, who kept getting in front of him to show him some pictures, and he told her frankly that it was too late. He edged by her and went to the hall and the elevator, with Margaret trailing behind him and pleading with him.

The elevator was late arriving. She maneuvered around so that she could slide her opened portfolio between Mr. Moskowitz and the elevator door at which he was staring. He had to look. The first picture was of the science building. Margaret let him see that and then turned the page over to the picture of the library Tower.

The elevator arrived. The door opened. Mr. Moskowitz ignored it. He was gazing wide-eyed at her portfolio. "Did you take those pictures?" he demanded. When she said yes, he turned on his heel and ordered her: "Bring those and come back to my office!"

What Do You Think?

1. Why did Margaret make dreamy, soft-focus pictures at first?
2. Why was her first attempt to sell her photographs so successful?
3. Why did Margaret's photographic style change?
4. Why did Margaret decide to become a photographer instead of working for the Museum of Natural History?

Taking a Closer Look

1. What was Margaret's reaction to the Cornell campus?
2. What idea did she get to earn some money for her last year at college?
3. What mistakes did she make at first?
4. Where did she get the idea of becoming an architectural photographer?
5. How did she get an executive at an architectural firm to look at her work?

Putting Ideas to Work

What kind of conversation do you think Margaret and Mr. Moskowitz had? Write a page of dialogue for them as they looked through Margaret's portfolio.

the artist

Isabelle C. Chang

There was once a king who loved the graceful curves of the rooster. He asked the court artist to paint a picture of a rooster for him. For one year he waited and still this order was not fulfilled. In a rage, he stomped into the studio and demanded to see the artist.

Quickly the artist brought out paper, paint, and brush. In five minutes a perfect picture of a rooster emerged from his skillful brush. The king turned purple with anger, saying, "If you can paint a perfect picture of a rooster in five minutes, why did you keep me waiting for over a year?"

"Come with me," begged the artist. He led the king to his storage room. Paper was piled from the floor to the ceiling. On every sheet was a painting of a rooster.

"Your Majesty," explained the artist, "it took me more than one year to learn how to paint a perfect rooster in five minutes."

Life is short, art is long.

The Pottery of Maria Martinez

Ellen Anne Jones

Great things take time. How does the pottery of Maria Martinez combine a mastery of the past with a spark of the present?

At the time of this writing, Maria Martinez is almost a hundred years old. She isn't sure of her exact age. She only knows that she was born sometime in the 1880s. To Maria, time doesn't mean much; the things that do matter are her family and the customs of her tribe. In the village of San Ildefonso in New Mexico, Maria Martinez and her family carry on the old Pueblo art of pottery-making. For the high beauty of her pottery and for her own special contributions to this craft, Maria Martinez has become famous.

She learned how to make pottery by watching her aunt Nicholassa at work. When still a child, Maria began to turn raw lumps of clay into beautiful pots. By the time she was a young woman, she had already become a skilled potter.

Then, in 1908, archaeologists working near San Ildefonso dug up some unusual pieces of ancient Indian pottery. The fragments were black, with a soft sheen. The archaeologists brought the pieces to Maria, in hopes that she could make pots like the ancient ones. Maria had never seen pottery with quite the same color and luster. But she decided to try to duplicate it.

In traditional Pueblo pottery-making, there are several steps.

First, the right kind of clay must be found. The clay is purified and then mixed with other substances to give it hardness and durability. Water is added to this mixture, and the pot is shaped while the clay is damp. After the pot has dried, it is sanded to remove roughness. Then a second layer of wet clay, called the "slip," is applied to the outside of the pot. The clay in the slip is different from the basic clay in the pot. The slip contains substances that will give the pot its color. There are several varieties of slip clay, each giving a different shade.

While the slip is still wet, the potter must polish it with a smooth stone. If the pot is to be painted with a design, this decoration is done after the slip dries. Finally, in a process called "firing," the pot is heated to a very high temperature. Firing brings out the pot's colors, strengthens the pot, and hardens its finish.

In trying to make new pots with the unusual black color, Maria began by following this same basic procedure. After shaping the pots, she applied a clay slip that usually turns red during firing. Normally, the pots are heated by a fire that is allowed to burn freely. But this time, Maria experimented. After the pots had been heated awhile, she suddenly smothered the fire.

When Maria pulled the pots from the fire, she saw that she had achieved her goal. Smothering the fire had made the clay slip turn black instead of red. Her pottery was the same color as the old fragments. But there was one important difference. Maria's pots were much more beautiful than the ancient pieces.

What began as a single experiment ended up becoming a lifelong endeavor. Maria continued to make the black pottery. Helped by her husband, Julian, she perfected the process by which the clay pots acquire their richly gleaming, black finish. She and her art became famous. Museums all over the world now display bowls, plates, boxes, and vases made by Maria Martinez. Pots that, years ago, she sold for a few dollars have recently become almost priceless.

Today Maria Martinez lives a quiet life in San Ildefonso. She is a member of the Tewa tribe, and she works to pass on its culture to the young people of her pueblo. In particular, she has taught many younger members of her family the art of making pottery. Her son Adam and daughter-in-law Santana are masters of the craft. And the pottery of Barbara Gonzales, Maria's great-granddaughter, is becoming famous in its own right.

Barbara's own children now watch her as she makes pottery. They are beginning to learn the art. The craft of Maria Martinez, partly Pueblo tradition and partly her own unique contribution, will live on.

In 1910, when this photograph was taken, Maria was a young woman. Her work was already beginning to be well known.

The red color of the bowl on the left (below) is typical of much Pueblo pottery. This shade is produced when posts are heated over a free-burning fire. Air circulates among the pots. Oxygen in the air combines with substances in the clay slip, and the red color results. In the heating of the pot on the right, however, the fire is smothered at a certain point. This makes the pottery turn black instead of red.

Photographs on pages 474-481 from the *Living Legend of Maria Martinez* by Susan Peterson, published by Kodansha International.

At her own house, Maria shows some of her great-grandchildren how to make pottery. The children learn by watching, just as Maria did when she was a child. Perhaps they will someday teach the craft to their own daughters and sons.

The clay that goes into the pots is found in the hills near the pueblo. Santana and Adam Martinez here dig up some of this clay. There are many different kinds of clay in the area of San Ildefonso, each producing a different quality of pottery. If the pot is to turn out well, the clay must be the right kind.

Santana mixes purified, dried clay with volcanic ash. The ash strengthens the pottery. Without it, the pottery would not be durable enough to withstand the heat of firing.

Santana makes a well in the center of the clay-ash mixture. Then she pours water into the hole (left). With her hands, she mixes the water and the clay (below). She kneads and pats it until the clay becomes soft and smooth. The wet clay is usually allowed to rest for a day. Then it is ready to be molded.

476

The smooth, moist clay is patted into a pancake shape. Santana will then press this onto a puki, *or mold. The* puki *provides support for the wet clay as it is being shaped into a pot. There are many different sizes and shapes of* puki.

The edges of the flat clay base are pinched up. The sides are built by adding coils of clay. Santana first makes a coil (above).

Then, by attaching the coil to the base, she begins to build up the sides. After the coil is added, the clay is smoothed.

Coil after coil, Santana builds up the pot. It is a very slow process. The potter needs a great deal of skill—and patience—to get the exact shape and thickness desired. After the pot has been shaped, it must dry for at least a week. Then it will be scraped and sanded until it is smooth.

478

To give color and sheen to the pot, a special clay cover, or slip, must be applied. Clay for the slip is mixed with water until it becomes a paste. The dry pot is coated with this clay paste. As shown, the wet clay slip is next polished with a smooth stone.

After the polished slip has dried, the pot may be decorated. Santana paints a design on a pot. The brush she uses is made from part of the yucca plant, which grows wild near the pueblo.

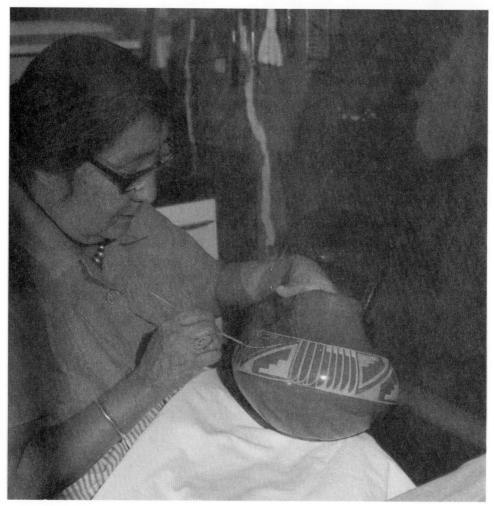

Now it is time for the pots to be fired. Santana carefully stacks them on a fireproof rack. Underneath the rack is wood for the fire. The pots will be covered loosely with pieces of metal, including old license plates. These will hold the heat in, but will not stop air from circulating.

After the fire has burned freely for a time, it is smothered. The fire smolders, because it has been deprived of oxygen. If the fire hadn't been smothered, the resulting pots would be red. Now they will be black.

At last, very carefully, the gleaming pieces of pottery must be removed from the hot pile of ashes (left).

Santana wipes the pots and dishes to remove the ash. They now have the characteristic black luster. The process of pottery-making, begun by digging clay, is now finished.

What Do You Think?

1. How has Maria Martinez's family and background been important in her art?
2. How does this story demonstrate the timelessness of art?
3. This type of story is called a "photo essay." How does the combination of photographs and captions contribute to your understanding of the pottery-making process?

Taking a Closer Look

1. What special contribution has Maria Martinez made to the art of pottery-making?
2. How did she learn pottery-making?
3. What is the difference between the slip clay and the basic clay for the pottery?
4. List the steps involved in the traditional process of making Pueblo pottery.
5. What special step turns the pots black instead of red?

Putting Ideas to Work

Create a photo essay. Choose a topic of interest, then collect photographs from magazines and newspapers. Arrange them in a logical order and write an explanatory caption for each.

How to Use the Yellow Pages

The Yellow Pages are the most helpful tool when it comes to locating places of business or products and services you may need.

To find things quickly, easily, use these time savers:

Product or service

Headings are always alphabetical. Think of the heading most likely to list what you want. Flip to it and you'll find names, addresses, and phone numbers of business people ready to serve you.

Forgotten the name?

Again, turn to the heading that best describes the firm's type of business. Glancing down the list will usually bring the name back to mind.

Brand names

Turn to the heading, then look for the trademark or trade name. Usually you'll find it listed—and in the advertisements carried under that heading.

Call ahead

You can save time by calling ahead to be sure the store has what you want. Ask them about delivery services.

Emergencies

Use the Yellow Pages to find out who can handle your emergency. For example, some of the headings include Physicians and Plumbers.

1. What three items are listed for all businesses and services?
2. What is another advantage to calling a store before you go there, other than to make sure the product is available? Can you think of others?
3. How are headings listed?
4. How do you locate a place or product if you cannot remember its name?
5. Under what headings would you look for the following:
   Dr. Wilbur Jenkins, M.D.
   Brando's Moving and Storage
   Quality Pest Control, Inc.
   Napoli Pizza Parlor
   Beauty and Flowers, Inc.
   Wheel & Spoke Bike Shop
   Ye Olde Donut Shoppe
   Dr. Flo Sanders, D.D.S.

There are two types of material in the Yellow Pages. There are alphabetical listings for categories of goods and services, and there are ads placed by businesses. Ads are to attract your attention. Look at the listings and ads on the next page. How well can you use the Yellow Pages?

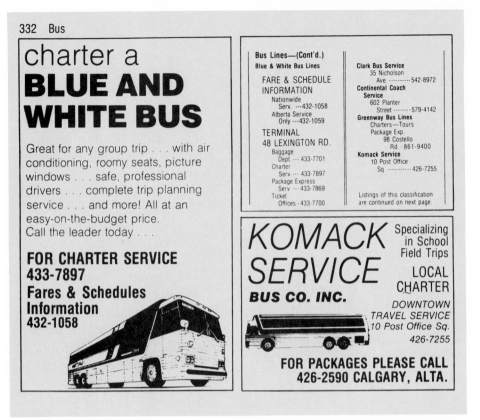

1. What is the difference between the information given in the ads and the information given in the alphabetical listings?
2. What are the advantages of having ads as well as listings?
3. If your class needed a bus for a school trip, which bus lines could you call for information?
4. What number would you call at Blue & White for lost baggage?
5. The ad for Blue & White Bus Lines gives only two telephone numbers, but the alphabetical listing has many more. Why?
6. Suppose the birthday of a member of your family was coming up soon. How would you use the Yellow Pages of your local directory to help you find the items listed below? Make a list of the places from your local Yellow Pages that can help you carry out your plans. Try to select places within the same area of town to save time. Be ready to give reasons for your selections.
Florist—*flowers*
Gift shops—*a present*
Greeting cards—*birthday card*
Restaurants—*Chinese dinner*

An Artist in Harlem

Romare Bearden and Harry Henderson

A poor, street-wise boy from New York proves in this story that art touches every part of human life.

Jacob Lawrence, The Migration of the Negro *(1940-1941). "In the North, the Negro had better educational facilities." No. 58. Tempera on gesso on composition board, 18" x 12". Collection, the Museum of Modern Art, New York. Gift of Mrs. David M. Levy.*

When the Lawrences moved to Harlem, Mrs. Lawrence was worried about her son Jacob. She was still at work when he came home from school. Although he was a quiet and serious boy, she was afraid that Jake, as everyone called him, would join a gang of wild boys in his search for new friends.

Nearly twelve years old, Jake was finding Harlem exciting. Everything seemed to happen on its streets. There were children playing games, families sitting on the steps of brownstones, gangs of boys everywhere.

Jake had been born in Atlantic City, New Jersey, on September 7, 1917. His father was a cook on railroad dining cars, and his job kept him moving from one city to another. During this moving about, Jake's parents separated. Finally Mrs. Lawrence and Jake moved to New York City. Although the big city had more jobs for black people, the Depression was just beginning, and Mrs. Lawrence barely managed to make ends meet.

She made up her mind to keep Jake "off the streets." One day she learned that a settlement house had classes in arts and crafts after school, so she enrolled Jake.

Charles Alston, a thin young man later to become a leading black artist himself, was in charge. He suggested that Jake could carve soap, work with carpenter's tools, weave baskets, draw, or paint.

"Can I color with crayons?" asked Jake.

"Of course," said Alston as he gave Jake a large box of crayons. "Draw what you like."

Soon Jake was drawing triangles, squares, and circles, each a different color. He delighted in working with patterns that often looked like those in his mother's rugs, but the bold colors were his own. Then Jake began to see different patterns all around him—the windows in buildings, people sitting around a table, the subway steps, the legs of people walking, fire escapes.

Alston was impressed with Jake's work and he was pleased that Jake didn't ask, "What should I do next, teacher?" Jake had ideas of his own. His questions were about *how* to do something. Alston decided it would be a mistake to try to teach Jake. Jake was teaching himself, finding his own way, and all the boy needed was a little encouragement.

Watching Jake develop, Alston became convinced that this quiet boy was one of the most naturally gifted artists he had ever seen. He proudly showed Jake's work to his artist friends in Harlem, and soon they too were encouraging young Jake Lawrence.

By this time Jake had outgrown the after-school program. He was now a high-school teenager, hunting eagerly for odd jobs. The Depression had become worse, and his mother had lost her job, so Jake signed up in the CCC. In a camp in northern New York State, Jake went to work with the CCC. Living out in the country, the workers planted trees, drained swamps, cleared dead trees from forests, and built dams.

Jacob Lawrence. Tombstones *(1942). Gouache on paper. 28¾" x 20½". Collection of Whitney Museum of American Art. Purchase. Acq. No. 43.14.*

The Depression got worse and worse, and millions more were out of work. To provide jobs, President Franklin D. Roosevelt started the WPA, which paid thousands of workers to build schools, hospitals, post offices, roads, and airports. They also set up theaters for actors and made jobs for writers and artists.

In Harlem some fifteen hundred people were attending art centers. There, for the first time, many black people learned that they had talented artists in their midst. One art center was directed by the sculptor Augusta Savage; another by Charles Alston, Jake's former teacher.

When Jake returned from the CCC, he went one day to an art center where he stopped at the door of a crowded meeting room. The speaker was saying that black people should know their own history and be proud of it. Describing the great things that black people had done in Africa, he told about the golden city of Timbuktu and the art treasures of the Benin in Nigeria.

"Who's talking?" asked Jake.

"Don't you know? That's Charles Seyfert."

Charles Seyfert had collected a sizable library on Africans and the contributions of black people to American life. His talks were the first of the "black studies" programs, and many Harlem people came regularly to listen to him.

Seyfert's talks were just what Jake Lawrence and other Harlem young people were looking for. Seyfert gave to these young persons a sense of pride, and soon Jake was reading

Jacob Lawrence, The Migration of the Negro *(1940-1941). "And the Migrants Kept Coming." No. 60. Tempera on gesso on composition board, 18" x 12". Collection, The Museum of Modern Art, New York. Gift of Mrs. David. M. Levy.*

Jacob Lawrence, The Migration of the Negro *(1940-1941). "One of the largest race riots occurred in St. Louis." No. 52. Tempera on gesso on composition board, 18" x 12". Collection, The Museum of Modern Art, New York. Gift of Mrs. David M. Levy.*

and studying black history. The vocational high school he attended provided none of this satisfaction in its courses on bookkeeping.

Jake left high school after his second year to devote more time to reading black history. This worried his mother, who had hoped that knowing bookkeeping would help Jake get a good job, but Jake was excited by what he was learning from Seyfert. He read avidly about anything or anyone that this unusual teacher mentioned—great African empires, black inventors, the Underground Railroad, Benjamin Banneker, black soldiers in the American Revolution and the Civil War.

Then in 1935 the Museum of Modern Art exhibited sculpture from West Africa. Seyfert took groups of Harlem artists there, but Jake missed going with a group and went alone. The carved figures greatly excited him. They were made by black people who did not know the art of the Western world, yet the carved figures were art also. Jake studied them carefully, and when he returned home, he got some blocks and made two small wooden sculptures. "I didn't have regular carving tools, so I whittled more than I carved," he recalled. "The show made a great impression on me." For weeks afterward the young Harlem artist talked of it.

Seyfert's talks helped Jake feel he was part of the past and present problems of black people, and he poured his deep feelings into his paintings. His work was increasingly winning the praise of other Harlem artists.

Yet Jake actually had less and less time to paint; he was too busy hurrying around trying to earn money. He delivered laundry, ran errands, and worked for a small printer who turned out notices and business cards.

One day the sculptor Augusta Savage learned from Jake that he hadn't been painting. Taking him by the arm, she headed down the street. "Where are we going?" asked Jake.

"To the WPA headquarters! We're going to get you on the artists' project. You're an artist, and you ought to be painting and getting paid for it."

At the WPA office Jake's application was turned down because he was not yet twenty-one years of age. Jake only shrugged. He hadn't really believed he was going to get on the project, but Augusta Savage had made up her mind. "I'm going to get you on that project," she said.

Jake forgot about it. By saving his money, he bought a newspaper delivery route. He gradually came to think of painting as something he would do as a hobby, and he was beginning to see he needed an education to get better paying jobs. As one job played out, he found another. But one day, when he dropped into the Harlem Art Center, Augusta Savage said, "Come on, Jake. We're going to the WPA again. You're old enough now!"

She had kept track of Jake's birthday. A year had already passed. It was July 1938, and Jake was nearly twenty-one. This time he was accepted as an artist and given a job. He could paint at home and was provided with materials and paid $23.86 a week. In return he had to complete two paintings every six weeks.

Later, looking back, Jake said, "If Augusta Savage hadn't insisted on getting me on the project, I would never have become an artist. It was a real turning point for me."

Today one of America's best-known artists, Jacob Lawrence has taught in the nation's leading art schools. He began by making colorful patterns, and his work now hangs in museums all over the United States.

What Do You Think?

1. "Alston decided it would be a mistake to try to teach Jake. Jake was teaching himself, finding his own way." Can you think of any other kinds of learning in which this rule would apply? Explain your answer.
2. Which of the paintings reproduced with this article do you like best? Tell why.
3. Do you think it would be easier to learn to be a painter in the city or the country? Explain your answer.
4. In what way did the Depression help Lawrence develop as an artist?

Taking a Closer Look

1. Why was Jake's mother concerned about keeping him "off the streets"?
2. Why did Mrs. Lawrence enroll Jake in art and craft classes?
3. Why was Charles Alston impressed and pleased with Jake's artwork?
4. How did Augusta Savage influence the art career of Jacob Lawrence?

Putting Ideas to Work

Create a picture of your own using bold colors and the shapes and patterns you see in your classroom. When you finish, show your work to a classmate.

CHOOSING A SUBJECT

How does an artist choose a subject? What inspires artists to use their talents? Two Christian artists and the source of their inspiration are discussed in the following articles.

The Story behind the Painting

Warner Sallman

Many times I have been asked how I happened to paint the *Head of Christ* that has received so wide circulation since it appeared as a painting in 1940.

"Did you have a vision beforehand?" they ask.

"Did you feel Christ's presence?"

"Did you have some kind of religious experience?"

The answer is Yes to all these questions, but the real story behind the picture begins with a change that took place in my life shortly after my wedding.

When I married Ruth Anderson, an attractive and dedicated choir member and organist, back in May 1916, I was twenty-five years old, was employed as an artist in the field of men's fashions, and was prospering financially. In all, it seemed like a cloudless sky, but the storm clouds already were forming below the horizon.

◄ *Sallman's* Head of Christ, *reproduced by permission of the copyright owners, Kriebel & Bates, Inc.*

493

Years before, I had had a tumor in my shoulder but a surgeon had removed it and it apparently was healed. Then came a major complication in the same area. By the following spring, 1917, the pain was acute. I went to several doctors and took various treatments, but the affliction grew worse. Finally, I consulted a specialist who made extensive tests.

"You're pretty sick, my boy," he said kindly.

"Tell me the whole truth, doctor," I replied. "I ought to know what's wrong with me."

"You have tuberculosis of the lymph glands," he continued. "I recommend surgery." He hesitated a moment, took my arm, then continued. "Otherwise I cannot give you much beyond three months."

The physician's words jolted me severely. I left his office in a daze, and with uncertain step made my way to a streetcar. On the car I moved up until I was close to the motorman, feeling some protection in his presence. It gave me an opportunity to do a little thinking.

"What shall I do?" I asked myself. "Shall I tell Ruth the whole truth or conceal what the doctor said until after the baby is born?" It was July, and our first little one was due in September. I feared the revelation would so upset her that serious complications might develop.

Warner and Ruth Sallman

I prayed for guidance, and believe God was directly speaking to me when the conviction suddenly came over me that "Ruth is brave, has a deep faith, and can take it. I'll tell her all."

This I did, not minimizing the "three months to live." Ruth received my words with utmost calm—a feeling came over me that she was like a rock and that through her the Lord would guide us aright.

"Let God's peace come into your heart, Warner," she told me, putting her arms around my neck and looking squarely into my face, her eyes aglow with love. "We'll pray, and whatever is God's will for us, we gladly will do it. In three months we can do a lot for Him, and if it be His will to spare our life together for a longer period, we will thank Him for it and go ahead serving Him."

I do not remember the words we used in our prayer together, but I do know we did *not* ask for a longer life span. We only asked God to guide and bless and use us. The heart of our prayer was a plea reminiscent of our Saviour's in Gethsemane: "Dear Lord, we pray that Thy will be our will, and that in all ways Thy will be done."

In no manner did we forgo medical or surgical help, but we felt that if the latter was to be for me, God would make it known. We continued the medical treatments as before, but no revelation came regarding the proposed surgery.

However, something else did happen; by the alchemy of nature or in the providence of God, the pain gradually grew less, and there were signs of amelioration of the disease. It took months, but complete healing finally took place. We do not minimize the powerful influence of mind over matter—we implicitly believe the Lord can and does heal.

What better proof can there be than that the predicted three months have stretched into forty-four busy, fruitful and happy years, with the added blessing of three sons born to our union and that now, as I near the seventy-year mark, I feel almost as vigorous as ever, am well occupied with my work and have the joy of Ruth's unfailing companionship?

Yet the important part of this experience is not that I was healed, but that I learned an exciting and dynamic principle.

When we turn our lives over to God, without reservation, He can and will do remarkable things through us.

It was this personal philosophy that made it possible for me to do the *Head of Christ.* It began as an assignment from a small Christian youth publication in January 1924, for a cover design. I thought to do the face of Christ. My first attempts were all wrong. Finally there were only twenty-four hours until delivery date. I tried again and again the preceding evening, but the impressions that came to my mind were futile. I felt disturbed and frustrated.

I went to bed at midnight, restless in spirit but did ask God once more to give me the vision I needed. Suddenly about two o'clock I came out of my fitful attempts at sleep with a clear, beautiful image of the head of Christ startlingly vivid in my mind. I hastened to my attic studio to record it. I made a thumb-nail sketch so the details of the dream might be captured before fading out of my mind. Next morning I made a charcoal drawing of it.

This *Head of Christ* hardly caused a ripple of comment when it first appeared, but in 1940 I made an oil painting of the "head" and in the years since, its distribution has attained phenomenal proportions. Yet I always think of the portrayal as something God did—through me.

For Ruth and I believe that as good disciples of Christ our task is primarily seed-sowing of good deeds, good thoughts, and good purposes.

Yet we are human enough to enjoy hearing or knowing of results, strong and unpredictable, accompanying our labors. For instance there was a recent incident in Los Angeles. A robber rang the doorbell to an apartment.

When the lady opened the door, he thrust a revolver in her face and snapped, "This is a hold-up. Give me your money and jewelry!"

Just then he looked up and saw behind the woman a large picture on the wall. It was the *Head of Christ.* For a moment he seemed to freeze. Slowly he lowered his gun.

"I can't do it, lady," he gasped. "Not in front of that picture." And he turned and ran down the stairs.

Praying Hands

Albrecht Dürer was born in Nuremburg. At fifteen, Albrecht was apprenticed to Michel Wohgemuth, a local artist who painted altar pictures. Four years later he crossed the Alps into Italy where he worked and studied. He was greatly influenced by the Italian masters and is credited with bringing the Italian style of painting into Germany and other northern European countries.

In 1497 he returned to Nuremburg where he set up his own studio. From this time on he lived a life of devotion to art and literature. He was very German in his attention to detail, yet all parts of his pictures fit together smoothly. They have the feeling of largeness and a simple grandeur. Nuremburg is famous for the woodcarvings done there, and perhaps this is the reason why Dürer's greatest expression is felt in his woodcuts. He received many royal favors in his lifetime. Ill health plagued him during the last few years of his life. He died in 1528.

Albrecht Dürer, A Man in a Fur Coat. Isabella Stewart Gardner Museum, Boston.

Albrecht Dürer, the artist who painted *Praying Hands*, was the son of a Hungarian goldsmith who was born in Nuremburg, Germany. Because of his very large family and lack of money, Dürer was obliged to work at his father's trade while he was a young boy. Always he wanted to draw and paint. Finally he was allowed to leave home and to go away to study with a great artist. Because he was very poor, it was hard for Dürer to study and make a living at the same time. During these days of struggle Albrecht Dürer found a friend, a man somewhat older than himself, who also had a desire to become a great artist. The two of them decided to live together, and one day when the struggle to earn enough food had discouraged both of them almost to the point of giving up their dreams, Dürer's friend made a suggestion.

"This way of working and trying to study," he said, "is intolerable. We are neither making a living, nor are we mastering our art. Let us try another way. One of us could make a living for us both while the other continued to study. Then when the paintings begin to sell, the one who has worked may have his chance."

"True," answered Dürer thoughtfully, "but let me be the one to work."

"No, I must be the one to work, because I already have a place to work in the restaurant. I am older, and I have not so much talent. Let it be as I say."

So the older man had his way. Albrecht Dürer worked faithfully to master his art while his friend worked at any kind of labor he could find to buy them food and to pay for their mean little room. He served in the restaurant, washed dishes, and scrubbed floors to add to the small sum he was paid. His hours were long and the work was menial and hard, but he did it cheerfully because he was helping his young friend and looking forward to the time when he would be able to use his brush again.

At last the day came when Albrecht Dürer came home bringing the money that he had received for the sale of a woodcarving. It was sufficient to buy food and to pay their rent for a considerable length of time.

Albrecht Dürer, Praying Hands. *Courtesy of the Albertina Museum, Vienna, Austria.* ➤

"Now," he said, "the time has come when I will be the breadwinner, and you shall go to your paints, my good friend. You need no longer work, for I will care for both of us."

So his good friend left his serving and dishwashing and scrubbing and took up his brush. But something had happened in those days during which he had worked so hard with his hands. The hard work had stiffened his muscles, enlarged his joints, and twisted his fingers so that they would no longer hold the brush with mastery and skill. He worked long and hard, only to find that his art would have to be sacrificed forever.

When Albrecht learned what had happened to his friend, he was filled with a great sorrow. Of course he would always care for him and give him a friend's love, but he could not give him back his skill. One day Albrecht returned to his room unexpectedly and heard the voice of his friend in prayer. He entered softly, and seeing the work-worn hands folded reverently, a great thought came to him.

I can never give back the lost skill of those hands, he thought, but I can show the world the feeling of love and gratitude which is in my heart for his noble deed. I will paint his hands as they are *now*, folded in prayer, and the world shall know my appreciation for a noble, unselfish character. It may be that when people look at the picture they will remember with love and devotion all hands that toil for others and like me express in some beautiful way their appreciation for such beautiful service.

As we look at the picture we can read the story. Look at these toil-worn hands. You can see evidences of the hard labor that earned the living for both artists. Notice the broken fingernails and the enlarged joints. Yet in spite of these disfigurements, are they not beautiful hands? Let us think silently of other toil-worn hands the world around that have labored to make things easier for others as we look at Dürer's picture of *Praying Hands*, and try to feel as the artist must have felt when he decided to paint the hands of his friend at prayer.

500

What Do You Think?

1. Which picture do you find more appealing, interesting, or artistic, *Head of Christ* or the *Praying Hands?* Explain your choice.
2. How do you think Dürer's friend felt when he found that he could no longer paint? Think of at least five words to describe his feelings.
3. If you could rename the painting, *Praying Hands,* what would you call it?
4. In your own words summarize the influences that caused Sallman to sketch the *Head of Christ.*
5. In what ways is there a parallel between *Praying Hands* and the quotation "Greater love has no man than this, that a man lay down his life for his friends"? John 15:13 RSV.

Taking a Closer Look

1. For what form of art was Nuremburg famous?
2. What happened in Warner Sallman's life that changed him?
3. How was Ruth Sallman, his wife, like a rock?
4. Are visions given to artists in the same way they are given to prophets? Explain your answer.

God is the author of all beauty.
—*Ellen G. White*

He hath made everything beautiful in its time.
—*Eccl. 3:11 RSV*

It is right to love beauty and to desire it.
—*Ellen G. White*

504

Reserved for Mark Anthony Crowder

Alison Smith

Chapter 1

Mrs. Prescott reached for the atlas. It was on the top shelf in the class library, as usual. Mark Anthony pulled himself down into his seat till his chin hovered two inches above his desk. He opened his math book and stared at the page, even though it was so close to the end of his nose the words were all blurred.

"Mark Anthony."

It was no use. "Yes, ma'am?"

"You're so nice and tall. Get that atlas down for me, would you?"

Mark Anthony groaned inside himself and stood up. As he walked down the aisle, he could hear the words hissing out behind him. "Mark Anthony's so nice and tall."

He reached for the atlas and handed it to Mrs. Prescott.

"Thank you, Mark Anthony."

The echoes followed him down the aisle, soft and with a snigger of laughter in them. "Thank you, Mark Anthony. Mark Anthony's sweet."

He sat down, staring at his math book, feeling his face burning. Anger filled him and pounded in his ears. If only she wouldn't ask him to help her like that. She was a nice woman, and she meant well, but every time she called on him like that, the kids gave him a hard time. Besides, he wasn't the only tall kid in the eighth grade. Lots of the girls were almost as tall as he was. But no—every time—"Mark Anthony, you're so nice and tall. . . ."

It hadn't helped that he'd always gotten good grades, either. It had made it worse. So, for the last six weeks he'd been really coasting—not much homework, no more speaking up in class, and no great effort on tests. Mrs. Prescott had noticed. She'd made a couple of comments about mental laziness and glanced in his direction.

The bell rang, and he got up instantly. He could go home. He gathered up all his books and headed out the door, toward the school-bus parking area.

Earl Jones caught up with him in the corridor. Earl was short. He was lucky. And he didn't have to wear glasses—

thick ones, like headlight lenses. Doubly lucky. He was Mark Anthony's best friend, his only friend, really, at school, and Mark Anthony had moved to Ridgedale a year ago.

"Let's go to the playground for a while before we go home. The guys are getting up a softball game."

"OK," Mark Anthony said, and felt his stomach tighten with apprehension.

"I'm going to catch for Brian's team. Come on."

Mark Anthony followed Earl as he slipped through the crowds in the corridor.

Outside, the spring sun was hot and blindingly bright, after the dim coolness of the school halls.

Mark Anthony set down his jacket and his books in a corner of the playground and followed Earl out to the softball diamond. The fellows were choosing up sides. This was the part he hated—the very worst part.

"Mark Anthony will be on our team," Earl said to Brian. "He can hold down first base."

Brian spat on the dusty ground.

"No way. We don't need another man."

"Yes, we do," Earl insisted. "Put Mark Anthony on first."

"Tommy's going to play first. At least he can see the ball coming."

"I can see," Mark Anthony said. "Nothing's going to get by me."

"He plays, or I quit," Earl said.

"Forget it," Mark Anthony said. "I've got things to do, anyway."

"All right, all right. Four Eyes can work the outfield," Brian said, scowling at Mark Anthony. "And you'd better not let anything get by you, Four Eyes."

"I won't," Mark Anthony promised.

"You'd better not."

Mark Anthony picked up a glove and walked out to the outfield. He knew he wouldn't be there if it weren't for Earl. Earl was a hot-shot catcher. Brian would let Mrs. Prescott play outfield to get Earl as catcher.

Brian and Earl had a short conference, and then Brian

motioned Mark Anthony to center field, right behind the pitcher. Two little guys—Shorty Travis and Johnny McGee—were playing right and left field. Neither of them was known for speed, having very short legs, so Mark Anthony knew he'd have a lot of ground to cover.

It was hot in the outfield, and dusty. Sweat ran down Mark Anthony's face and neck. Little dust devils swirled around him and left a gritty feeling in his mouth and a scratchy sensation in his eyes. He blinked repeatedly to keep them clear.

The teams were pretty evenly matched, and no one on either team was a great hitter. The innings marched by uneventfully: 1-0; 1-1; 3-1; 3-2; 3-4; 4-4; 5-4; 5-5. Mark Anthony kept his eyes on the ball every minute. His head ached from the concentration.

The sun was getting lower, and it was getting harder to see the ball. He wished he'd brought his clip-on dark glasses.

It was the bottom of the ninth. The other team was up to bat, with two men out, two on base, and a fairly good hitter, Steven Smith, at the plate. Mark Anthony could hardly see Steven, against the glare of the lowering sun. He shifted his position several times, uneasy, trying to find a spot from which he could see Steven and the ball more clearly. The score was still 5-5. Two strikes. One more strike would do it. The next two batters after Steven weren't much better than Mark Anthony was.

There was a sharp crack and a yell. The ball had been hit hard, but he couldn't see it. Now he saw it—flashing toward him—high. He jumped, stretching every muscle, reaching, straining, and heard the ball whistle past his glove, about an inch to the left. A home run. Three men in. 8-5. He'd blown it.

He went after the ball and threw it in, grateful for the noisy celebration of the other team. If his team was saying anything to him, he couldn't hear it. He did notice that even Earl wouldn't look at him.

The game was over. Mark Anthony turned his glove in, and went after his books and jacket. Greg said, "Great going,

Mark Anthony," and Brian said, "That's the last time you play outfield for me, kid." He couldn't blame them. He headed for home.

Earl caught up with him. "Hey! Wait up! Everyone makes mistakes. They're not so great themselves."

"Face it, Earl. I can't catch, I can't run without falling over my own big feet, I can't pitch and I can't hit. Who'd want me on their team? The harder I try, the worse I get, and you know it."

"Aw, come on, Mark Anthony. It's not that bad."

"Yes, it is. See you tomorrow, Earl."

He walked home alone. It was a long walk, if you were hot, and tired, and thirsty. He was kind of glad not to have to talk to anyone, for a while.

His sister, Georgette, and some of her friends were in the playroom when he got home. He could hear them laughing and talking. All his good stuff was in there—in the old toy chest or on the shelves. He wandered out to the kitchen.

His mother was starting supper. She seemed like she had eight arms, at times like this. She covered a lot of ground fast. During the day, she worked in an office, with statistics and figures. She was very good at it. She was also a very good cook.

He took a couple of cookies and a glass of milk.

"How long are they going to be in there, Ma?"

"I don't know, dear. Why?"

"Oh, I just need some stuff."

"Well, go on in and get it—and tell them there are cookies here, and some milk, if they'd like some. Dinner won't be ready for an hour and a half."

The girls emptied out of the playroom like water down a drain. Mark Anthony went over to the storage shelves, where he kept some of his Indian things and rocks and shells in shoe boxes. Everything was jumbled up together and wedged in tight. Everyone in the family stored stuff there. He pulled out a couple of shoe boxes, but they weren't the right ones. His boxes were probably under something else.

He thought about the ball game. Boy, just once he'd like to hit a home run with the bases loaded. He sighed, and put back another shoe box full of his father's old wristwatch bands and buttons.

He walked over to the toy chest and lifted the lid. The arrowheads were in there, somewhere, and lots of other things he had found in the woods nearby.

He pulled them out, one by one, from under Georgette's old Noah's Ark set. As he collected them, he stuffed them into the front of his flannel shirt. He had almost everything when he heard footsteps coming.

He grabbed the rest of his stuff and slammed the chest lid down.

Doris came around the corner.

"Hi, there, Mark Anthony. What have you got?"

"Just some of my stuff."

"Like what?"

"You want to let me past, Doris?"

He tried to ease by her as she stood in the doorway. It wasn't easy, with all that stuff in his shirt. Then, to his horror, he felt something begin to slip and slide, and fall. An arrowhead bounced on the linoleum at his feet. Then, a rock and two shells. Everything was going, even though he was clutching it all frantically . . . and then—oh no!—a rubbery monkey and a little blue giraffe from Noah's Ark. They must have gotten caught up on something when he heard footsteps coming.

Doris pointed at the pile of toys at his feet. "Oh, look at that. Little Mark Anthony's playing with a monkey and a teeny tiny blue giraffe."

Mark Anthony wanted to yell at her. Instead, he just stepped over the toys and walked down the hall and out the front door. As it slammed to, behind him, he could hear the girls.

"Mark Anthony's playing with a little blue giraffe. Sweet little Mark Anthony."

He didn't think he would ever go home again.

His mother was still in the kitchen, cleaning up after supper, when he walked in.

"Where have you been, dear? We've been so worried."

"I'm sorry, Ma. Just walking." Mark Anthony got out the ingredients for a filling sandwich. "Ma, I need a place of my own to put things in."

"You've got all that space in the playroom."

"Come on, Ma, every time I want something, Georgette and her nutty friends are holed up in there. You saw what happened this afternoon."

His mother sighed. "Now, Mark Anthony, Georgette and her friends are just at that stage. They'll grow out of it, eventually."

"I don't care about eventually. Tomorrow morning, Doris will be spreading the word around that I was playing with Georgette's Noah's Ark animals." Mark Anthony sat down at the table. "I don't need that. I'm not exactly popular at that school as it is."

His mother dried her hands on her apron and sat down across from him. "You had a bad day?"

Mark Anthony shrugged.

"I'll speak to Georgette. Maybe she can ask Doris to restrain herself."

"That won't do any good. Don't do that, Ma, please. I just need my own space, for my old stuff and my collections and my books."

"Well, if it will help. . . ."

"How about Grandma Hooper's old dresser? We could move it up from the basement to the hall. It could be just mine. There are ten drawers in it—plenty of room. No one's using it."

Mrs. Crowder nodded slowly. "That's a good idea. I'm sure Grandma would want you to have it. I'll have your father move it up tonight, before he goes to bed."

"Thanks, Ma. Thanks a lot."

Mrs. Crowder called to him as he left the kitchen. "But nothing alive in there, Mark Anthony. You hear me? Nothing alive."

Uncle Edward was in his room. Mark Anthony could tell because the light crept under Uncle Edward's bedroom door into the hallway outside his room.

"Uncle Edward?"

"Come in, my boy. Come in."

Uncle Edward was a great big man. He had a very large, white and yellow moustache. His hair was thinning and silvery white, but his voice was strong, and deep.

Mark Anthony loved to talk with Uncle Edward. He always made a person feel listened to. When you were conversing with Uncle Edward, you were doing something. He used uncommon words, and rolled them out into the air proudly, and loaded them with meaning. Even listening to him was an event, a happening, particularly when he felt strongly about something. Actually, Uncle Edward felt strongly about everything. He was not a wishy-washy person.

"I see that the slings and arrows of outrageous fortune have pierced your soul again," he said, brushing newspapers off the bed so Mark Anthony could sit down.

"Yes, sir."

"Would you care to tell me about it, or do you prefer not to relive the more painful moments?"

"It's the same old stuff—this time it's Prescott and softball."

"I see."

" 'Nice and tall,' and 'Four Eyes.' "

"Ah, yes."

"It's getting so I hate to go to school."

Uncle Edward nodded. "Understandable. Indeed—inevitable."

"I tried. I really tried, but that ball got past me, and the other team won."

"Hmmmmm." Uncle Edward stroked his moustache and stared down at the little oval braided rug beside his bed. The clock on his bureau ticked loudly, solemnly, on, while he stroked and thought. Finally, he raised his head.

"Mark Anthony, do you relish playing softball? Do you do

it for pleasure?"

"It's OK."

"But there are other pastimes that nourish your spirit more fully?"

"Sure. Like reading, and collecting Indian stuff."

"Then why do you do it?"

"Because the other kids do it."

"But, if you would rather be doing something else. . . ."

"Look, Uncle Edward, I don't always want to be doing my own thing—alone. It gets awful lonely, if you want to know."

"Ah, yes. I do know."

Suddenly, Mark Anthony remembered that Aunt Betsy had died less than a year ago.

"I'm sorry. I didn't think."

"Of course, my boy. It's all right. Now, back to our problem."

"I try to do the things they like to do so they'll like me."

"But it isn't working."

"Well, what will work?"

Uncle Edward sighed. "I don't know." Then he drew himself up and said loudly, "I'm not admitting defeat, you understand. We are temporarily stalemated, you and I. We will, of course, find a satisfactory solution and implement it."

Mark Anthony didn't want to spread the gloom any more than he had already. "Sure, Uncle Edward. Thanks for listening."

"Have you done your words today?"

"Not yet. I'll pick them out as I go to bed."

"Good idea. May I suggest *bibulous, bigamy, bilge water, billet-doux,* and *bigot*?" He winked at Mark Anthony. "They are all close together, interesting, and related in some way to human nature."

Shortly after Uncle Edward had come to live with the Crowders, being freshly widowed and Mrs. Crowder's only surviving elderly relative, Mark Anthony had been forced to buy a small dictionary so he could understand Uncle

Edward. A month or so later, Uncle Edward had talked him into memorizing and using five new words every day. At first, it had become interesting in its own right, and now he was constantly on the lookout for words which Uncle Edward might not know, or words he could use on Georgette which would leave her uncertain as to whether she had been insulted or complimented.

Naturally, he kept this ever-increasing store of satisfying, fascinating, mouth-filling words hidden. At school, he was constantly on guard—carefully restricting himself to short, common words, and weeding out anything ornate or unusual. It made for very slow talking sometimes, but Mark Anthony knew it was the wise thing to do. All he needed, at this point, was for the guys to think he was trying to put on the dog. That would finish him. The big thing was to maintain a very low profile—use short, regular words, and stoop as much as possible.

He went into his room and sat down. On the bed. The only chair in the room was one of those wooden folding chairs you find in church basements. When Uncle Edward had arrived, and his big brother Wellington had come home from college, his father had to partition one room to make three bedrooms. He and Georgette and Wellington were all packed in, now, side by side, in three skinny little rooms that would have made good closets. Uncle Edward had gotten Georgette's old room across the hall. It was great—having Wellington back and Uncle Edward there, and Mark Anthony didn't complain, but now he had a room to sleep in, and that was about all.

His father opened the door. Straight arm. Never a knock, or a request to enter. No. Just *zap!* and there he was. He might as well have an Open House sign over his door, and a Do Come In doormat.

His mother once told Mark Anthony that his father did this because he was high-strung, and because all the doors in the athletic building at the college where he was a coach opened that way. After a few months of this kind of treatment, so did all the doors in the Crowder house.

514

"Your mother's been after me to move that old dresser upstairs."

"Yes, Dad. I really need a place to put my things."

"Your stuff is all over the house already."

"That's just what I mean."

"You've got to have this?"

"It would really help."

"All right. Let's get it over with. Come on."

They brought the dresser up and set it up in the hall. It took up a lot of space, but you could get by it if you turned sideways—unless the drawers were open.

"This thing is a hazard to life and limb," his father said. "What if there were a fire, and we all had to get out quickly?"

"We'd go out our bedroom windows, dear, and step right down onto the ground," Mrs. Crowder said.

"We'd better keep a light on it," his father grumbled. "We'll all be running right into it in the dark on the way to the bathroom."

"I'll bring up Georgette's little night-light from the basement. It'll look very nice," his mother said.

"What do we need this here for anyway? He's got a room of his own."

"I have to step out into the hall to make his bed," Mark Anthony's mother said crisply. "He needs more space. We'll all adjust beautifully, I'm sure."

When his mother used that tone, and talked about all of them adjusting, it meant that she was drawing a line and daring someone else to step over it.

"All these kids have too much stuff anyway," his father said, and stumped off to bed.

Chapter 2

He got up wishing it was the weekend already. A holiday weekend was always great. Three days with no school. He checked his forehead for fever. It was hard to tell on yourself, but he didn't think he had any. He looked in the bathroom mirror at his throat. Pale pink. Healthy. It was no good saying he felt sick to his stomach, which was true. His father would just say, "Eat something and go to school. You'll feel better."

He walked up the long flight of steps to the school with a churning, ready-to-heave-at-any-moment stomach. It was almost a relief when he ran into Brian and Arnold Janssen in the hallway right away, and they let him have it.

"Well, here comes the famous baseball player—Butterfingers Crowder."

"Hey, Butterfingers, you play for the other team next time, you hear?"

Mark Anthony kept on walking. Arnold grabbed at his sleeve, missed, and ran after him.

"Hey—Baby Ruth, when are you going to learn how to catch a ball?"

His voice carried over the shuffling and chatter of the kids in the corridor. The noise around them died down a little. Everyone was watching and listening, waiting to see what Mark Anthony would do.

He felt his face burn. "Look, it was just a game, Arnold. You've let balls get past you."

"You could have caught that one, easy."

"I tried."

"No, you didn't. You just reached up like . . . you were dancing." Arnold stretched out his arms for an instant, like a ballet dancer. An appreciative ripple of giggles ran around the circle of kids around them.

"Do you want a fight?" Mark Anthony asked. "Is that what you want?"

"You take your glasses off first. I can't hit a guy with glasses on."

"I can't see without them. I need them. Don't worry about me, Arnold. They've been tempered. They won't break easy."

"We're not supposed to fight in the corridors. You're trying to get me in trouble."

"I'll be in trouble too." For a minute, Arnold hesitated, and Mark Anthony hoped he was going to back down. But he

didn't. Mark Anthony watched as he put his lunch and books down near the wall. Arnold was a squat, beefy kid, with a build like a bulldozer. He had long arms, and he swaggered when he walked. Now, he straightened up and rolled up his sleeves. Mark Anthony put his own things down.

"This is it," he thought. "He's going to kill me." He moved in closer to Arnold, fists up.

Arnold squinted down the corridor over Mark Anthony's shoulder.

"Cool it, you creep. A teacher's coming."

As Mark Anthony turned, Arnold's fist caught him right under the rib cage, and drove every bit of air out of his body. He doubled up, struggling to get his breath, making long, horrible, gasping sounds. The other kids in the corridor backed away from him, leaving him the center of a tight little circle. He heard someone say, "Go get a teacher."

Finally, he managed to inhale a little air, and then a little more. The pain in his chest eased, and the mist over his sight cleared.

"Are you all right, Mark Anthony?"

He looked up. Mr. Dobbs. Science and track.

He nodded, not daring to try to talk yet.

"What happened here?" Mr. Dobbs asked, looking around the circle.

No one answered. The other kids started to drift away, and the circle melted into a hallway full of hurrying kids.

Mr. Dobbs bent down. "Will you be OK?"

"Yes, sir."

"All right. If you feel sick later, better stop in at the nurse's office."

"Yes, sir."

He picked up his stuff and walked to his first class. He had to bend over a little, still. He ached where Arnold had hit him. And it had all been for nothing.

The door to the classroom closed behind him. Mrs. Prescott rapped on her desk, and the school day had started.

After the fight, the little singsong that Doris directed at him during lunch hour hardly mattered. He didn't even bother to look up.

"How're you doing, Mark Anthony? Got your little blue giraffe with you today?"

Unable to get a rise out of him, she turned to her friends. "Mark Anthony plays with little toy animals. Would you believe it?"

Her friends laughed nervously, uncertainly. She walked away.

Earl came over and sat down beside him. He opened up his lunch bag. "That Doris is a pain. What've you got?"

"Cheese. Again. And brownies. Want one?"

"Sure." Earl accepted one of Mark Anthony's brownies and took a bite, slowly and thoughtfully. "Your Ma sure makes good brownies. You want to trade my sandwich for the other brownie?"

"No." Mark Anthony thought it over and changed his mind. "You can have half of it. Keep your sandwich."

"Thanks, Pal. What are you doing on this long weekend?"

"I'm going to get all my Indian stuff out and organize it. I'm setting everything up in one spot. Ma let me have a big, old dresser for my collections."

"It sounds neat. Can I come over Sunday afternoon and see the Indian things?"

"Sure."

"OK. I'll see you about two."

"Hey, that's terrific! You'll really like it, Earl. I got some good things. I collected most of them right here in town, too, in the woods and along Bowditch Creek."

"How come you never showed them to me before?"

"I didn't know you liked Indian things."

"Everyone likes Indian things."

The bell rang, and he had only two more hours to go to the end of the school day—a Friday school day.

Uncle Edward was in his room when Mark Anthony came home.

"Uncle Edward?"

"Ah, yes—it is the ruddy stripling."

"May I come in?"

"You'd better. It's difficult to talk through the door like this."

Uncle Edward was lying on the bed, with three pillows under his head and a book on his chest. *Webster's Unabridged Dictionary* supported his elbow.

"How goes it, Mark Anthony?"

"Lousy."

"Bad word. Expressive, but too general. Try another one."

Mark Anthony was in no mood for word games. "I had a fight with Arnold—only it wasn't a fight. It only lasted for one punch. He got me right in the bread basket."

"Knocked the wind out of you, did he?"

"Did he ever!"

"Are you all right, my boy?"

"I'm healthy, if that's what you mean, but I'm not all right."

Uncle Edward nodded. "This Arnold—is he the school bully?"

"I don't know if you could say that. He's just not afraid of anything or anyone. He walks around like he's in charge of the whole world. Everyone says, 'Yes, Arnold,' and, 'Sure, Arnold,' and if he doesn't like you, you've had it."

"Is he bigger than everyone else?"

Mark Anthony frowned. "No. Actually, he's kind of short. Short and square, if you know what I mean."

"Yes. Well, now. We must take prudent action. Such as a course in self-defense." He shook his finger in Mark Anthony's face. "I am against violence, you understand, whether it's directed against you or against Arnold, but merely the knowledge that you are expertly prepared to defend yourself might serve as a deterrent. If not, at least he won't find you an easy mark. No pun intended."

Mark Anthony shook his head. "Where am I going to get the money for that?"

Uncle Edward said sadly, "Finances have never been one of my strong points. When it comes to managing money, my boy, I am a weak reed."

"Maybe I can earn the money this summer."

"That's possible. In fact, I think it's our best hope, so far. Doing what?"

"I don't know. I'll have to think about it."

"Do. And while you give that some thought, it may help to remember that people like Arnold frequently have a great deal of trouble coping with adult life, after they leave school."

"Uncle Edward, if I don't find some way to slow Arnold down, I may not reach adult life."

"Don't be pessimistic. It takes all the starch out of you." Uncle Edward stood up, shoved his feet into his slippers, and shuffled to the door.

Mark Anthony got to work on the dresser. He scrubbed it,

waxed it, and polished it till it glowed. Then he started combing through the shelves, drawers, pockets and shoe boxes to gather together the bits and pieces of his collections. It took all afternoon.

When he was finished, he was astonished at the variety and value of his own possessions. He went to bed tired but happy. Sunday he would arrange it all and show it off to Earl.

He was busy labeling and grouping arrowheads when Earl called, around ten, Sunday morning.

"What's up?" Mark Anthony asked. "You're still coming, aren't you?"

"Oh, I'm coming, all right. The thing is, I wondered if I could bring someone. Actually, two people."

"Who?"

There was a short silence. "Arnold and Brian."

"Are you kidding? Don't be silly, Earl. Knock it off." Privately, Mark Anthony thought it was not all that funny for Earl to call up and ask if he could bring the guy who had floored him the day before.

"I'm not kidding. They really want to come."

"Why?"

"To see your Indian stuff."

"Sure. If I'd believe that, I'd believe anything. Quit fooling around, Earl. I've got to get back to work."

"Look, Mark Anthony, can't I bring them along?"

"Just give me one good reason."

"I told you—everyone likes Indian things."

Mark Anthony felt a pleasant little thrill of pride. He had something the other kids wanted to see.

"OK. They can come, I guess."

"Thanks. That's great. We'll be there about two."

Mark Anthony hung up. He hadn't wanted to turn Earl down. If he had, maybe even Earl wouldn't have come. Besides, it sounded as if Brian and Arnold were really interested in seeing his Indian collection. Maybe they collected arrowheads and spearpoints too.

He went back to the hall and stood there, looking down at his collections. All of a sudden, the displays looked skimpy.

Especially the Indian things. Maybe he shouldn't have made such a big deal out of it.

He finished the labeling—where, when and how he'd found each arrowhead, spearpoint or tool—and then he worked on his rocks and minerals, as a sort of backup attraction. He was just getting going on his shells when his mother called him for lunch.

Last night, this stuff had looked like a million dollars to him. Now, with Brian and Arnold and Earl due in an hour or so, it looked like a lot of nothing.

Chapter 3

They arrived right at two o'clock, on their bicycles. He heard them coming and ran to the front door. He was nervous. When he grabbed the doorknob, his hands were so sweaty, they slipped. Part of him wanted them to be so impressed by his collection that they would like him more. The other part of him didn't even want to let them come in, particularly Arnold.

"Hey, Mark Anthony, I hear you got some good Indian things here." Brian looked really interested.

Arnold didn't say anything.

Mark Anthony shrugged. "I like to collect stuff like that." He opened the screen door slightly, as they came up the steps onto the porch.

Earl fidgeted in the background while Arnold and Brian leaned their bikes against the porch railing. Then he followed them into the front hall. It made Mark Anthony mad to see him so anxious. He grabbed Earl's arm and pulled him along the hall, ahead of the others.

"Come on, Earl—the Indian things are down here."

"You say you found all this stuff around here?" Arnold sounded as though he could hardly believe it. Mark Anthony felt another tingle of pride run through him.

"Yes. I found the first arrowheads in the root hole where a big tree had blown down, and then I found one at the entrance to a woodchuck's burrow, and three of those spearpoints in Bowditch Creek, when it was real low. The rest I found digging for worms, or under rocks—when I was collecting rocks and minerals—or just lying on the ground, under leaves and stuff."

Mark Anthony opened another drawer. "The beadwork came from a reservation. My father brought it home from a trip. The hatchet blade was dug up in Massachusetts. My brother went to college there."

"Wow," Earl said, "this is really neat. I never knew there was anything like this around." He picked up a small white "bird-point" in his hand and looked at it closely, testing its sharpness against his palm.

"Where'd you find that?" Arnold demanded.

"I got that digging for worms, in Eberhart's woods."

"It's funny," Arnold said to Brian. "I've gone through those woods a million times. I never saw one of those," and he picked up a spearhead.

"Maybe you didn't look in the right places," Brian said.

Earl put the bird-point down and picked up a quartz crystal from the rock collection. "Hey, fellows, look at this."

"You find that in Eberhart's woods too?" Brian asked. There was a nasty tone to his voice.

"Are you saying you don't believe me?" Mark Anthony asked. He could feel his face burning red and hot.

"No, man. We're just saying it's funny how no one else ever found things like these along the creek or in the woods before. Then you come along, and there's Indian stuff all over," Brian said.

"You know," Arnold said thoughtfully, "I saw arrowheads just like these in a store, once. They were real cheap. I should have gotten some."

"Where was the store?" Brian asked. "In Eberhart's woods?"

"Hey, fellows," Earl said, "look at this abalone shell. It's from California."

"Listen, Brian," Mark Anthony said, "I found all that stuff just where I said I found it. It was there all the time. I could take you out there right now and show you where I found it."

"Sure you could."

Mark Anthony was conscious of his breath coming hard and fast, like he had just run the mile. "That's right, I could."

A door down the hall swung open, creaking a little. Uncle Edward came out into the hallway and noticed the boys. Mark Anthony had seen him do that double take a hundred times.

"Hello, there," he said warmly. "Who are your friends, Mark Anthony?"

Mark Anthony glared at Arnold. "This is Arnold Janssen. This is Brian Miller. You already know Earl."

Uncle Edward came closer. "Hello, boys. I'm Mr. Hooper, Mark Anthony's Uncle Edward." He stood in front of the group now, smiling benevolently down on them.

"Showing them your Indian things, are you? That's nice. It's a shame to be indoors on such a great day, though. Boys your age should be out, most of the time."

The group found themselves drifting toward the front door.

"When I was your age, I had to be hog-tied to be kept indoors in the springtime. Yes, yes. I remember those days with pleasure. Running through the fields . . . busy from morning til night." They were at the front door now.

"It's been interesting meeting you—Arnold, was it?— and Brian. After you've said your good-bys, Mark Anthony, I'd like to see you and Earl in my room. There's a small errand I need run. Good-by, now," and he ushered Brian and Arnold out onto the porch with a sweeping gesture of his left hand, nodding and smiling all the while.

The screen door slammed behind them. They walked over to their bikes and pushed them over to the steps, and down onto the walk. Arnold turned.

"Who do you think you're kidding? That stuff was all bought and paid for. Trying to be a big shot, aren't you?"

Brian nodded, and they got on their bikes and left.

"You shouldn't have come out," Mark Anthony said.

"I know," Uncle Edward said with a deep sigh.

"I'm glad he came out," Earl said with feeling.

"You were listening, weren't you?" Mark Anthony asked Uncle Edward.

"These walls are so thin," Uncle Edward said apologetically, "and I became aware that the situation was worsening. It sounded as though you might be forced to take on both Brian and Arnold in defense of your integrity. A fair fight is one thing, but human sacrifice is something else." He paused, and threw up his hands. "I concluded that I would have to intervene at some point, and that it would be easier to prevent an altercation than to break one up."

"I would have had Earl on my side."

Earl spoke up bravely. "Yuh."

Uncle Edward smiled at Earl. "True. But, while Earl is stout of heart, he is still slender of stature. His body has not yet caught up with his spirit. You boys were not outclassed, merely outweighed." He shook his head. "Brian and Arnold would have gone over you like Sherman marching through Georgia."

"Those guys didn't believe me."

"They have closed minds. Tragic! At their age!" He turned on Earl, shaking his finger in Earl's face. "You must never, ever, allow your mind to become closed."

Earl nodded vigorously, wide-eyed.

Mark Anthony said, "You want to look at the collections some more, Earl?"

Earl shook his head. "No. Everything's really neat, but I think I'll go home now."

"They're not going to beat you up or anything, Earl. You didn't lie to them. If they don't believe anyone, it's me."

Earl stepped out onto the porch. "See you Tuesday, at school."

"Sure."

Mark Anthony watched him ride away, and felt very lonely. The long weekend he had looked forward to stretched out ahead of him now as something to be gotten through.

On top of everything else, Brian and Arnold hadn't been impressed by the collection—they'd figured it was phony—

a collection of lies. They must think he'd sat down and made up every single label. They'd probably spread it all around school that he had tried to pull a fast one on them. This was the last time he'd show that collection to anyone, if he had anything to say about it.

He decided to go for a walk. Sometimes, walking made him feel better. Besides, if he found anything new, he'd have a place to put it now.

Chapter 4

The trees were full of bird songs. Chipmunks and squirrels bounced along the tops of old stone walls. Everything smelled cool and fresh and green. He could hear Bowditch Creek from a long way off. The spring rains had left it high, and shoving at its banks.

He found his favorite spot, overlooking the creek. Moss, like a brilliant green carpet, covered rocks and tree stumps. Ferns hung out over the brook below. Sunlight and shadow dappled the soft, brown layer of last year's leaves at his feet. He sat down and watched the creek for a long time, till it didn't matter anymore what anyone else said or did.

Finally, the dampness came through the seat of his blue jeans, and it was time to move on. He worked his way upstream. It was tricky going. The stream had eaten away at the clay under its banks. A solid-looking piece of ground might suddenly give way under the least little pressure and toss him into the creek. Here and there, a tall, slender tree had fallen across the creek when its root system was undermined.

He climbed out onto one of those trees and sat down, dangling his legs over the creek so his toes hung just inches above the water. A chickadee landed on the tree trunk not five feet away from him and watched him for a while.

He got up and walked back along the trunk to the point where its roots had pulled away from the bank. They looked like gnarled old hands, clawing at the air.

Below him, in the gaping root hole, he saw an irregular line of reddened rocks and blackened soil. He poked gently at the clay around the area with his pocketknife, and dislodged some of the rocks, opening up a small hole in the bank. Some of the rocks were shattered, and there were small lumps of charcoal packed in among them. He sat back on his haunches and studied the hole. This had to be an old hearth site. Very old. The Indians again. They had built at least one fire here, long ago, and the remains had been trapped and preserved under layers of clay carried down by spring floods. He scraped out a handful of rocks and rock chips and charcoal pieces, and put it all in a big square of aluminum foil. It just barely fit in his shirt pocket.

He always carried his knife and some foil with him—just in case he found something interesting.

Then he worked his way up the creek bank, going from rock to rock, just above the water, scanning the sides of the freshly exposed bank.

He was just about to give up when he saw another line of reddened rocks and black soil, and something that didn't look like a rock or a piece of tree root. He worked at it gently, scraping the damp clay away layer by layer till it lay in his hand. He couldn't believe it! It was a piece of a broken clay pot. An Indian pot. Wow! This had been one of the most exciting afternoons of his whole life, after all. He put the piece of pot in his other shirt pocket and started home. Earl would get a big kick out of this. Maybe he'd even bring him back here and show him the campfire traces. If that's what they were.

Earl's line was busy.

Mark Anthony wandered into the kitchen. His mother was cooking dinner. She glanced up, flushed and hurried looking.

"Oh, good. Mark Anthony. You can set the table for me. Dinner's almost ready."

"Sure, Ma. Hey—I found something, today—along Bowditch Creek. You'll never guess."

"I wonder if this roast is really cooked. Last time I did it this way, it wasn't done and your father wouldn't eat it."

"It's cooked. It's all dark brown, isn't it? Did you hear what I said about Bowditch Creek?"

His mother looked up at him. "You didn't get wet, did you, dear? If you did, you go and take off your socks and put on dry ones right away. There are a lot of colds going around."

Mark Anthony took a deep breath. "Ma—will you listen, please?"

"Why not wait and tell me after dinner, dear? Everything's just about ready. Did you set the table yet?"

Mark Anthony walked into the dining room and started counting out the silverware.

The roast was cooked, and everyone said how good it was. Dessert was rhubarb pie. It always set Mark Anthony's teeth on edge, no matter how much sugar his mother added. He decided to pass it up, this time. He excused himself from the table and headed for his room. Georgette could help clear. He'd set the table.

He laid the piece of pot under the lamp on his night table, and studied it closely. It still needed a careful cleaning. He took out the aluminum-foil packet from his other pocket and labeled it. Someday, if he found someone he could really trust, who knew a lot about Indians, maybe he'd ask them about these rocks, and the pot. He got up and went out into the hall to store them safely in one of his Indian drawers. Georgette was just closing the top drawer—where he kept his smallest shells.

"What are you doing in my stuff?"

"Don't you yell at me."

"I'll yell at you whenever you get into my things. What were you doing?"

"I was just borrowing a couple of shells, for school. We're studying the Pacific Ocean, and I told my teacher about your shells, and she said to bring some in."

"Oh, she did. Well, they're not your shells, and you can't. Put them back."

"Ma!" Georgette yelled, "Ma!"

"You can yell all you want, Georgette. You're not helping yourself to my shells."

His mother came around the corner.

"What's the matter?"

"Mrs. Reilly asked me to bring in some shells for a geography project and Mark Anthony won't let me borrow any."

"She just barged right in and helped herself—never asked or anything."

"It's for school. My teacher told me."

Mark Anthony's mother looked at him. "If it's for school, Mark Anthony, it does seem to me that you could let her borrow some."

"That's not the point, Ma. The point is, they're supposed to be mine—and she just waltzes in and takes what she wants without even asking."

"Well, of course she should ask." His mother turned to Georgette. "Let Mark Anthony see what you're borrowing."

Georgette opened her fists reluctantly.

Her mother said, "Oh, dear."

Mark Anthony felt sick to his stomach.

She had just grabbed two handfuls of the smallest, lightest shells—and in the excitement, she must have squeezed. Three of his most delicate shells were crumpled into little flakes, like crushed eggshells. Another shell had been cracked.

"Oh, Georgette," his mother said. "You should have been more careful."

"I'm sorry, Ma," Georgette said, and started to cry. His mother put her arms around her. Mark Anthony shoved by them, hard, and ran—down the hall to the front door, down the walk, and out into the dark. He didn't want to cry in front of Georgette.

It was late when he got back. He didn't want to come home, but he was getting awfully tired, and cold, and there was no place else to go. The lights were out in the living room. That meant the television set was off—and they had probably all gone to bed. The front door was still unlocked.

He was halfway through the living room when his father spoke. "Where have you been?"

Mark Anthony finally located him. He was sitting in the big wing chair in the corner, in the dark.

"I was walking."

"All evening?"

"Yes."

"Well, you just about ruined the whole evening for all of us. Your mother worried all evening. I finally sent her off to bed and said I'd wait up. Do you ever think of anyone else but yourself?"

"Do you know what happened?"

"Yes. I know. All this over a handful of little shells that you can replace any day in the week."

"That's not true. I'll have to order them, and they cost a lot of money—and I paid for them."

"With my money." His father's voice was like a slap, coming at him out of the dark.

Mark Anthony was silent. There wasn't any comeback to that. If his allowance was still really his father's money—not ever his own—then his father was right.

"What's the matter with you, anyway? I won't have it. If you run out of here again and stay away till this hour, I'll call the police. So help me!"

Mark Anthony still couldn't think of anything he could say that would make any difference.

"Haven't you got anything to say for yourself?" His father sounded as if he was getting even more angry. Mark Anthony began to panic. He'd better come up with something, fast, no matter what.

"I'm sorry Ma was upset."

"Now you look here. I let you put that dresser in the hall —against my better judgment—to keep your stuff in, but if it's going to be a bone of contention, it goes. Do you understand me?"

"Yes, sir."

"Now, go to bed."

Mark Anthony lay in bed, staring up at the ceiling. He wondered if it was different when you were grown-up. It must be. When he was six feet tall and weighed two hundred pounds, just let someone try and mess with his personal possessions. He'd live by himself, far away from here, and have everything fixed just the way he wanted it. And if he never saw Georgette—ever—it would be just fine with him.

There was a very light knock on his door. Then two more, close together. Uncle Edward. He didn't want to see or talk to anyone. He lay still.

The single knock came again—then two more. He got up and opened the door. Uncle Edward slipped in and closed the door softly behind him.

"Get back in bed and cover up."

"You heard?"

"Yes." Uncle Edward laid his hand on Mark Anthony's shoulder and began to slide it slowly, firmly, up and down over his back.

"Mark Anthony, have you ever heard anyone say that childhood is marvelous, enchanted . . . the best time of our lives?"

"Sure. Everyone says that."

Uncle Edward's hand worked over the muscles in Mark Anthony's back, coaxing them to let up a little.

"Well, that's a lot of bilge water. Don't believe it. I wouldn't be a child again for a million dollars—tax free."

"But this afternoon, you said. . . ."

"Of course, there were times when I was on top of the world—when everything was golden. Every child has moments . . . whole days, maybe . . . like that. And that kind of glory never comes around again—except on very rare occasions. I felt like that the day I got married. I think parents must feel like that when their child is born."

The back rub continued. Mark Anthony worked down deeper into the pillow, finding the most comfortable spot.

"But being young is hard. Very hard. For every peak, there is a valley—no, a pit, full of creeping fear, or raging frustration, or black despair." Uncle Edward's voice painted the pits of fear, frustration, and despair on the darkness before them.

"And you are so vulnerable when you're young, and so powerless." The words trailed away to a whisper. Then his voice rang out again, strong and confident. "Being an adult is like walking across a rolling prairie—some clouds, some sunshine, lots of open sky. There are great days when you can't see over the next little rise, and you're so tired, you can hardly go on—but the reins are in your hands."

He paused, and repeated, "The reins are in your hands then, and that makes all the difference, Mark Anthony. You may be frightened at times, and you may carry a heavy load —but you will be in charge of your own life." His voice rang out, filling the tiny room and vibrating through Mark Anthony's head. Mark Anthony could feel goose bumps rise all over his body, and the hairs on his arms stand up.

"It will only get better as you grow up, I promise." His voice sank to a whisper. "Until you get to be very old."

Mark Anthony's eyes closed. Still, he had to be sure of something before he let go. "Even for me—you're sure it will really get better, Uncle Edward?"

"You have my word. Hold on for just a few more years, and you'll know what I mean. We've all been through it. Things will get better. Just hang on."

Mark Anthony sighed deeply, and slept.

Chapter 5

He woke up Monday morning to the voice of the floor polisher zinging around the living room, bouncing off the wallboards and the furniture. His father ran household equipment like he drove. Good luck to anything that got in his way, Uncle Edward said. All this activity must mean company was coming. Some holiday.

Mark Anthony groaned. He rolled over and tried to go back to sleep. The minute he poked his head out his door, he'd get his marching orders. He'd be stuck with yard work, probably, or getting the screened porch ready. He didn't mind getting things tidy, or helping out, but if important company was coming, like someone from the college, his parents practically went into orbit. Everything had to be perfect. Not just clean. Super clean. He couldn't see it, himself. Not that he'd be asked. Just told.

His throat felt scratchy. He sat up. Where was this scratchy throat Friday, when he needed it? His head pounded a little in front, over his sinuses.

"Oh, no," he thought, "not sinus. Please. Not sinus again."

The pounding eased, but it didn't go away. Mark Anthony sighed. Some great holiday this was going to be.

Breakfast was a drag. Everyone was polite, especially Georgette. She was trying—he had to admit it. She passed him the sugar for his cereal three times, and smiled at him once. When he pushed his chair back, she leaned forward quickly and whispered, "I'm going to get you some new shells, Mark Anthony."

He stood up. "Don't worry about it, Georgette." The kid

got such a small allowance, it would be like taking candy from a baby.

His father cleared his throat loudly, and said, "Mark Anthony, you have something to say."

"I'm sorry I stayed out so late, Ma."

"That's all right, dear. I know you were upset." His mother reached over and patted his hand.

"It's not all right," his father said. "Now go straighten up your room. Company's coming."

Mark Anthony marched out of the room and down the hall.

His head pounded, and his face felt hot and dry, as if he had a bad sunburn.

His mother came to his door in the middle of the morning.

"Mark Anthony, may I come in?"

"Sure, Ma."

"I wonder if you'd like to help me with the porch."

"Where's Dad?"

"He's taken a load of trash to the dump. Then he'll get some extra ice, and stop by the fruit market."

"OK. I'll be out in a minute."

"Thank you, dear."

The porch ran along the back of the house. He could stay out there and work all day without running into anyone else. As long as he didn't make a lot of noise and call attention to himself, everything would stay copacetic. It was better to have something to do, anyway.

His mother brought him a sandwich and some lemonade for lunch. He was terribly thirsty. The lemonade tasted great. But he couldn't get the sandwich down. The next time his mother flashed past the doorway from the porch to the living room, he flagged her down.

"Ma, could I have some more lemonade—and maybe two aspirin?"

"What's the matter, Mark Anthony? Don't you feel well?"

"Sinus."

"Oh, dear. Do you have a fever?" She reached towards

him—inside of the wrist out and positioned to register the temperature of his forehead. He ducked.

"No fever, Ma. Just headache."

"All right, dear."

The lemonade and aspirin helped a lot. By three, the porch was ready. The Queen of England could come for dinner on that porch and feel right at home. Mark Anthony slipped into the house and made it to his room without running into anyone. The whole house smelled of floor wax and lemon oil and pine disinfectant.

He lay down on his bed and it felt good. The sinus attack was really getting him down. Maybe if he could sleep, he'd wake up feeling better.

It was getting dark when the headache woke him up. His throat burned and stung when he swallowed. The sheets scratched where they touched his skin. He got up to go to the bathroom and get some more aspirin. On his way back, he noticed the dresser. One end was piled high with men's sports jackets. His father's briefcase and his brother Wellington's tennis racket rested on the other. Wellington must be home.

Mark Anthony stood there in the hallway, looking at the dresser for a moment. If he'd been a little kid, he might have cried, he felt so bad. He thought of moving everything somewhere else—maybe even just shoving it all onto the floor, so the shiny top he'd worked so hard on would glow back up at him again. Then he shook his head and went back to his room. If he could just get rid of this headache, he'd feel a lot better.

He went back to sleep almost immediately, but it was a tough way to spend a night. When he wasn't being chased by something the size of the Empire State Building, he was falling—down elevator shafts, off bridges, into empty black space. His fingers ached from grabbing and digging in, but still he fell. It was a tremendous relief when his mother woke him up.

"Mark Anthony, it's seven-thirty. You'll miss the bus."

Mark Anthony sat up. His head hurt so much he closed his eyes quickly and lay back down. His throat felt as if he'd been swallowing hot swords.

"I can't get up, Ma."

He felt the wrist on his forehead.

"Oh my, you're running a temperature."

"Yes, ma'am."

"Well, you certainly can't go to school in this condition."

Mark Anthony slid back down under the covers, silently.

His mother went through the whole sick-child routine. She took his temperature, gave him aspirin, and spent ten minutes out in the hall in conference with Uncle Edward over his care and feeding during the day.

Georgette poked her head in the door. "I'm sorry you're sick. Can I have some more shells for school?"

He just waved his right hand at her.

His father came in and said, "You mind Uncle Edward, now. Don't give him any trouble."

Mark Anthony nodded.

"I expect this is the result of your evening ramble."

Mark Anthony didn't respond. He was too tired and sick to argue, anyway.

"See you tonight. I hope you feel better," and his father was gone.

The rest of Tuesday was a haze—mostly sleeping, sweating, and going to the bathroom. Wednesday was more of the same, with a hacking cough thrown in. Thursday, he woke up around nine in the morning to find Dr. Thorndike holding his wrist, taking his pulse.

"How do you feel, Mark Anthony?"

"Sort of fuzzy."

"I'm sure you do. Let me listen to your chest."

The stethoscope felt like an ice cube on his back. The room tilted and spun around him slowly while he breathed in and out on command. He fell asleep while Dr. Thorndike was still packing up his case.

Friday, the cough felt like it was tearing him apart. His

throat hurt, his chest ached, even the muscles in his stomach pulled painfully with every deep breath. There were more pills on his tray, and a medicine that burned all the way down to his stomach.

Saturday, he really woke up, clearheaded, in the afternoon, and noticed that Uncle Edward had taken the church basement chair out and brought his own rocker into the bedroom and was sitting in it, reading.

"You've been here all the time, haven't you?"

"You know I have. I think I've developed saddle sores from sitting here rocking."

"Am I getting better?"

"Yes. For which I hourly give thanks."

"What'd I have?"

"You opened with sinus, followed that up with the flu, and peaked on Thursday with a touch of pneumonia in your left lung. What a performance!"

"Wow!"

"Wow, indeed. You came very close to being hospitalized."

"Did I almost die?"

"No. Although I imagine you must have felt like it, on occasion."

Mark Anthony nodded. The effort made his head hurt again. He groaned, and coughed.

"Please, my boy, take it very easy. You are my responsibility right now, and a relapse would be awkward to explain. My position here is precarious, at best."

Mark Anthony reached out towards Uncle Edward. "Don't say that. Even kidding," and to his amazement, he felt hot tears running out of his eyes and down into his hair. He turned his face into his pillow.

Uncle Edward got up instantly and leaned over him. "I'm sorry, Mark Anthony. I was only joking. I'll be here as long as you need me, probably longer. Don't let my warped humor alarm you." He patted Mark Anthony's shoulder. "Rest. You must be exhausted from your recent struggle."

He took Mark Anthony's hand between his own hands,

and sat down gently on the edge of the bed. "I'll stay here. You go to sleep," and Mark Anthony did.

Sunday, they decided to let Earl visit him for five minutes. Dr. Thorndike said it couldn't hurt, and it might help. Mark Anthony heard the doctor talking to his mother out in the hall, but he couldn't catch much of what was being said. He asked Uncle Edward, later.

"He was concerned that you got so very sick, so fast. He was wondering if there might be an underlying problem."

"Like what?"

"Like a chronic infection, or something similar. He ran tests. So far—nothing."

"So Earl can come over?"

"He may, if he can," Uncle Edward said, correcting him.

"Will you call him?"

"When you have finished that eggnog, I shall call," Uncle Edward said, sitting back down.

Mark Anthony said, "I don't want the eggnog. Couldn't get it down. Honest."

"I see," Uncle Edward said thoughtfully. "Perhaps you would prefer your egg soft-boiled, with dry toast."

Mark Anthony shuddered and drank the eggnog. It wasn't easy, but he finished it. He hoped fervently it would not come right back up. "There. Are you satisfied?"

Uncle Edward nodded and picked up the empty glass with a very satisfied smile, and went to the phone.

Earl was impressed. "Boy—you've really got it made. I hear you've been real sick."

"I know."

"How do you feel now?"

"Tired. I can't do anything, but I'm always tired."

"Don't knock it. At least, you don't have to go to school."

"Anything new happen?"

Earl clammed up. Mark Anthony could see it happen. Everything Earl thought showed up simultaneously on his face. "Nothing special," he said.

"What's going on? You'd better tell me, Earl."

"Nothing important. When will you be coming back to school?"

"I don't know. Earl—there's something you're dying to tell me, but aren't. What is it?"

"I'm not supposed to excite you."

"Not knowing is exciting me."

Earl leaned forward. "At first, before they knew how sick you were, Brian and Arnold were going all around school saying how all that Indian stuff was fake, and that was why you weren't in school. They told everyone you weren't even really sick. Then, when the teacher said you might even have pneumonia, boy! did they look dumb."

"I don't even care anymore what they think. But don't you shoot your mouth off and get yourself involved, Earl, because I'm not having them over again for you or anyone else."

"Sure, sure, Mark Anthony."

"I found some more stuff, just before I got sick."

"What'd you find?"

"There's an aluminum-foil envelope and a piece of clay pot—top right-hand drawer in the dresser. Bring them in here."

Earl came back in a minute. He laid the envelope and the potsherd on the bed. "There's all doll stuff in there, too," he said.

"There is? In the drawer?" Mark Anthony started to get up, but thought better of it.

"Yeah. I guess that's Georgette's stuff, right?"

"Sure it is. She must have moved right in!"

"I thought that was supposed to be all your space."

"That's what I thought. You go get that doll stuff out of there and put it on her bed."

"I don't want to get into trouble."

"You won't. Go do it, now."

Mark Anthony leaned back and looked out the window. The trees on the lawn were full of tender new leaves, fluttering and glinting in the sun and wind. The sky was a deep, beautiful blue. A small bird darted from one tree to another, and disappeared among the leaves.

Suddenly, he had an idea. A really great idea. Earl came back into the room.

"Earl—when I'm well, I'm going to build a tree house—a real, big tree house."

"Fantastic!" Earl said. "Can I help?"

"Sure. We'll work on it together, and use it together."

"Oh, boy. That'll really be neat."

"It sure will. There's just one thing, Earl. You don't go spreading this all over school, now. You promise?"

Mark Anthony's mother came to the door. "Time's up, Earl. If Mark Anthony's doing all right, maybe you could come back tomorrow?"

"OK. I'll call in the morning." Earl got up and started out.

"Remember," Mark Anthony called, "don't say anything."

"OK," Earl said.

Mark Anthony buried his face in the pillow so his mother wouldn't hear him coughing from talking too much.

Earl dropped by every day to discuss plans for their tree house and relay all the news from school. Uncle Edward sat and rocked, and kept Mark Anthony company whenever Earl wasn't there. Mark Anthony's mother and father popped in and out constantly during the early mornings and evenings. Still, Mark Anthony felt restless, and bored, and edgy.

One morning, Uncle Edward left him alone briefly, and walked down to the university library and carried home an armful of books about Indians.

"This is terrific, Uncle Edward. Thanks a lot."

"You're quite welcome, my boy." Uncle Edward sat down heavily in his rocker. "By the way, I met a young man at the library. He was quite interested in your Indian collection. I think he might like to see it."

Mark Anthony sat up. "Forget that, Uncle Edward. I'm not having anyone else over to see my collection."

"This young man is very knowledgeable. He is an archaeology major—you know what that means. He may be able to shed some light on the origins of your artifacts."

"No way. I'm not going through that again. Please don't ask me, Uncle Edward. You don't understand. These things are important to me, see, but to anyone else, they're not so great. No one else sees them."

"It's entirely up to you. If you change your mind, I'll get in touch with him for you."

"I appreciate your help—but let's leave him out of it."

"Consider him out."

They settled down to their reading.

A week later, Dr. Thorndike told Mark Anthony he was ready to go back to school.

"I'm not ready. I'll never be ready to go back to that school," Mark Anthony said to Uncle Edward.

"You've been gone quite a while, my boy. You will find yourself to be quite the conquering hero, I think. Pale, thinner, the survivor of a harrowing ordeal—an unbeatable combination."

"I don't think Arnold or Brian or the other kids in my class will be all that impressed. And if the teachers make a fuss over me, I've had it."

Uncle Edward nodded. "I see your point."

"Also, we're getting report cards pretty soon."

"Surely yours will be marked 'Incomplete.' "

"Yes. But before that, it'll be marked 'Unsatisfactory.' "

"Come now, Mark Anthony, the one thing that has never given you any trouble is your schoolwork."

"Well, lately I haven't been doing all that well."

"Really? May I ask why?"

"You know how they were making fun of me every time I answered correctly in class—and when tests came back, and everyone asked what everyone else got, how they would say stuff like, 'Mark Anthony's got another A. He's Mrs. Prescott's pet. All the teachers like Mark Anthony.' They just never let up. So—I sort of coasted for a while, to see if they would leave me alone."

"Did it work?"

"Not really. I began to get C's a lot, and I hardly ever answered in class. They started giving Heidi Mueller a hard time too. But they still don't like me."

"And the day of reckoning approacheth."

"You said it."

"Your father will be upset."

"Will he ever!"

Uncle Edward sighed. Mark Anthony's mother called him from the living room.

"Ma's home. I've got to go."

"Come back anytime."

Mark Anthony's mother had some packages.

"Here, dear. I got you a new pair of blue jeans and a shirt to match. To wear on your first day back. We're so glad you're all recovered and ready to return to school," and she hugged him lightly and handed him one of the bags.

"Thanks, Ma."

He opened the bag. Blue jeans. Neat. No big copper rivets. No thick leather patch on one hip in back, like everyone else wore. Neat—very neat. Too neat. And a blue and white checked shirt. The country-boy type. Except that no country boy he'd ever known would wear that shirt—it would look too much like his mother's tablecloth. There was just one chance. He'd lost some weight, being sick. Maybe they were too big.

His mother was standing there, waiting for a reaction.

"Why don't you try them on now, to see how they fit?"

"Sure thing," Mark Anthony said. At the doorway, he turned and added, "I really appreciate your getting me these things, Ma . . . on your lunch hour, and all."

His mother smiled at him and bent to pick up the rest of her things.

Well, he'd been right about one thing. They were too big. His arms looked like bleached toothpicks, hanging down out of those starchy short sleeves, and the blue jeans were so big

542

around his middle, he had to hold them on with a leather belt. But he knew they weren't so big that they'd be returned.

"Once you get some of that weight back, they'll be perfect," his mother said cheerfully.

"He's growing, anyway," his father said.

Uncle Edward said, "You look like an ad for 'Send this boy to camp.' "

"I know."

"Is there anything I can do?"

"No. She probably took her whole lunch hour looking for these, and she thinks they look great."

"She loves you very much."

"I know she does."

"Haven't you ever asked her to let you pick out your own things?"

"Sure I have."

"And?"

"She says we should shop together—to be sure and get good value, and the right size—which means about two sizes too large. She thinks the things all the kids are wearing look kind of tacky."

"They do. But that's not the point, is it? Perhaps when the opportunity presents itself, I shall rush in where angels fear to tread, on your behalf. In the meantime. . . ."

"I'll wear them. And I will grow into them."

"True. And after school, you can certainly make a case for wearing your older, smaller things."

"Right."

In spite of the shirt and jeans, and Mrs. Prescott's hovering over him like an angel in a painting, the first few days of school went by fairly peacefully. Arnold, the real ringleader in any group action, pretty well ignored Mark Anthony. Mark Anthony gratefully went out of his way not to rock the boat. He studiously maintained his low profile and stayed as far away from Arnold as possible.

When three days of school had gone by, and Mark Anthony had not started running a temperature again, Dr.

Thorndike said he could resume all normal activity.

To Mark Anthony, that meant work on the tree house. He and Earl lived in a constant state of suppressed excitement as the weekend drew closer.

Chapter 6

Sunday morning, they rendezvoused very early at the edge of Eberhart's woods and began the search for the perfect tree. There were trees in the Crowder and Jones yards, but they were young, development trees, like all the others in the neighborhood. Young maples, mostly. What they needed was a great big, old oak, or broad, spreading beech.

The woods were jumping. Things were growing, blossoming, spreading, singing, chirruping, climbing, and dashing. Nothing was staying the same except for the rocks. Mark Anthony felt as if he might become airborne at any moment, floating and bouncing along in the shimmering sunlight like a helium-filled balloon.

Earl darted from one side of the path to the other, like a chipmunk, checking out dozens of trees, talking all the time. Mark Anthony remembered Uncle Edward's words, from the night before he got sick. This must be one of those golden times. Only now he knew it, so he could really feel it and promise himself to remember.

At last, they found it. It was a very old oak.

Broad branches spread out all around the trunk. Any one of them would support a small tree house. If they built it so it was supported by two branches, it would be even safer. They found two branches on the far side of the tree, growing almost parallel to each other, less than six feet apart, for quite a distance. It was perfect, as if it had been designed for a tree house from the start.

Earl tied his handkerchief to one branch, to mark it, and they started home. It was settled. Now all they needed was the wood to build the tree house.

They went to Earl's house first, for lunch. His father was home. Earl brought up the subject of scrap lumber very casually, while they ate.

His father said, "Why don't you go over to Maple Drive, where they're building those new houses? They pile all their scraps in one place, so they can burn them later. Just don't take anything that isn't in a pile with a lot of scraps."

"Sure, Dad."

"Hey, you haven't finished your lunch."

"That's all I want, Dad. Come on, Mark Anthony."

"Good-by, Mr. Jones," Mark Anthony said, and took off after Earl, who had a good start on him already.

The scrap piles were full of interesting things. Most of the pieces of wood were small, though. By carefully sifting through several piles on several lots, they got quite a pile of their own.

"How do we get it to the tree?" Earl asked, standing back and studying it.

"A wheelbarrow. I'll borrow my parents'."

"Sure. That will work fine." And Earl was off again.

They worked all day. By Sunday evening, the tree house looked just as good as Mark Anthony had dreamed it would. Over the door, he proudly nailed a small sign:

No Trespassing Stay Out
Property of
Mark Anthony Crowder & Earl Jones

The wheelbarrow had come from the Crowders' basement, along with two rusty hinges for the door and half the nails. The hammers, an old window with only one pane missing, half the nails, and the saw came from the Jones's utility room.

"Did your parents let you have this neat window?"

"Sure," Earl said. "They said anything to keep me busy and out of their hair while they worked on the records. They're being audited."

"What's that?"

"The government wants to know if they cheated on their income tax."

"Did they?"

"No, but they can't find half the records. They put them in a box when they were through with them, and now they can't find the box. They think someone may have thrown it out. It's making them tense. How about you? What'd you tell your parents?"

"They were working. Dad was at a play-off, but I called him up. He said I could borrow anything but the power tools, just to bring it all back in good shape."

"Didn't he ask what you were building?"

"No. Did your parents?"

"No," Earl said.

"Well, then, no one but us knows about it." Somehow, that made the tree house even more special to Mark Anthony.

Earl frowned. "I sure would like to be able to show it off to just one other person."

"Why?"

"Oh, I don't know. Just so they could say how neat it was—or tell us what's wrong with it."

"Aw, come on, Earl. We don't need anyone else butting in."

"How about your Uncle Edward?"

Mark Anthony thought about that for a moment. "Yes. He'd be all right. And he'd come too, if we asked him."

"Sure he would. OK. Let's ask him to come tomorrow afternoon."

"OK. I'll meet you here—right here—at the tree, at three-thirty tomorrow."

They shook on it, formally.

Then they picked up the tools and loaded them into the wheelbarrow and started off down the path. At the bend, they stopped and turned back. The tree house rested in the arms of the tree like a small box. The fresh, new wood looked naked, somehow, surrounded by rough, weathered bark and shining bronze leaves.

"Maybe we should paint it," Earl said.

"Right. Camouflage it. Dark brown and green, maybe."

"Right."

"It's a good house. Wait till we get it fixed up."

"You said it."

Uncle Edward was impressed. "You mean to tell me you boys did all this in one day? Why, it's just about perfect."

Mark Anthony said, "Would you like to climb up and go in?"

"Thank you, no. I am honored, of course, but climbing is out of the question. It's all I can do, some nights, to climb into bed."

"We're going to paint it brown and green, to camouflage it," Earl said proudly.

"Sound idea. Aesthetically very sound. It will blend in with its surroundings."

"It's perfectly safe too," Mark Anthony said. "See how it rests on two of the biggest branches?"

"It does indeed. This tree is magnificent, isn't it? One of the tallest in these woods, I would imagine." He paused and then continued thoughtfully, "I expect the owner is very proud of it."

"The owner?" Mark Anthony asked. "What owner?"

"Every bit of land in these continental United States is owned by someone. Therefore, we must assume someone owns this tree."

"Eberhart does," Earl said. "Mr. Eberhart. He lives in that big, old house on the other side of the woods. The one with all the fancy carving around the porch and roof."

"Yes, I remember, on Peach Street. So there really is an Eberhart, who owns Eberhart's woods. Is the house a faded yellow? Three stories? Heavily encrusted with Victorian gingerbread? There is a very interesting octagonal room at the top, is there not—with windows all around?"

"That's it."

"Well," Uncle Edward said, "it might be diplomatic for you fellows to drop by someday soon, and let Mr. Eberhart know what you've accomplished in his oak tree. It's always better to bring the subject up, in a polite way, than to wait for him to find it out himself."

"He'll never find this tree house," Mark Anthony said.

"Possibly. Possibly. However, I must call your attention to this path. You used it to traverse these woods effortlessly. It would not be here if someone else had not been using it, and kept it open. I think you'd better approach Mr. Eberhart for his permission."

"All right," Mark Anthony said. "After we've painted it. I don't want anyone else noticing it."

"You'd better get busy then," Uncle Edward said. "There is a front due here Wednesday night—if the forecast is to be believed."

"Wow, we'd better paint it tomorrow," Earl said.

"Right after school," Mark Anthony agreed.

Uncle Edward walked down the path, turned and studied

the tree house. "I think you boys did a first-class piece of work here. Are you going to show this to your parents?"

"No way," Mark Anthony said. "Next thing you know, Georgette and her friends would be up there, we'd be out."

Earl nodded. "Besides, they wouldn't be interested."

Uncle Edward shook his head. "Not true. However, I am a guest, not a member, so I must abide by your decision. I hope you change your minds about that later on." He waved good-by and walked on around the curve in the path.

"Will he tell?" Earl asked fearfully.

"No. Not unless we say he can."

"What about Mr. Eberhart?"

"First we paint—to beat the rain. Then we worry about telling Mr. Eberhart."

"OK. You got any paint?"

"We've got a lot of old cans with a little left in them. Don't you have any brown or green?"

"No. I don't think so. Some white, maybe, and some purple, from the bathroom."

"What'll we do? We can't paint it in stripes."

"Mix it all up together. It'll probably come out close to brown. I remember when I was a little kid, once, I mixed all my poster paints together, and I got a real muddy color."

"Well, it won't hurt to try it. I'll meet you here tomorrow with all the paint you can find. Bring a brush too."

"Right. Shake."

Tuesday afternoon was hot and sticky. Mark Anthony scrounged around through the basement and found five cans with a little paint left in each of them, and one can of brush cleaner. He called his father at the college.

"Dad, can I have all those old cans of leftover paint and some of your rags?"

"I guess so. What for?"

"We're painting something. Can I borrow a brush?"

"OK, but I want it back when you're through—clean."

"Right. I found some brush cleaner."

"All right. And don't paint in the house—you hear?"

"OK, Dad."

Earl was waiting for him at the tree. He had three small cans and a brush with him.

"Is this all you could find?"

"Yes. What are we going to mix it in?"

"One of my big cans, I guess. Did your father mind you taking the stuff?"

"He's out of town. My mother was glad to get rid of it. She wanted me to keep on going and work on clearing out the whole utility room. I thought I'd had it. I told her I'd promised to meet you."

"Well, here goes."

The resulting paint mixture was a dull, neutral color—somewhere between purple and brown and gray.

"It's not very pretty," Earl said sadly.

"We don't want pretty. We want camouflaged. This will do it."

They cleaned the brushes and piled the paint pots neatly in a corner of the tree house, along with the rags and the can full of brush cleaner.

"We can paint the inside any day," Mark Anthony said. "The rain won't matter."

"Do you think this roof will leak?"

Mark Anthony looked up. Here and there he could see tiny slivers of light.

"It might. I'll get a couple of plastic trash bags and cover the roof with them. Maybe I'll put rocks on them to weigh them down."

"That'll do it," Earl said. "Then the stuff we put in here will be one hundred percent safe."

"It's coming along great, isn't it?"

"It sure is. When are you going to Eberhart's place?"

"Me? Why just me? You helped build—you help talk."

"OK, OK. When will we go?"

"Tomorrow, I guess—unless it rains."

"All right. If it doesn't rain, I'll come over to your house after school."

"Come anyway. We can do something."

They stopped for a moment at the edge of the woods, where Earl usually peeled off to go to his house.

"Boy!" Earl said, "if the kids at school could see that tree house, they'd go bananas."

"Well, they aren't going to see it, are they?" Mark Anthony demanded. "This is going to be just our place, right?"

"Sure, sure. I've got to go. My parents will be getting mad if I'm late."

It worried Mark Anthony, what Earl had said. He stood there and watched Earl cut across the empty corner lot. Maybe that little sign over the tree-house door wasn't enough. Some people didn't think you meant what you said unless you shouted. A small sign sort of whispered politely.

He jogged back down the path leading into the woods till he ran out of breath and had to walk. When he reached the tree house, he found the bucket of white paint—there was a little left in the bottom—and a brush. He painted KEEP OUT in very large letters on every side of the tree house but the front. Then he put the brush and bucket back, and climbed down to study the effect.

The white paint had started to run a little, but anyone who could read would still get the point.

He started home again, his mind more at ease.

Chapter 7

It was cloudy when Mark Anthony woke up Wednesday. Very cloudy. The rain was coming, after all. He hoped all the paint on the tree house had dried. The air was heavy. It felt almost thick and hot on the skin.

The storm arrived while he was in school. It started with a black sky. The teachers had to turn the lights on in the classrooms, and everyone kept looking out the windows and saying how dark it was getting. Mark Anthony was delighted. It was one of the most exciting mornings he'd ever spent in school.

As they were getting ready to go into the cafeteria for lunch, the PA system came on.

The principal, Mr. Farnum, always started his announcements by clearing his throat and saying "Testing. One, two, three, four." Mark Anthony could never figure out what he thought he was testing. You could always hear him—clear out to the playground.

"This area has been placed on a tornado watch, starting at twelve noon and continuing until seven this evening. Teachers are asked to review their storm-alert sheets, and run through the evacuation drill procedure with their students. That is all."

Mark Anthony felt a shiver of excitement run down his back. He was pleasantly scared, and fascinated by the stormy sky outside. He heard Mrs. Prescott outlining the evacuation procedure. Her voice was higher pitched than usual, so he guessed she was a little frightened herself. But his attention was on the windows as he watched the small trees around the school tugging at their roots in a fitful wind.

He thought about the big oak in the middle of Eberhart's woods, and the little tree house in its lowest branches, and wondered if they had nailed it down firmly enough. They should have used more nails, but they hadn't wanted to hurt the tree. It was really a great old tree.

Everyone filed into the cafeteria, talking about the storm. He saw Earl, and made his way over to Earl's table.

"How about this storm?" Mark Anthony said.

"Do you think the tree house will be OK?"

"I don't know. Most of the time these watches end up with just plain old thunderstorms."

"This one is awfully dark," Earl said, and looked out the window. His voice was light, and his face was kind of pale. Mark Anthony realized that Earl was really scared.

"Come on, Earl—we're not going to have a tornado. They're just getting all excited about nothing."

They had just gotten back to class when Mr. Farnum came on again. He cleared his throat.

"Testing. One, two, three, four. The Weather Bureau has

just issued a tornado warning for Dorr County. Please remain calm. Do not panic. It is important, however, to monitor the sky for possible tornadoes in this area. We are advised to watch for trouble in the southwest quadrant of the sky. The teachers on that side of the building will keep us informed, and I am on my way up to the roof at this moment. I repeat—please remain calm. Everything will be all right."

Mark Anthony could feel the vibrations around him. Everyone was psyched up. Dorr County was only a short drive away from Ridgedale. He'd gone over there lots of times in the fall, to get cider with his father. Mrs. Prescott started to speak, had trouble with the first word, and started again.

"Now, children, it is important to remain calm. We will continue with our daily work. In the event of a tornado, we all know what to do. I'm sure the people on the southwest side will give us plenty of warning."

Outside, Mark Anthony could see lightning flicker over the trees near the horizon. Around the school, the air had become still. The sky was a sickly orange color, and the light coming through the windows was a murky greenish yellow. Like a bruise, he thought, a couple of days after it first shows up.

The lightning on the horizon slowly died away. But the color of the clouds over the school changed gradually to a heavy purple gray color. The air was still, except for an occasional odd little gust, coming out of nowhere and going nowhere. Mark Anthony could hardly sit in his seat. It was as if everything on earth was poised—waiting—holding its breath.

Suddenly, a tremendous sheet of lightning flashed through the air. Even with the classroom lights on, it was blinding. The kids all reacted. Some yelped, some drew in their breath sharply. Mrs. Prescott said "Oh!" very loudly, and sat down, as if she was feeling faint.

There was a single, sharp cracking sound, like a gunshot. The lightning had struck something nearby.

The thunder, coming right afterwards, was so close, so

loud, Mark Anthony could feel it vibrate up through his feet, where they rested on the floor, and through his arms, which touched his desk. The lightning flashed again, and as it dimmed, all the lights in the classroom went out.

From all over the school, Mark Anthony could hear the cries and small shouts of startled children, and, more faintly, the undertone of teachers' voices, firm, controlled, penetrating. His heart pounded up in his throat. His palms were sweaty. This was no joke. Poor Earl. He must be really scared by now. Earl was frightened of thunderstorms, although he hid it pretty well, most of the time. Mark Anthony wished he could go to Earl's room and sit with him, to keep him company. The thunder pounded down onto them as if it were trying to drive the school into the ground.

Then, from the village, he heard the volunteer fire company's siren. Sometimes lightning set it off when there wasn't a fire. But usually, hearing the siren during a storm meant something had been hit and was burning. Mark Anthony thought of their oak—"One of the tallest in these woods," Uncle Edward had said.

The siren wailed on and on. All over town, Mark Anthony knew, men were dropping their pens or paintbrushes or wrenches and racing to their cars. They would speed through the village towards the firehouse, headlights on, horns blaring. They should be there, some of them, in a minute . . . running past the rack where their hats and waterproof coats hung, snatching them as they ran, springing up onto the fire trucks, and revving up the motors. Mark Anthony planned to be a volunteer fireman when he got old enough. He dreamed about it, sometimes.

The lightning flashed almost continuously now. The thunder rolled first from one side of the school—then from the other. Some of the kids had their heads down on their desks and were crying softly. Little Shorty Travis looked sick. Sometimes Shorty threw up if he got upset. Mrs. Prescott must have noticed. She was walking towards Shorty's desk.

Some big drops of rain spattered on the windows near

Mark Anthony's desk. Then the downpour started. The rain was so heavy, it cut off his view, like a curtain made of wrinkled cellophane.

Down in the village, the first truck had its own siren going. He could hear it, in between the explosions of the thunder and the drumming of the rain. In another thirty seconds, it would be on its way, and the second would be warming up and sounding off. He wished he could be either at the fire station, climbing up on a truck, or sitting with Earl while all this was going on. He hoped Earl wouldn't get sick like Shorty had, poor kid.

Little by little, the electric storm wore itself out. By the regular dismissal time, the sky was still hanging over them, heavy and threatening, but the rain had stopped. The power was still out. Mr. Farnum came around to each class and started them out to the buses. No one was allowed to walk home today. Every walker was assigned to a bus and told to go straight home after getting off it. Mark Anthony saw Earl in the corridor, walking silently out to his bus. He looked as if he might have been crying, but it was hard to tell in the dark corridor. Poor Earl. He'd call him up as soon as he got home. Earl's mother would never let him come over with a tornado watch on.

Georgette wasn't on the bus. She must have taken the other bus and gone to Doris's house. His father's car was in the driveway. He didn't often get home during the afternoon. And there was a pickup truck, a very old one, pulled up in front of the house. Mark Anthony didn't recognize it.

His father was sitting in the wing chair.

"Mark Anthony?"

"Yes, sir?"

"This is Mr. Eberhart." And his father pointed to a small elderly man hunched up on their sofa, holding an old cap between his hands.

"Hello, Mr. Eberhart." Mark Anthony knew something was wrong. His father sounded strange. Cold, sort of, and very formal. Like he didn't even know Mark Anthony.

555

"Hello, young man," Mr. Eberhart said. "I have just told your father about the damage you did to my tree. Nearly burned my woods down, that's what you did. And what I want to know is, what's he going to do about it."

Mark Anthony felt as if everyone was talking to him in a foreign language.

"I didn't burn your woods down, Mr. Eberhart."

"Awfully close, let me tell you. Just lucky for you we have this tornado watch on."

Mark Anthony sat down. He glanced at his father. His father's face looked like it had been carved out of rock, like those men on Mount Rushmore. He turned back to Mr. Eberhart.

"I'm sorry, but I don't know what you're talking about."

"You don't, huh? Did you and a friend of yours—an Earl Jones—build a tree house on my property."

"Yes." Mark Anthony felt trapped, somehow. He knew he must be in real trouble, but he didn't know what . . . or why.

"Did you ask me if you could?"

"No, sir. I was going to see you this afternoon."

"You were, were you? That's convenient. It's also after the fact."

"What happened?" Mark Anthony could hardly hear himself, his voice was so low.

"What happened was that shack you built burned down. Nearly took my tree—my whole woods—with it."

"How could it?"

"Well, I'll tell you. First off, I thought the old tree had been hit by lightning, when I saw the smoke. But when we got over there, we found a pile of paint cans and rags and all, blazing away merry as could be. If that shack hadn't been made of green lumber, and the heavens hadn't opened and dumped a load of rain on it, I'd have lost the whole kit and caboodle. Didn't you ever hear of spontaneous combustion?"

"Yes, sir. I've heard of it. I thought the house was too well ventilated for it to be a problem. There were little holes in the roof, and everything. I'm awfully sorry about the tree."

"Did you ever hear of trespassing?"

"Yes, sir."

"Good, because you're going to hear a lot more about it, you are. I'm posting my land, and if you so much as set foot on it—you or that Earl Jones—I'll have the law on both of you."

Mark Anthony looked at his father.

There was no answering movement of the eyes, nothing to show his father was aware of his appeal.

Mr. Eberhart stood up. "I've never had to post my land. Never wanted to. Now, you're responsible for me having to close it off. I'll be going now. I can see I'm not going to get any satisfaction here. I'll give you twenty-four hours to get every splinter, every nail of that tree house off my property."

Mr. Eberhart turned suddenly, on Mr. Crowder. "What kind of a father are you, anyway, mister? You don't know what your own son's up to, and you don't stir yourself to make good when he does some damage, and you don't even stick up for him or stand by him."

"We'll get the tree house out of there—don't worry," Mr. Crowder said.

"See that you do." And Mr. Eberhart stumped off toward the front door. Mark Anthony came to life again and followed him.

"Mr. Eberhart, I'm sorry. Honest. And I was going to see you. You can ask my uncle. This afternoon. I wouldn't have done anything to hurt that tree—that's just about the best tree in your whole woods."

Mr. Eberhart stopped and looked at him for a minute. Then he said, "I reckon you are sorry. So am I. Crazy thing to do—leaving all that inflammable stuff around. Kids today aren't ever taught anything sensible—all about how to run a computer, but nothing about not burning your own house down. Feel sorry for all of us, I do. Lot of nonsense, not much common sense, that's what I say. I'll let myself out." And he did.

Mark Anthony turned back to the living room. His father still sat in the wing chair.

"I'm sorry I got you in trouble, Dad."

"I trusted you."

"What do you mean?"

"I left you alone, and you never told me you were building a tree house on someone else's land."

"I never really thought about it that way—till someone else pointed it out. I never really thought it was that important."

"You didn't think. You never think—of anyone but yourself. You have no team spirit—It's always just I . . . I . . . I."

"Dad, please."

"The volunteer fire department saw that house—with your name on it. Everyone in town will know about it by tonight."

"I didn't do anything bad. Just to build a tree house isn't bad."

"It resulted in the destruction of private property, didn't it? That Mr. Eberhart thinks you're a juvenile delinquent and I'm a delinquent parent. How could you do this to me?"

"I didn't *do* anything. I should have asked first, I should have taken the paint stuff away, but I didn't mean to hurt anything."

Mark Anthony's stomach tightened into a painful ball just under his ribs, and the first hot wave of nausea swept up into his throat. He gulped hard and said, "Excuse me," and ran towards the bathroom.

He could hear his father calling after him. "OK—duck out. But we'll talk more about this when I've cooled down. This subject is not closed yet, young man. You're going to have to rejoin the human race. Yes, sir!"

Mark hated to throw up. He always fought it till he had to give in and let it happen. He kept flushing the toilet and running the water, so no one could hear him.

When it was really all over, and the pain in his stomach had quit, he washed his face and combed his hair. He looked OK. Pale and kind of damp, but OK.

The house was quiet. His father must be in the den, at the southwest corner of the house—keeping an eye on the weather. His mother wouldn't be home yet, and Georgette was probably having a great time at Doris's house. He made it to his bedroom without having to talk to anyone . . . or listen to anyone.

Uncle Edward waited an hour before he knocked.

"May I come in?"

"Yes."

Uncle Edward felt his way over to the bed and sat down.

"It's dark as an abandoned mine in here."

"That's the way I want it."

"You heard?"

"Of course."

"Uncle Edward, is your position here really precarious?"

Uncle Edward sat on the bed, silent, for a full minute. Then he answered slowly.

"I don't know. I've never felt free to test its stability."

"That's why you wouldn't stick up for me this afternoon—if you heard?"

"Mark Anthony, right now, you and I need each other very much. That's what we might call a primary consideration. Everything else is secondary. Do you understand me, so far?"

"I think so."

"Frequently, I must decide how I can best help you on a long-term basis. The answer is usually to avoid making my position here untenable. Do you follow me?"

"I guess so."

"Therefore, to put it in the vernacular, I keep my mouth shut for five minutes so I can converse with you, later, for sixty minutes."

"I understand."

"Good. It has bothered me for some time now—what you must think of me in circumstances like those of this afternoon. However, I did not wish to add anxiety about me to your burdens. Now that you've brought it up, it's best to be candid."

Mark Anthony said, "Don't worry, Uncle Edward. I can fight my own battles. You just stay cool."

"Well, in this particular situation, there may actually be something concrete I can do for you. But it's going to take time—maybe as long as a week or more."

"What?"

"I won't say. In case it doesn't work—or I have to change my approach. But, if I do succeed, you will know immediately."

Mark Anthony reached out and touched Uncle Edward's arm. "Don't rock the boat here, will you? Don't get my father mad at you or anything else, please."

"Have no fear, my boy. We understand each other perfectly, you and I. I will not, as you put it, 'rock the boat.'" He stood up. "It must be almost seven. The worst is over. Time to blow the all clear."

They took the tree house down Thursday afternoon. Mark Anthony's father was due at six—to inspect the area and make sure there was nothing left to mark where the house had been.

Mark Anthony had been dreading it—coming back to the tree. He was afraid one whole side of the tree would be burned off or scarred. He even dreamed about it. In his dreams, the whole woods had eventually gone up in flames, leaving a smoking, blackened wasteland around a newly painted tree house—still intact.

When he actually saw the oak, he felt about one hundred percent better. The corner of the tree house where the paint cans had been stored, and the window—framed in old, dry wood—had been burned out. But the damage to the tree itself was limited to a few leaves and twigs overhead, and a bit of charred bark underneath. The house itself lay on its side on the ground—crumpled, streaked, and blackened. But the tree was OK.

They used the wheelbarrow and trucked it all back to the scrap heaps on Maple Drive. By six, Mark Anthony could not see a single nail or bit of painted wood anywhere near the tree.

His father took one long, silent look around, nodded, and walked back down the path. Mark Anthony fell into step a

560

few paces behind him. They walked home without talking. His father was still plenty angry. Mark Anthony could even see it in the way he walked.

Report cards were handed out just as school closed, Friday afternoon.

Mark Anthony slid his card out of its envelope in his lap. It was kind of a shock at first . . . C's, D's, and Incompletes, in red ink, like pimples, all over. Well, no one could call him a teacher's pet with a card like this.

Arnold caught up with him in the hall. "How's it going, Mark Anthony? All A's?"

Mark Anthony thought Arnold's voice would rank right up there with chalk going the wrong way on a blackboard.

"No. Not all A's."

"So, let's see it."

Mark Anthony held his card out. Arnold's eyes widened. He handed it back.

"Boy, your father's going to be ripping." He sounded almost friendly.

"Don't I know it." Mark Anthony shoved the card back into its envelope and put it in his pocket. "I've got to get the bus."

"What'll he do to you?" Arnold kept up with him as the kids surged out to the line of buses drawn up to the curb.

"I don't know. Cut back on my allowance or something. Who knows?" Mark Anthony tried to sound casual. He swung himself up into the bus and let himself down into his seat. Arnold leaned up into the stairwell.

"See you tomorrow, kid."

Mr. Goss, the bus driver, tapped Arnold's shoulder. "You want to move on, Janssen? I'd like to close the door now, if it's all the same with you."

"Sure thing, Mr. Goss," Arnold said, and backed away.

The bus door squeaked shut, and the bus backed ponderously out into the school drive. Mark Anthony slumped in his seat. Now, all he had to do was show this card to his father . . . and his mother . . . and Uncle Edward. He groaned.

Chapter 8

He went right to his room, and stayed busy all afternoon. He read some, and left his radio on good and loud, but the report card hung in the back of his mind like a dark cloud. Things might ease up a little at school now, but they were sure going to tighten up some at home, when this card had to be signed. He toyed with the idea of forgery, for a minute, but decided against it. First of all, he'd never get away with it, and boy! when that came out, he'd really be in trouble. Second, it was wrong—maybe even a crime.

Maybe the subject just wouldn't come up. Maybe the moon would fall down out of the sky. He was the last one to the dinner table.

Georgette brought it up, of course. "We got report cards, today. May I have the gravy, please?"

"Did you, dear?" his mother said, handing down the gravy boat. "Did you get yours, too, Mark Anthony?"

"Yes."

"Well, let's see them," his father said heartily. Mark Anthony thought he'd rather get the silent treatment than that hearty, team spirit ho-ho-ho, like a department store Santa Claus.

He pulled the card out of his pocket and handed it to his father.

"Shouldn't let it get all dog-eared like this," his father said. "It doesn't look neat. Doesn't look as if we took proper care of it."

He opened it.

He read it all the way down.

Then he handed it to Mark Anthony's mother.

"I don't know. You figure him out. I quit." And he got up and left the table.

His mother dropped the card on the table and stood up. She picked up his father's plate and silverware, and followed him into the hall.

"Whatever it is, Harry, why not finish your supper? We can all talk it over later, calmly."

"That card isn't going to look any better on a full stomach,"

his father shouted. "In fact, it makes me want to throw up."

Their voices blended and trailed away as they went into their bedroom at the end of the hall.

Georgette reached for the card. "Boy, that must be some report card."

Mark Anthony grabbed it away from her. "Leave it alone."

"Ma," Georgette yelled, "Ma!"

Uncle Edward rapped his knife handle on the table. "Eat your dinner, Georgette."

She look up at him, startled.

"I said, eat your dinner. It'll get cold. I'll take this till your mother gets back," and he pulled the card out of Mark

Anthony's hand. "You eat something too."

Mark Anthony studied Georgette under his eyelashes once or twice.

The three of them sat there, shoving the food around on their plates. Mark Anthony's mother came back.

She sat down, and Uncle Edward handed over the card. She slipped it out and studied it silently. Then she looked up, not at Mark Anthony, but at Uncle Edward.

After a moment or two, she asked, "Did you look at it?"

"I have a rough idea."

"I see." She looked at Mark Anthony. "Your father wants to talk to you later." She sighed. "I don't know what the problem is, but I do know you've always been a good student till now, and you're still intelligent. Something is wrong, somewhere. Can you talk about it?"

"Not right here, right now, Ma."

"All right, dear. Later." She glanced at Uncle Edward nervously, and laughed. " 'Later' is filling up fast, isn't it?" Then she reached over and squeezed Mark Anthony's hand. "Everything will work out, somehow."

She turned to Georgette. "Let's see your card, dear."

Georgette went to get hers from her room. "She always likes to make a big production out of it," Mark Anthony thought. He pushed back his chair.

"May I be excused, Ma?"

"Yes, dear."

He went to his room to wait for the summons to the family conference. He really hated family conferences. Groups of people couldn't sit down and talk things over like two people could. In a group, someone was always yelling, and talking about seventy-five percent of the time; and someone else was always trying to say something and not getting anywhere. He lay down on the bed. "Of course," he thought, "sometimes it can be like that when just two people are discussing something." He groaned out loud.

They called him into the living room about eight-thirty. Uncle Edward got up to leave as he came in, but Mark Anthony's mother said, "Sit down, Uncle Edward, you don't have to go. We're all family."

Mark Anthony saw his father's eyebrows go up, but he didn't say anything.

Uncle Edward sat down.

Mark Anthony found a seat beside his mother. He wondered, for a moment, if this was what it was like to be on trial.

His father cleared his throat.

"Mark Anthony, you're getting further and further out of line every day. Something's got to be done about it."

Uncle Edward stirred restlessly in his chair.

"I'm sorry about the report card."

" 'Sorry' doesn't help, mister. 'Sorry' doesn't get you into college. 'Sorry' doesn't get you a good job. 'Sorry' doesn't support a family."

"He's just a boy," Mark Anthony's mother protested.

"Oh, really? He's grown up enough to almost burn down Eberhart's woods. He's big enough to stay out till all hours 'walking' without permission or a word to anyone else. Just when do you think we should start bringing him up right?"

"We have been bringing him up right," Mark Anthony's mother said angrily. "For heaven's sake, Harry, the child hasn't killed someone."

"This 'child' has caused us to be held up to public and private ridicule. This 'child' will be in trouble with the police, next."

Georgette said, "I heard he burned a whole oak tree down."

"I did not. Just a few leaves got scorched, and a little bark burned."

"Well, that's what Patricia Reilly said, and her father should know. He's a volunteer fireman, so there."

His father banged on the coffee table.

"The point is, we've got to nip this in the bud. You have got too much time on your hands. What you'll get into this summer, who knows. The first thing is, I want you to register for the sports-camp program at the college. It'll be good for you to think of the team first."

Mark Anthony stood up. "No! I can't. I won't do it."

His father stood up also. "Why not? You're always saying you can't pitch, you can't run, you can't do this or that. Here's an opportunity to learn, from professionals. We couldn't even afford it if I didn't get a faculty discount. You'll be training right at the college. You can even ride over with me. It's a great opportunity."

"I can't do it. The kids who do that are good to begin with. I stink. It'll be awful. And with my own father working on the coaching staff. It'll be just like school, only worse. You'll see. And you'll hate it."

Mark Anthony was yelling now, but he didn't care. "You know why? Because I'll blow it. I won't be good at anything and everyone will know I'm your son."

He ran out of the room.

His father yelled after him, "You stay out till all hours and I'll call the police. You hear me?"

The front door banged to, behind him, and he was out . . . into the cool, quiet, moist darkness.

He circled the common in the village. There was a four-sided clock in the lighted tower of a church near the common, and he could keep track of the time. He figured he'd better be in by ten, or he might find himself down at the station.

His father and mother were watching television. He walked through the living room fast, but not fast enough.

His mother called him back.

"Mark Anthony, now that you've had a chance to consider, do you still refuse to go to the sports camp?"

"Yes, Ma. I'm not refusing, really, I just very strongly don't want to do it."

His father snorted.

"Well, your father feels that you must learn to be more responsible. So he—we—have decided that you will be in charge of the vegetable garden this year."

"The whole garden?"

566

"That's right," his father said very low and gravelly. "By the end of the summer, sports camp will look good to you."

"You may charge the seeds and sprays and things at Billy's Hardware, and we will expect the garden to look well cared for at all times," his mother said.

"Thanks," Mark Anthony said. He was seething with anger. This was his father's idea—getting back. He'd never have time for anything else all summer.

"Don't be fresh to your mother," his father snapped.

"Harry, will you please let me handle this?" His mother turned back to Mark Anthony. "Maybe Uncle Edward will lend a hand, if you ask him."

"He's not to work that old man to death, out in the hot sun," his father said.

His mother threw her hands in the air. "I've had it, Harry. This is your son we're talking to, not Attila the Hun. Now handle this yourself, or let me do it. And Uncle Edward is not 'that old man.' "

His father said, "See the trouble you cause?" to Mark Anthony.

His mother said briskly, "Nothing of the kind. Go on to your room, Mark Anthony. Tomorrow is another day. It won't really be so bad." She caught his hand and pulled him closer to her and kissed his cheek. She smelled very nice. In his ear, she whispered, "It'll all work out, dear," and then she released him. For just a second or two, he stayed where he was, bent over her, and kissed her cheek very quickly. Then he straightened up and bolted for his room.

Uncle Edward shuffled across the hall around eleven o'clock. Mark Anthony heard him coming and yelled, "Come in," before he could knock.

Uncle Edward opened the door and winked at Mark Anthony. "I heard."

"Boy, I'm sunk."

"Not so. I think it all turned out very well, considering."

Mark Anthony sat up. "Maybe you *didn't* hear. I've got the whole vegetable garden to take care of."

"Wellington did it for four summers, and had time left over for tennis and swimming and girls."

"Wellington is a lot bigger than I am, and he knows a lot about gardening."

"You'll grow," Uncle Edward said comfortably, "and in a week, you'll be an expert on gardening."

"Uncle Edward, listen to me. I don't know anything about it. Honest. Nothing."

"I understand that. Tomorrow, we shall visit the local library and accept all the help it can extend to us. If the library fails us, we shall stop in at Bookworld. Books on gardening probably proliferate like books on cooking. Between the printed word and our ingenuity, we shall achieve horticultural brilliance."

"It'll mean slaving out there, every day, in the sun."

"'Tote that barge, lift that bale'? Come now, Mark Anthony, an hour a day should do it, once it's established. On the other hand, I'm sure your father would be delighted to enroll you at the college, and assume responsibility for the garden himself."

Mark Anthony slid down under the covers. "What time does the library open?"

"Nine o'clock. I will give you a shake at eight."

"I can't wait."

The library had one whole section—five shelves—on gardening. Mark Anthony and Uncle Edward went through the titles systematically, chose a dozen of the more likely ones, and retired to a big round table nearby, to browse through those twelve.

Mark Anthony found most of the books confusing and dull . . . the kind of book that could give you a headache if you read it too long. Even the pictures, which were almost all black-and-white, were boring.

Uncle Edward laid down the last of his group with a sigh.

"It beats me," he said, "why anyone would ever take up gardening if they approached it through this type of book."

"Dull?"

"Dull. And pedantic. Let us wend our weary way to Bookworld."

Bookworld had a much smaller selection of gardening books, but Mark Anthony found several with colored pictures, a text he could actually make some sense out of, and step-by-step, simplified instruction. Uncle Edward scanned each one as Mark Anthony finished with it. When they were through, Uncle Edward said, "This one."

He held up a soft-cover book called *Practical Vegetable Gardening.*

"Why that one?"

"Well, the fellow who wrote it is in all the pictures—it's his garden. He's not much to look at himself, but he grows a lovely cabbage. And look here—pages of instructions a five-year-old could follow. I vote for this one."

"It's your money, Uncle Edward."

"But your responsibility, and your time. I want you to be content with our selection."

Mark Anthony shrugged. "I'm content. I'm not going to be ecstatic, no matter what the book looks like."

"Good word. Well used. You're really making progress. Let us celebrate your verbal acuity with an ice cream cone on the way home."

It was the first bright spot in Mark Anthony's day.

They took turns reading the book. Mark Anthony found himself experiencing a mild interest, now and then, to his surprise. Once or twice, a definite feeling of eagerness to get started stirred and subsided. He was intrigued by the variety of vegetables available, and their names. Lots of them had never appeared on the Crowder table. He thought it was great to call a tomato "Valiant," and he grinned when he read about an onion called "Ebenezer," and he'd never heard of spaghetti squash.

Uncle Edward was also intrigued, but cautious. "Let us be wildly successful with some standard products, for the most part. We can razzle-dazzle them next year—if we're called upon to do this again next year."

"Just how big is that garden out there?"

"I haven't the faintest idea."

"Well, we'd better pace it off and find out."

"Already, you're beginning to sound professional," Uncle Edward said proudly.

Mark Anthony bent down to tie his sneakers.

"Do you still think we can do it?"

"Child's play, my boy. Absolute child's play. We will open with something exotic, quick growing and easy, to amaze and astound them . . . like these black and white radishes, perhaps. Can't fail. Then, while we have their attention, we'll follow up with several kinds of lettuce. We must get some seedlings tomorrow. And after that, they'll be so impressed they'll leave us alone, to carry on in our own way. If this fellow can do it—an earnest man, but not an outstanding one—we can do it. We may even come to enjoy it."

Mark Anthony felt this was going too far, but Uncle Edward's confidence was comforting. He let the last statement go by unchallenged. However, he did feel that something basic had been overlooked.

"Don't you think we'd better get the garden plowed first?"

Uncle Edward nodded approvingly. "In another year, you'll be putting out your own gardening book."

His father was home for supper. It was a quiet meal. Mark Anthony could hear everyone chewing. It seemed to him the chewing sound started as a murmur and built to a deafening roar. He couldn't stand it. All he could hear was chewing— and forks clacking on plates. He asked for the butter, which he didn't need, just to break the spell.

As his father got up to leave the table, Mark Anthony asked, "Is it all right if I call Mr. Leyden to come and plow?"

His father said, "Yes. He can bill me. And I will expect you to keep records. Expenses, of course—item by item—and projects completed each week. 'Weeded the carrots' or 'sprayed the squash' or whatever. It would also be interesting to keep a record of your hours."

His mother spoke up. "We never insisted on that with Wellington, Harry. Expenses and jobs completed will be fine."

"It sounds like you don't trust me," Mark Anthony said.

His father said, "If the shoe fits. . . ."

His mother cut in sharply. "That isn't it, at all. A record of expenses tell us what everything costs, Mark Anthony. And a record of jobs completed is a good idea, for your own information. If the corn is weedy on a Thursday, and you can say, 'I weeded it last Friday,' we'll all just have to accept the fact that the weeds grew more rapidly than usual." She shot a glance at his father, still standing at the other end of the table.

"Write down what you do, and what you plan to do, in a little notebook. No one else has to see it—it will just help you keep track, that's all." She smiled at him as if she hoped he'd go along with the idea, and not make waves.

He made the notebook that night, and he found an old manila envelope and wrote *Expenses* on it—for the cash register receipts, and bills, and other money records. He also called Mr. Leyden, who promised to come by Sunday afternoon, to "turn the garden over," as he put it. Mark Anthony had a mental picture of Mr. Leyden turning the garden over with one great swing, like he and his mother turned the mattresses every spring and fall.

He fell asleep rereading *Practical Vegetable Gardening*, and dreamed of squashes big as baseball bats, and melons that looked like footballs, and a scarecrow who kept ticking away like a taxi meter while Mark Anthony was working in the garden, keeping track of his hours.

The lettuce plants were such a delicate green, and so small and fragile looking, Mark Anthony thought they must be the rejects; but Mr. Roccio, the roadside-stand man, said they were just the right size to transplant. Mark Anthony bought forty-eight plants—four varieties. Then he and Uncle Edward went to Billy's Hardware and bought seed for red, black, and white radishes, and several bags of fertilizer. They got back just in time to say hello to Mr. Leyden, who was plowing.

"You fellows sure are eager," he said. "What have you got there?"

"Lettuce and radishes," Mark Anthony said, spreading out the flats and seed packages.

"Aren't you going to raise anything else?"

"Of course we are," Mark Anthony said stiffly. "We are using succession planting."

"You'd better," Mr. Leyden said, and chuckled. He waved good-by and chugged around the corner of the house.

"What does he know?" Mark Anthony said scornfully. "Our family eats a lot of lettuce."

Uncle Edward said, "True. But, in this case, we may have been a little overeager. We must proceed with restraint in the future, dear boy. You keep an eye on me, and I'll keep an eye on you. I am afraid we should both have been born Texans."

They raked the freshly turned soil till it looked like brown cornmeal, and set out all the little lettuce plants, following the advice of the Practical Vegetable Gardener—or PVG, as Uncle Edward was beginning to refer to him—to the smallest detail. Then they planted a row of radishes—one-third black, one-third white, and one-third red.

"A stunning color scheme," Uncle Edward said proudly, straightening up with difficulty.

"The tops will all be green. Only the earthworms will know about the black, white, and red," Mark Anthony said.

"We'll know they're there."

"Well, let's go in for dinner," Mark Anthony said.

"You have forgotten something," Uncle Edward said, pointing to page 32 in PVG. "Hats. For the lettuce."

Mark Anthony folded them—little triangular toy soldiers' hats—out of newspaper, and Uncle Edward set them in place and weighted down the edges with soil. Forty-eight of them.

As he handed the last cap to Uncle Edward, Mark Anthony realized that the sun had set. It was getting dark.

"What time is it?"

"After seven," Uncle Edward said.

"After seven! You see—three hours—just to plant some

radishes and lettuce. This is going to be a full-time job."

"I think it's more interesting that you didn't realize it was that late. Doesn't that tell you something?"

"Yes. It tells me that if I'm not careful, I'm going to miss meals on account of this garden."

Uncle Edward smiled. "I'll believe that when I see it. To the parapets, men!" and they marched towards the kitchen.

That night, tired and stiff to the bone, Mark Anthony got out his notebook and made his first entry.

April 23—April 29

April 24—Planted too many radishes today—whole, long row, ⅓ black, ⅓ red, ⅓ white. Also bought more lettuce than necessary. They looked so small— hardly a mouthful each. Planted and put little newspaper caps over each one— 48!—to keep the sun and wind off them till they settle in.

April 25—Lettuces looked real neat this morning—like the garden was being invaded by rows of tiny soldiers wearing big hats. Should put in lots of spinach, so Georgette will *have* to eat it, and a bunch of cabbage too.

April 26—Found doll clothes in arrowhead drawer AGAIN. Put in bags and stored in attic for safekeeping. Will tell Georgette, later.

April 29—Planted ½ row of spinach, and six big pots snow peas—strings all around edges tied to dowel in middle, like a maypole. Peas will grow up strings—PVG idea. Ma will be tickled. She loves snow peas. Radishes up. At least, we think those are radishes.

April 30—May 6

April 30—Had to rake whole entire garden—*millions* of little weeds, all over. Planted Swiss chard in rest of spinach row. Uncle Edward says when all else fails, Swiss chard succeeds. I say, who cares? You might as well be eating tough spinach. Wellington wants two drawers for his extra clothes. If he has all that much money for clothes, why can't he buy his own dresser????? Ma made me "adjust," so Wellington's got one of my drawers, now—PLUS the top where he keeps his old tennis racket.

May 1—Hats off cabbages—watered them. Planted ½ row beets, ½ row carrots. Put some of the leftover radish seeds in row. PVG says to—to mark the row. How do you get the radishes out without pulling up the other stuff? PVG doesn't say.

May 2—Uncle Edward says he talked to Mr. Eberhart and I can walk in the woods again if I keep my nose clean and stay out of trouble. Uncle Edward gave his personal word. Good old Uncle Edward. Got an A on social studies test. Arnold is starting in again. I knew he would. The thing is, if I have to choose between Arnold giving me a hard time at school and the whole family treating me as if I had a fungus disease, I guess I can take it better from Arnold. At least I don't have to see him after school gets out every day. I wish I lived in a cave somewhere.

May 7—May 13

May 7—Had to water everything. Hot and dry. Went for walk in Eberhart's woods. Didn't find anything, but I sure was glad to be able to go back. Bought one flat of Marglobe tomatoes, one flat of Valiants. That's a neat name for something—Valiant. Waiting for cloudy day to plant.

May 9—Mother's Day. Peas not up yet, but gave pots to Ma anyway. Put bows on tops. She thought it was great.

May 11—Cloudy. Planted tomatoes.

May 13—Had to water AGAIN. Tomatoes looking pretty sad. Still cloudy, no rain. Cut some outer leaves off lettuce for salad. Not bad. Georgette took some shells to school for crafts. Didn't ask. I took all the rest and dumped them on her bed. She can have them. There's another drawer for Wellington. Dad still mad about camp.

May 14—May 20

May 14—Picked a few red radishes. They're still too skinny. White radishes must be almost ready. Weeds coming up everywhere I watered. You can't win. Spent two hours raking and hoeing. Hard to tell weeds from seeds, sometimes. I think I hoed up some Swiss chard. By accident. I really thought it was weeds, at first, and that's the truth. Uncle Edward said I should be more careful. It's hard to be all that concerned about something that tastes like Swiss chard. But—if that's what it was, then it proves the Swiss chard is coming up—was coming up. Adults have some very strange tastes.

May 15—Over at Eberhart's woods. Found the charcoal places again, and one more piece of pot. Put with first piece in white shoe box, under bed.

May 18—Planted three hills muskmelons, two hills Big Max pumpkins.

May 20—The big news is BEANS. We followed along behind a state highway truck cleaning out the right-of-way along Hardscrabble Road and got twenty long, skinny saplings. Made a maypole thing out of them, only as big as a tent. Planted scarlet runner and Kentucky Wonder beans round the base of each pole. They should look really wild when they've grown up the poles and bloomed. Scarlet runner has red flowers. Uncle Edward says it will be our pièce de résistance—our big number. And we hung a big, bright red college-type banner, with HARD KNOCKS U. in white felt letters, from the top. This gardening is more fun than I thought it might be.

May 21—May 27

May 21—Picked a lot of red radishes. Planted some more in same row. Very nice.

May 23—Got an A in math. Could not believe it. Also an A in English. Arnold "accidently" knocked my books on floor going to lunch. Here we go again. My only hope is if Arnold moves, or gets smart suddenly, during the summer—which is not likely. He's worse now than he was before the last report card . . . as if he thought I'd tricked him into talking to me for a while back then. Big deal.

May 26—Melons—muskmelons, that is—coming up. I love the way the earth cracks over them before they poke through—like we had miniature earthquakes all over.

May 28—June 3

May 28—Uncle Edward went through woods with me to see campfire site. We sat and talked for a couple of hours.

May 30—A few beans are up. The ground is cracking all around every pole, so lots more are coming. Memorial Day. Went to parade in town—met Mr. Eberhart. Talked to Uncle Edward and me for half an hour just as if nothing had ever happened. Said we should try watering our Big Max pumpkins with "manure tea" every week or so. Sounds gross to me. He gave the recipe to Uncle Edward. Uncle Edward said we would get some manure and try it.

June 1—Georgette's birthday. Gave her a little suitcase to put her doll stuff in with a lock and everything. Hope she takes the hint. She had about eight friends over for supper.

June 3—Came home from school, saw big brown hill in back—manure. Gift from Mr. Eberhart to Uncle Edward. I never knew he had an old horse back there—and a cow and some hens. Uncle Edward says they're not productive any longer, but Mr. Eberhart keeps them for company. He must be awful lonely. Anyhow—there it was. We got to work, top-dressing with the manure, right away. Dad came home and went around slamming all the windows shut. Uncle Edward and I thought it smelled kind of nice. And it was all crumbly and dry—easy to handle. We started a big pail of manure tea too. Took some lettuce over to Mr. Eberhart after supper. Uncle Edward asked Dad if, hypothetically speaking, I ever grew so much stuff Ma couldn't use it, could I sell it and keep the money? Dad said that would never happen, but yes. Uncle Edward came back out and said, "Shovel on more coal, Mark Anthony"—meaning more manure.

June 4—June 10

June 4—We got desperate, so I took some sample lettuce down to the vegetable stand. The guy down there, Mr. Roccio, said he'd take anything that was really fresh, and the price was right. To come back at the end of the day for the unsold stuff. Uncle Edward arranged all our surplus lettuce in a wooden box, with radishes here and there as bonuses.

Then he sprinkled the box with water. It looked like a picture in a cookbook. Mr. Roccio sold every lettuce! Bought some bush bean seed, and more loose-leaf lettuce seed. Took Uncle Edward for ice cream with some of the lettuce money, to celebrate.

June 5—Rained. Heavy. Uncle Edward said it could only do us good . . . working manure down in.

June 11—June 17

June 11—Took some more lettuce and radishes to Mr. Roccio for weekend sales. Sold every one by nightfall. Wants more stuff.

June 15—Cut first Swiss chard. Uncle Edward and I opened account at bank—$5.00. We put it in both of our names, so either one could get it out without the other—which was a very good idea. That way, if I should happen to keel over from heatstroke or something, weeding, Uncle Edward could still get to our money. It could happen.

June 17—Last day of school. Three cheers. Report cards. 3 A's, rest B's. Plus lots of comment. Arnold was all over me like slither on a snake—"What'd you get, Mark Anthony? Teacher's pet, Mark Anthony." I figured, just let me get out of here, I don't have to see him till September. But as I climb up into the bus, he grabs my leg and pulls, and I give him a shove, to get loose, and over he goes—PLUS two of his buddies standing behind him. So—it was back to the office for fighting . . . which was a new experience. Everyone passing the office looked in and kept on going, as if they were glad it was us and not them in there. The principal bawled us all out, as if we were a gang. Arnold looked disgusted. I had to walk home because the bus had left without me. Uncle Edward said I got "mixed reviews" at supper. Dad looked at my card and grunted. Then he said, "By the way, while I certainly do not approve of fighting—you understand?—I'm glad you're starting to stick up for yourself." Ma was happy about the card and upset about the fighting. Georgette looked impressed, which doesn't happen too often. I felt like a phony, to tell the truth. It was just a real lucky shove.

June 18—June 24

June 18—Took some Swiss chard to Mr. Roccio, arranged it with white icicle radishes. A little still unsold by suppertime. It figures. You couldn't give it away to me. Everyone says, "If he grows it himself, and sees it coming up and all, he'll learn to love it." No way. I could sit there and watch it grow all day, and when I put a forkful in my mouth, it would still taste like rusty nails.

June 19—Got up early in honor of Father's Day. Gave Dad some shaving lotion. He said he liked it.

June 20—First beets are in. I'm going to plant more beans—the maypole sure is a sight. The green creeps up the sides every day now. I can see the difference. I water it whenever I can. Dad says it looks like a circus tent out there. Actually, with the red banner at the top, it looks more like something out of King Arthur's court. Very classy.

June 21—Earl came over. Nothing to do in the garden today. I feel like I must have forgotten something—but even gardeners get a day off once in a while, I guess.

June 29—July 1

June 29—Got up very early, while it was cool, and went over to Eberhart's woods. Found small cave, going way back under hill. Entrance is all overgrown. Actually, I tripped into it, sort of by accident. Anyway, I brought out some pieces of charcoal, which could be from Indian fires, and a scraper—I think it's a scraper—for animal skins. Hid them in the shoe boxes under my bed.

June 30—Made up two small mixed boxes in morning, took them down to Mr. Roccio. He went crazy—little vegetables sell for more than big ones. Can you beat that! They're supposed to be more tender and tasty. The people driving by on the highway stop at his stand in droves. He was sold out by six. I watered for an hour this evening. The garden sure smells nice. Uncle Edward says I should consider becoming a farmer, but I want to be an archaeologist. That's all I've ever wanted to be, really. It's kind of an oddball thing to be, though.

July 2—July 8

July 4—Our own tomatoes, peas. Got two small boxes down to Mr. Roccio. Cleaned out the garden to do it. Hope Ma doesn't ask for anything tonight. Fireworks display over the lake, if it doesn't rain. The whole family is going. I'm going to ask for potato salad, specifically, for the picnic supper—otherwise, Ma might try to scrounge up a big tossed salad. We'd have to give her radish tops and dandelion greens because everything else is down at Mr. Roccio's stand.

July 5—Hot! Great fireworks last night. Had to hoe for one hour. Uncle Edward gave up and sat on the porch drinking lemonade.

July 7—Some of the beans have made it all the way to the top of their poles. The whole maypole is green now, and with the red banner on top, it's a sight. It looks like a tent for royalty, if you look at it with your eyes almost closed. Earl brought his dad over to see it. Mr. Jones said it was something else.

July 9—July 15

July 9—Nothing for Mr. Roccio. He called to see if we could spare him a couple of boxes of stuff. I had to say no. He called back later, and asked if we were mad about something or wanted a bigger cut. Uncle Edward said we had a deal—we weren't holding him up—and went into his "Who steals my purse steals trash . . ." bit. Everybody here is eating as if it's going out of style. Ma makes big salads every night. I don't dare say anything, in case Dad blows the whistle on our deal with Mr. Roccio. But I'm watering a lot, and we've used up the last of the manure. It's all in there, somewhere.

July 11—Succession planting. Carrots, beets—one row each. Bush beans and lettuce—half a row. Stiff all over when I got through. Soaked in a hot tub till I was bright red—then liniment, again.

July 16—July 22

July 16—Three boxes for Mr. Roccio . . . a little of

everything. Uncle Edward sure does a great job. When he gets through arranging things and spraying them with water, I feel like buying them myself. Mr. Roccio happy again.

July 18—Back to the bank. Weeded, sprayed beans for an hour—early in the day. Discovered space inside bean tent is really neat. Cool and shady. Set up two chairs in there in afternoon. Uncle Edward and I spent a couple of hours reading. Planted more beans at base of each pole.

July 19—Rabbits giving us trouble. Nibbling. Just a little here, a little there, but people don't like to eat something a rabbit's been eating first. Even if you wash it. Uncle Edward and Mr. Eberhart say a chicken-wire fence will do the trick.

July 20—Asked Dad to go in with me on chicken wire. He said it would be cheaper to buy the vegetables. Ma said it would not. She'd go in with me on the wire, 50-50, if I put it up. I think Dad is mad at me again.

July 21—Georgette asked for a couple of drawers in dresser, "like Wellington's got." She's running out of space for her stuffed animals. Ma said she could have one drawer. Which means the whole dresser.

July 23—July 29

July 23—Put in chicken-wire fencing. Earl helped. Paid him a dollar an hour. He says if I've got any more jobs, call him.

July 25—Moved an orange crate full of books out to the bean maypole and covered it with plastic to keep rain and dew off. Hot today. Read in the afternoon. Weeded after supper. Mosquitoes are really getting to me.

July 26—Big thunderstorm last night. Nice and cool this morning. Have all my Indian stuff safe in shoe boxes under my bed now. . .sorted, labeled and everything. I label it by how and where and when I found it, but that's all, because I don't know the rest. I don't think it was all done by the same tribe, because the chipping and shaping aren't the same on all the points, and several different kinds of rocks were used. Uncle Edward went through it with me this afternoon. He said I should show it to that fellow at the university. NO WAY! I'm not going to be called a liar, or made fun of again, if I can help it.

July 30—August 5

July 30—Beans for Mr. Roccio—plus an assorted crate. He snapped a couple of beans between his fingers, and then he ate one raw. He said they would go in his "deluxe case." Uncle Edward went over to visit Mr. Eberhart this afternoon. He took some tomatoes, beans, radishes, lettuce, and a bag of cookies Ma had made. We called it our "We Care" box. Mr. Eberhart and Uncle Edward are getting to be real good friends.

August 3—The melons are ready. Man! My mouth has been watering for a month. Got one sweet little cantaloupe and one small watermelon. I ate them both—gave everyone else a tiny slice—and I never ate anything so good in all my life. Spent afternoon in maypole. Mr. Eberhart came by and sat and talked with Uncle Edward while I read. Said pumpkins were coming right along. Took off ends of vines to stop more vine growth, and picked all the little pumpkins but one off two vines, so those two vines will concentrate on one pumpkin each. I might end up with a couple of pumpkins that weigh as much as Ma does. Went to bank. Our account is really growing.

August 4—Uncle Edward put my old toys and stuff in the bottom of his closet. My books are all over—mostly out in the maypole. Hot sticky day—you could practically see things grow. Uncle Edward says out in Kansas, on a day like today, if you stood in a cornfield, you could *hear* the corn grow.

August 6—August 12

August 6—Mr. Eberhart came by. I could tell he was leading up to something. Sure enough, after an hour of "Isn't it hot?" and "Those are the best beans I ever ate," he got down to it. Could he see my Indian stuff? I said no. Nicely. Uncle Edward gave me the fisheye. So I said I'd bring it out—and I did. But not all of it. I never thought Uncle

582

Edward would put the squeeze on me like that—in front of someone else. I just dumped the stuff down and left. I don't care what anyone else thinks about my stuff. I like it. I like to pick it up, and hold it, and think about the people who made it and depended on it years ago. I wonder about whether or not the "bird-points" brought down any birds for them when they were hungry. About the lady who cooked with the pot—did she have any children? If I wanted to fool around and collect this stuff, that's my business, isn't it—and I wish everyone else would just leave me alone. I think Uncle Edward is so sold on Mr. Eberhart now, that he doesn't care whether I mind or not.

August 7—Still angry with Uncle Edward. I wish I wasn't. He's the best friend I ever had. But I can't help it. That's all over now. Everytime he tries to talk with me—as if everything were OK—I get nasty or clam up. Sometimes I think, "That's like my father is," and I hate that—but I just keep on slamming doors or giving him the silent treatment.

August 8—Four boxes to Mr. Roccio, plus a lot of stuff for Ma. Uncle Edward came by last night, after I'd gone to bed, and knocked. I didn't answer. He came in anyway. He said Mr. Eberhart had been very interested in the Indian collection, and that it had been found on his property, after all. I said that wasn't why I was mad. He said he knew—that I resented being pushed to satisfy someone else's curiosity. Then he said, "I'm sorry, Mark Anthony. I was wrong." Just like that. What could I do? I had to tell him it was all right, right? So we're friends again, and I'm glad. I feel about a thousand pounds lighter.

August 13—August 19

August 13—Three weeks and a few days till school. At night, it's already getting colder. I feel like I'm slipping back into one of those pits of despair Uncle Edward was talking about. I wish it were June again. Ma's canning like mad. Mr. Roccio will take all the beans we can send over. Between the two of them, hardly a bean on the whole maypole gets to grow to its full length. Went to the bank. I never had a lot of money of my own before. It feels real good.

August 15—Weighed biggest pumpkin. *Ninety-eight pounds!* I couldn't believe it. Uncle Edward says it's all that manure tea.

August 16—Went for walk in woods—ran into Mr. Eberhart. I knew it. I'll bet he's out there every day now, looking for Indian stuff. What can I say? It's his land, isn't it? I showed him the campfire sites. He told me a lot of stories about when he was a kid. He really likes Uncle Edward. That's one thing we agree on. As we left, he said, "You've got the touch, Mark Anthony. Been looking all day, and haven't found a thing." I felt guilty, but it made me feel good too.

August 19—Ma and Dad and Georgette are going to Indianapolis, tomorrow. Uncle Edward and I get to stay home. At first, Dad said I should go; I didn't want to. They're going to stay with Uncle Julius—my father's brother—Julius Caesar Crowder. Everyone in Dad's family has a big name—Julius Caesar Crowder, Light-Horse Harry Lee Crowder, Mark Anthony Crowder, Wellington Waterloo Crowder, Georgette Sands Crowder—I mean, what are they trying to prove! If I have a son, I'm going to call him Sam. Period. Anyway, Uncle Julius is just like Dad, so they get on each other's nerves sometimes, and after a few days of doors slamming, suppers with no one speaking to anyone else, I've had it. Besides, we can't leave the garden. Ma said I could stay. Ma looked as if she would like to stay too.

August 20—August 26

August 20—Two weeks and a few days till school. Lots of things in the garden are slowing down. I can see it. Fall's coming. Little spaces between vines on maypole.

August 24—Fall lettuce perking up again. Uncle Edward wants to go to university library some day soon—asked me to go along to help carry books home. His back is bothering him. I hope I haven't let him do too much in garden. Mr. Roccio wants at least one of biggest pumpkins for display. Said he'd pay me ten cents a pound. When I told him how

584

many pounds I was shooting for, and that they might not be good eating pumpkins, he said, "I don't care about eating, these are advertising pumpkins." Uncle Edward said to take the money and run. Way back, Georgette said she wanted one for Halloween, and I thought she would get one of the biggest, but Ma said, "Nonsense, Georgette. Two of the small ones will be fine." And that was that. Ma's really neat, sometimes.

August 26—Everybody home again. When I asked Ma how it went, she said, "Don't ask." Dad just sort of growled.

August 27—September 2

August 27—Turned pumpkins, *very* carefully. Took two boxes of mixed produce to Mr. Roccio early in the day. Needs more if I can get it away from Ma. Went to library with Uncle Edward—met that fellow who's an archaeology major—does some assistant teaching, even. "Rodger Dodger," Uncle Edward calls him. He is so *short*—and wiry. I'll bet he doesn't weigh over one hundred and twenty pounds. Hey—not much more than one of my pumpkins! But he was really nice. Took us out for lunch. He said, "Mark Anthony, I believe we have a problem in common." I said, "Oh, yeah?" He said, "Yes—height." I guess my mouth fell open. He laughed and said, "Hey—don't you think being short has its drawbacks?" I said, "At least you don't stick out like a sore thumb, in a crowd." He said, "No, but I get stepped on a lot. Besides—the rest of them will grow, and catch up with you, but no one's going to shrink, and come down to my size." I said, "Hey, Rodger, size doesn't matter with a guy like you," and he said, "That's funny, I heard someone say just the same thing about you, Mark Anthony." Uncle Edward picked out only about four books, after all that. I sure feel bad about his back. Used to be, he'd carry home eight or ten books with no trouble.

September 3—September 9

September 4—Mr. Roccio called—more produce. I scraped up one small boxful and took it over. Watered early, sprayed late in day. Spent afternoon in maypole. It's really something, to sit in there. The light inside is green, like you were underwater. But, if you sit in the right place, the sun will fall on your book. No one can see you unless they're standing right in the entrance. All the house noises are kind of distant, once you're inside. It's sort of restful, and hidden, and private.

September 5—I think I can see gaps in the vines at the top, now. I'm going to miss this old maypole. It's Labor Day—a holiday. I sure don't feel like celebrating.

September 6—To the bank. Every time I look at the amount, I am really sort of surprised. Of course, a lot of that hundred dollars really should go to Uncle Edward. He says he won't take a penny. Ma made me go shopping for clothes with her. School tomorrow. We compromised a lot. Naturally, I had grown some more. Sometimes I think I have a glandular problem. Overheard Georgette and Wellington arguing about space in the dresser. Dad's easing up a little now that the sports camp is closed. I guess that was a constant reminder of how much I'd let him down. It's cold tonight. Cold weather means the only places I can be are in the house or in school. The maypole will be getting patchy, and after that, it'll be just a matter till first frost—I'd look sort of foolish, sitting out there where everyone could see me through the bare poles.

September 7—Got Mr. Dobbs for homeroom. Arnold and his friends are back. I wonder if there's any way someone my age could get out of going to school. Even if there was, my father wouldn't let me do it. Rodger Dodger came by tonight, to see Uncle Edward. I went across the hall, and we all sat around and talked. He really knows a lot about Indians.

September 10—September 16

September 10—Maypole definitely thinning out. Moved books and stuff indoors—to closets, etc. Wrote down what I did with everything. Put the paper in shoe box with potsherds.

September 11—Rodger Dodger came by but Uncle Edward

was gone—out for his paper and a walk. Took him into my room to wait. We got to talking about Indians, and he kept hinting around. And finally I ended up showing him all my stuff. He was really nice about it—and said it was a surprising collection, that the area they came from should be investigated. Well, he's really keen on Uncle Edward, so what else could he say? He took a couple of things with him, back to the university, for some reason. Promised to return them real soon.

September 15—Rodger Dodger came by and asked if he could take the rest of my Indian things for a couple of days. He was really cagey about why. It worries me, to tell the truth, but Uncle Edward says Rodger can be trusted. I guess the damage is done now, anyway.

September 17—September 23

September 17—Hubbards and pumpkins harvested!! Took two pumpkins to Mr. Roccio, after we weighed them on the bathroom scale. One weighed one hundred and twenty pounds, the other one hundred and fifteen. Uncle Edward helped me load them into the wheelbarrow. I guess his back is OK now. I had to make two trips. Mr. Roccio gave me $23.50 for the pumpkins alone. He also bought six Hubbard squashes—cash on the barrelhead—at 6¢ a pound. That's $28.90, total. And another trip with the wheelbarrow. I put six Hubbard squashes in the basement. Ma says that will hold us for one winter, at least.

September 18—Dad is in Cleveland. Rodger Dodger came by. For a minute, I panicked. He didn't have one shoe box with him. He asked me if we could walk through Eberhart's woods, to see the places where I found the stuff. I said sure. We walked all day. Rodger took a lot of notes, and poked and dug around. He's an easy guy to be with. I can see why Uncle Edward likes him. He says my stuff will be back next week, without fail, unless I'd like to leave it all with him a little longer. I didn't know what to say, so I didn't say anything. I hope he can figure that out. I want the stuff back. I'm really tired of waiting already. I miss it.

September 19—WOW! Today has been one of the best days of my whole life. I was sitting in the maypole, feeling like just taking off. The summer's over, Arnold and Brian are back on my neck, I'm taller, my stuff is spread out all over, hidden away again, the garden's dying . . . when I looked up at the sky, through the top of the maypole, and said to myself, "If this were a tipi, that would be the smoke hole, and I'd have a little fire here, which would be neat." And then I said, "Why not, man?" and that was it. I'm going to convert the maypole into a small tipi for the winter, with real Indian backrests, and a fire hole, and everything. I have enough money from the garden to pay for the materials, and the waterproofing, and the paints. I have the instructions in my books. So—I'll have my own place, even in cold weather. Only this time, it will really be my own place. I'll have Mr. Leyden turn the garden under but leave this place in the center alone. By the time the bean vines are dead, my tipi cover, and the lining, will be ready. Hardly anyone will even know it's back here. You can't see the garden from the street. Maybe Uncle Edward and Rodger Dodger will lend a hand.

September 20—Dad still in Cleveland. Uncle Edward thought the tipi was a great idea. He's at the library today, but he said he'd help when I was ready. Went to the bank after school and drew out enough money. Laid out all the cloth for the outer tipi and cut it out. Will do homework in the morning.

September 21—Laid out lining for tipi—cut it out. Drew decorations and designs on lining and outer tipi cover. Ma helped. She really can draw. Dad in Indiana.

September 22—Rearranged poles correctly—just to see what tipi would look like when it was done. A tipi is not a straight cone. It's sort of a tilted cone. It wasn't easy moving the poles with bearing bean vines still attached to most of them. Had to sort of coax them into place. It's going to look great. Dug fire hole. Ma nervous about fire. Had to show her the book so she'd quit worrying about me burning up. She still wanted me to put a Sterno stove in the fire hole instead. What Indians use Sterno in a tipi? Dad due home Friday. Will take some butternut squashes to Mr. Roccio, Friday.

September 23—Dug root cellar—*four hours!* Found spearhead in trench I dug. Called Rodger Dodger—he said I had the knack, ought to be an archaeologist. How about that! Maybe I will be, after all. Uncle Edward had to work on my back—stiff as a board. Georgette and Wellington had an argument about the dresser. Ma yelled at both of them. In a way I was sad, because I used to think that was going to be sort of my private museum; but in a way, I couldn't help feeling satisfied. Arnold and Brian had a fight—with each other for a change. Uncle Edward says it must be the barometric pressure. Mr. Leyden due to plow tomorrow. Uncle Edward was right—I even got to enjoy the garden.

September 24—September 30

September 25—Well, if September 19 was one of the best days of my life, September 24 was one of the worst—probably the worst. Mr. Leyden came to plow in the afternoon. Dad had gotten home at lunch, so he went out to talk to Mr. Leyden. When I got home from Mr. Eberhart's, they were starting to pull up the tipi poles and shove them into the back of Mr. Leyden's pickup truck, with the poor bean vines still hanging on and everything. I ran out there, yelling for them to stop. Dad said, "We're taking this eyesore down, so Mr. Leyden can cart it away and plow." I said, "It's not an eyesore. It's still a set of bean poles, and it's going to be a tipi." Dad said, "Look at it—it's falling over already. I want it down." When I told him that was how tipis were built, he gave me one of those looks, and said, "You don't know anything about tipis, and you don't need one. Now, we're taking this thing down." Ma heard us yelling and came out and said I had gotten everything ready to make the tipi and what would it hurt? Dad said, "You mean you knew about this? And you let him?" And Mr. Leyden said he could come back another day. Georgette came out and said everyone at school would laugh at her because she had such a weird brother, and I told her to be quiet, and Dad swung at me. He missed, but I got out of there fast.

I spent a couple of hours in the woods, but then I was getting so cold I couldn't take it any longer, so I went to Mr. Eberhart's house. I figured Dad would never look there, but he'd call Earl right away. Mr. Eberhart gave me some hot cocoa, which made me feel a lot warmer and sleepy. Then he called my house and asked for Uncle Edward, and told him that an unexpected guest had come by, and Uncle Edward caught on right away.

I didn't want him to call, but I figured I wasn't going back anyway, no matter what. So if they came to get me, I'd just leave. Mr. Eberhart said I could trust Uncle Edward to do right by everyone concerned, and I knew he was right. I wanted Ma to know just enough so she wouldn't worry. Dad wouldn't worry. He'd get madder, but he wouldn't worry. Uncle Edward called back later and said everything was OK, and he hoped Mr. Eberhart could accommodate his guest overnight, and we'd all talk in the morning.

Mr. Eberhart put me in a tiny room off his kitchen, in a little old bed that creaked. He piled the quilts up on me, in case I kept on feeling cold all the time—and three of his cats came and slept on the bed with me, which helped. We were all very compatible and comfortable. He left a fire going in the old stove in the kitchen, and a small light burning—which was really nice because even someone my age can feel kind of spooked sleeping in a totally dark place they don't know.

I knew I was never going home again, but I tried not to think of it too much in case I cried in front of Mr. Eberhart.

Mr. Eberhart got me up the next morning and gave me breakfast. We talked—but not about my walking out. Mostly we talked about gardening. Then Uncle Edward called and asked us to come over around eleven. Mr. Eberhart said yes, but I said no. So Mr. Eberhart got me to promise not to leave till he got back, and he went.

I sat there in the kitchen with the cats, and thought about things. I was feeling pretty bad. The cats kept jumping up into my lap, or rubbing up against my leg—trying to make me feel better. I didn't fit in at school. I didn't fit in at home.

My own father couldn't stand me. My Indian stuff was gone, and who knew when it would come back—if ever. My one hope for a place of my own was shot down. By now, the tipi poles were probably at the town dump. And I'd spent almost all my money for the stuff to finish the tipi—so I had no grubstake, except the little left in the bank. I felt about as down and out as I ever had. All I could see, when I closed my eyes, was Dad, taking a swing at me.

I heard Mr. Eberhart's pickup door slam—very tinny—and I looked out. He'd brought back Rodger Dodger and Uncle Edward. I figured he'd sold me out. The state police were probably on the way, was how I figured it. I started out the back door, moving very quietly, very carefully, and just as I thought I was in the clear, someone got me from behind and took me down. Rodger Dodger. He said, "An old trick," and helped me up. He brought me back into the kitchen and said, "Sit down and listen. You might learn something."

I sat down, but I didn't plan to listen. No way.

Well, Rodger Dodger started talking, and he said he had kept my Indian artifacts so long because they were being appraised by the university archaeology department, and they had done their best to figure when everything was made, and by whom, and the big news was that they had decided that my things had been made and left behind by lots of Indians, living in our area over a very long stretch of time. So—they were going to include my things in a special showing of local Indian artifacts, and mine would have a plaque attached: From the Collection of Mark Anthony Crowder. Rodger and Uncle Edward had kept it real quiet till they knew for sure it would all work out, because, Uncle Edward said, "Once was enough," whatever he meant by that.

So—my stuff was important. I couldn't believe it. And Rodger said that they'd be taking pictures, and if I could get the tipi ready in time, they'd want pictures of that, because I *had* done it right. It was really authentic. He said that I would be invited to a special showing of the exhibit, the night before it opened, and my family could all come too.

I said, "Thanks" a lot, but that was about it. Then I remembered that the tipi was probably already down at the dump and not likely to go up again.

Uncle Edward said, "The tipi still stands, Mark Anthony. Your father picked up the two poles that he'd helped pull down, and he put them back up, himself."

I guess I looked as if I didn't believe him.

Uncle Edward said, "I started to help him, and he waved me off. He sent Mr. Leyden home, and he worked on the tipi himself."

Naturally, I wanted to know why.

Uncle Edward said, "I think it was that moment when he swung at you, and you ran away from him. Have you ever heard of a moment of truth—when someone suddenly wakes up to what's happening, and sees everything clearly? Well, I think he saw things clearly, and now, Mark Anthony, the question is—how clearly do you see him?"

I walked home, alone. Dad was in the living room, sitting in the wing chair. Just sitting—no lights, no TV. I sat down too.

He said, "I'm sorry."

I said, "I should have asked—like with the tree house," and that was the truth. I am a slow learner, all right.

He said, "I do my best, Mark Anthony. I do care about you, very much. But most of the time, I just don't understand you. You'll have to talk more to me, and I'll try to listen, or I'll just keep on making this kind of mistake forever. But I do care."

And I said, "I know you do. Listen—they didn't put the squeeze on you about the tipi, did they?"

He said, "No. They did say that you were very, very good at what you like to do. And your mother said she thought you were entitled. And she was right."

It bothered me to see him sitting there, quiet, and kind of down. I couldn't leave the room with him like that. I got up and went over to him and shook his hand. It was a dumb thing to do, but it was all I could think of. Anyhow, it worked. He got up and gave me a little smile, and put his arm around my shoulder and said, "So—let's go and tell your mother the crisis is over, before *she* leaves me."

October 16

October 16—The tipi's up, the exhibit's open—I'm what Uncle Edward calls a ninety-day wonder. Next week, Arnold will go back to heckling me, but he isn't likely to mention Indian collections. Not now. He's got to believe the university. I'm still too tall, and my glasses still look like headlight lenses, but I guess I can live with that. Dad and I are trying to talk more. Sometimes I catch him looking at me with his head on one side, as if he was trying to figure me out. But if both of us keep trying, something will get through.

I'm getting older, and Uncle Edward was right—it does get better.

Glossary*

Pronunciation Key

The pronunciation of each word is shown just after the word, in this way:
ab bre vi ate (ə brē′vē āt).

The letters and signs used are pronounced as in the words below.

The mark ′ is placed after a syllable with primary or heavy accent, as in the example to the left.

The mark ′ after a syllable shows a secondary or lighter accent, as in
ab bre vi a tion (ə brē′vē ā′shən).

a	hat, cap	l	land, coal	u	cup, butter
ā	age, face	m	me, am	u̇	full, put
ä	father, far	n	no, in	ü	rule, move
b	bad, rob	ng	long, bring	v	very, save
ch	child, much	o	hot, rock	w	will, woman
d	did, red	ō	open, go	y	young, yet
e	let, best	ô	order, all	z	zero, breeze
ē	equal, be	oi	oil, voice	zh	measure, seizure
ėr	term, learn	ou	house, out	ə	represents:
f	fat, if	p	paper, cup		a in about
g	go, bag	r	run, try		e in taken
h	he, how	s	say, yes		i in pencil
i	it, pin	sh	she, rush		o in lemon
ī	ice, five	t	tell, it		u in circus
j	jam, enjoy	th	thin, both		
k	kind, seek	ᴛʜ	then, smooth		

A

ab sorp tion (ab sôrp′shən) *noun*. A being absorbed; great interest: The children's *absorption* in their game was so complete that they did not hear the doorbell.

ac ces si ble (ak ses′ə bəl) *adjective*. Easy to get at; easy to reach or enter: A telephone should be put where it will be *accessible*.

ac co lade (ak′ə lād) *noun*. Something awarded as an honor; praise or recognition.

a cous tics (ə kü′stiks) *noun*. The science of sound: *Acoustics* is taught in some colleges.

ac tu ate (ak′chü āt) *verb*. Put into action: This pump is *actuated* by a belt driven by an electric motor.

a cute (ə kyüt′) *adjective*. Quick in perceiving and responding to impressions; keen: Dogs have an *acute* sense of smell. —**acutely** *adverb*.

ad o les cence (ad′l es′ns) *noun*. Period of growth from childhood to adulthood; youth.

ad ren a lin (ə dren′l ən) *noun*. Hormone in the body that speeds up the heartbeat and increases bodily energy and resistance to fatigue.

aer o nau tics (er′ə nô′tiks or ar′ə nô′tiks) *noun*. (Plural in form but used with a singular verb.) Science or art having to do with the design, manufacture, and operation of aircraft.

af fa ble (af′ə bəl) *adjective*. Easy to talk to; courteous and pleasant: Our principal is very *affable*.

af flic tion (ə flik′shən) *noun*. State of pain, trouble, or distress; misery: the *affliction* of war.

af ter math (af′tər math) *noun*. A result or consequence: The *aftermath* of war is hunger and disease.

a gog (ə gog′) *adjective*. Full of expectation or excitement; eager.

a kin (ə kin′) *adjective*. Of the same kind; similar: His tastes in music seem *akin* to mine.

al che my (al′kə mē) *noun*. Magical power of transforming one thing into another.

* The Pronunciation Key, respellings, and dictionary entries are from *Scott, Foresman Intermediate Dictionary* by E. L. Thorndike and Clarence L. Barnhart. Copyright © 1979 by Scott, Foresman and Company. Reprinted by permission.

al cove (al'kōv) *noun.* Recess or large, hollow space in a wall.

a lum ni (ə lum'nī) *noun.* Graduates or former students of a school, college, or university.

am bi dex trous (am'bə dek'strəs) *adjective.* Able to use both hands equally well. **—ambidextrously** *adverb.*

a mel io ra tion (ə mē'lyə rā'shən) *noun.* An improvement.

a mi a ble (ā'mē ə bəl) *adjective.* Having a good-natured and friendly disposition; pleasant and agreeable. **—amiably** *adverb.* **amiability** *noun.*

an es thet ic (an'əs thet'ik) *noun.* Substance that causes entire or partial loss of the feeling of pain, touch, cold, etc.

an i line or **an i lin** (an'l ən) *noun.* A colorless, poisonous, oily liquid, obtained from coal tar and used in making dyes, medicines, plastics, etc.

an i ma tion (an'ə mā'shən) *noun.* Liveliness; vigor: The boy acted his part as a pirate with great *animation.*

an tic i pa tion (an tis'ə pā'shən) *noun.* Act of looking forward to; expectation: In *anticipation* of a cold winter, they cut extra firewood.

an ti dote (an'ti dōt) *noun.* Medicine or remedy that counteracts the harmful effects of a poison: Milk is an *antidote* for some poisons.

a pol o get i cal ly (ə pol'ə jet'ik lē) *adverb.* In a manner expressing regret or making excuses.

ap pa ra tus (ap'ə rā'təs *or* ap'ə rat'əs) *noun.* The tools, machines, or other equipment necessary to carry out a purpose or for a particular use. **apparatus** or **apparatuses.**

ap prox i mate (ə prok'sə māt) *verb.* To come near to; approach. **approximated, approximating.**

ar bi tra tor (är'bə trā'tər) *noun.* Person chosen to decide or settle a dispute.

ar dent (ärd'nt) *adjective.* Full of enthusiasm; eager. **—ardently** *adverb.*

ar o mat ic (ar'ə mat'ik) *adjective.* Spicy; fragrant.

ar ti fice (är'tə fis) *noun.* A clever device; trick; ruse: The child used every *artifice* to avoid going to the dentist.

at tain (ə tān') *verb.* Arrive at; come to; reach: Grandfather has *attained* the age of 80. **attained, attaining.**

at tire (ə tīr') *noun.* Clothing or dress: The queen wore rich *attire* to her coronation.

at trib ute (ə trib'yüt) *verb.* Regard as an effect of: She *attributes* her good health to a carefully planned diet. **attributed, attributing.**

au top sy (ô'top sē) *noun.* Medical examination of a dead body to find the cause of death; postmortem.

aux il iar y (ôg zil'yər ē) *adjective.* Giving help or support; assisting: Some sailboats have *auxiliary* engines.

av id (av'id) *adjective.* Extremely eager: an *avid* desire for fame. **—avidly** *adverb.*

awe (ô) *noun.* Great fear and wonder; fear and reverence: The sight of the great waterfall filled us with *awe.* **—verb.** Cause to feel awe; fill with awe: The majesty of the mountains *awed* us. **awed, awing.**

B

bac ter i ol o gist (bak tir'ē ol'ə jist) *noun.* An expert in the branch of biology that deals with bacteria.

band saw (band'sô) *noun.* Saw in the form of an endless steel belt running over two pulleys.

ban ter (ban'tər) *noun.* Playful teasing; joking. **—verb.** To tease playfully; talk in a joking way. **bantered, bantering.**

be lat ed (bi lā'tid) *adjective.* Happening or coming late; delayed.

bel fry (bel'frē) *noun.* Tower for a bell or bells. **belfries.**

bel lig er ent (bə lij'ər ənt) *adjective.* 1. At war; engaged in war; fighting. 2. Fond of fighting; quarrelsome. **—belligerently** *adverb.*

be mused (bi myüzd') *adjective.* 1. Confused; bewildered. 2. Absorbed in thought or daydreaming.

bil low (bil'ō) *verb.* 1. To rise or roll in big waves; surge. 2. To swell out; bulge. **billowed, billowing.**

biped (bī'ped) *noun.* Any animal having two feet.

blight er (blī'tər) *noun.* A worthless or contemptible person; fellow; guy.

bliss (blis) *noun.* Great happiness; perfect joy: What *bliss* it is to plunge into the cool waves on a hot day!

blunt (blunt) *adjective.* 1. Without a sharp edge or point; dull. 2. Saying what one thinks very frankly, without trying to be tactful; outspoken. **—bluntly** *adverb.*

bob bin (bob'ən) *noun.* Reel or spool for holding thread, yarn, wire, etc.

bold (bōld) *adjective.* 1. Without fear; brave: Lancelot was a *bold* knight. 2. Sharp and clear to the eye; striking: The mountains stood in *bold* outline against the sky. **—boldly** *adverb.*

boon (bün) *noun.* A great benefit; blessing.

boun ti ful (boun'tə fəl) *adjective.* 1. Giving freely; generous. 2. More than enough; plentiful; abundant.

bow (bou) *noun.* The forward part of a ship, boat, or aircraft.

bow ie knife. (bō'ē *or* bü'ē nīf) *noun.* A long, single-edged hunting knife carried in a sheath. **— bowie knives** (bō'ē *or* bü'ē nīvz) plural.

bread win ner (bred'win'ər) *noun.* Person who earns a living and supports a family.

breech (brēch) *noun.* Part of a gun behind the barrel. **breeches.**

brim stone (brim'stōn') *noun.* Sulfur.

brown stone (broun'stōn') *noun.* 1. A reddish-brown sandstone, used as a building material. 2. House with exterior walls built of this material.

bru tal (brü'tl) *adjective.* Savagely cruel; inhuman. **—brutally** *adverb.*

buoy (bȯi *or* bü'ē) *noun.* A floating object anchored on the water to warn against hidden rocks or shallows or to show the safe part of a channel.

buoy ant (boi'ənt *or* bü'yənt) *adjective.* Able to float: Wood and cork are *buoyant* in water; iron and lead are not. —**buoyantly** *adverb.*

bur eau crat ic (byür′ə krat′ik) *adjective.* Of a bureaucracy or a bureaucrat. —**bureaucratically** *adverb.*

bur ly (bėr′lē) *adjective.* Big and strong; sturdy: *a* burly *lumberjack.* **burlier, burliest.**

bush veld (bush′velt) *noun.* Open country in South Africa, having grass or bushes but few trees.

bust (bust) *noun.* Statue of a person's head, shoulders, and upper chest.

C

ca coph o nic (kə kof′ə nik) *adjective.* Harsh sounding; dissonant.

cal a bash (kal′ə bash) *noun.* 1. Gourd or gourdlike fruit whose dried shell is used to make bottles, bowls, drums, and rattles. 2. Bottle, bowl, drum, or rattle made from such a dried shell. **calabashes.**

ca lam i ty (kə lam′ə tē) *noun.* 1. A great misfortune. 2. Serious trouble; misery. **calamities.**

ca ma ra der ie (ka′mə rä′dər ē) *noun.* Friendliness and loyalty among companions, friends, or fellow workers; comradeship.

ca nine (kā′nīn) *noun.* 1. Dog. 2. One of the four pointed teeth next to the incisors; cuspid. —*adjective.* Of or like a dog.

car cass (kär′kəs) *noun.* Body of a dead animal. **carcasses.**

car ri on (kar′ē ən) *noun.* Dead and decaying flesh: *Some crows feed largely on* carrion.

cas cade (ka skād′) *noun.* 1. A small waterfall. 2. Anything like this: *A* cascade *of ivy was hanging from the flower box.*

cas u al ty (kazh′ü əl tē) *noun.* Accident, especially a fatal or serious one: *a* casualty *at sea.* **casualties.**

cav ern ous (kav′ər nəs) *adjective.* 1. Like a cavern; large and hollow: *a* cavernous *cellar.* 2. Full of caverns: *cavernous mountains.* — **cavernously** *adverb.*

ca vort (kə vôrt′) *verb.* Prance about; jump around: *The children* cavorted *about the field, racing and tumbling.* **cavorted, cavorting.**

ces sa tion (se sā′shən) *noun.* A ceasing: a stopping.

cha me le on (kə mē′lē ən) *noun.* A small lizard that can change the color of its skin to blend with its surroundings.

chan nel (chan′l) *noun.* Body of water joining two larger bodies of water.

cha os (kā′os) *noun.* Very great confusion; complete disorder: *The tornado left the town in* chaos.

char (chär) *verb.* Burn enough to blacken; scorch.

char ac ter is tic (kar′ik tə ris′tik) *noun.* A special quality or feature; whatever distinguishes one person or thing from others; trait.

chiv al ry (shiv′əl rē) *noun.* 1. The qualities of an ideal knight in the Middle Ages; bravery, honor, courtesy, protection of the weak, respect for women, and fairness to enemies.

chro mi um (krō′mē əm) *noun.* A grayish, hard, brittle metallic element that does not rust or become dull easily when exposed to air, used as plating, as part of stainless steel and other alloys, for making dyes and paints, in photography, etc.

cir clet (sėr′klit) *noun.* A small circle.

cir cuit (sėr′kit) *noun.* Route over which a person or group makes repeated journeys at certain times.

cir cu late (sėr′kyə lāt) *verb.* To go around; pass from place to place or from person to person. **circulated, circulating.**

cir cum cise (sėr′kəm sīz) *verb.* Cut off the foreskin of. **circumcised, circumcise.**

Civilian Conservation Corps. (sə vil′yən kon′sėr vā′shən kôr) *noun.* Agency begun in the U.S. by President Franklin D. Roosevelt to provide jobs for young men to work in parks and forests. —**CCC** *Abbreviation.*

clar i ty (klar′ə tē) *noun.* Clearness.

clas sic (klas′ik) *noun.* Simple and fine in form: *the* classic *design of a Greek temple.*

cli max (klī′maks) *noun.* The highest point of interest; most exciting part.

co balt (kō′bôlt) *noun.* 1. A hard, silver-white metallic element with a pinkish tint, which occurs only in combination with other elements. 2. A dark-blue coloring matter made from cobalt.

col o ny (kol′ə nē) *noun.* Group of animals, people, or plants of the same kind, living or growing together: *a* colony *of ants.* **colonies.**

com bat ive (kəm bat′iv) *adjective.* Ready to fight; fond of fighting. —**combatively** *adverb.* —**combativeness** *noun.*

con ceiv a ble (kən sē′və bəl) *adjective.* Able to be conceived or thought of; imaginable: *We take every* conceivable *precaution against fire.*

con clu sive (kən klü′siv) *adjective.* Decisive, convincing, final. —**conclusively** *adverb.*

con dens er (kən den′sər) *noun.* Apparatus for changing gas or vapor into a liquid.

con do lence (kən dō′ləns) *noun.* Expression of sympathy.

con du cive (kən dü′siv *or* kən dyü′siv) *adjective.* Favorable; helpful.

con sci en tious (kon′shē en′shəs) *adjective.* Careful to do what one knows is right; controlled by conscience. —**conscientiously** *adverb.*

con ser va tion (kon′sėr vā′shən) *noun.* A preserving from harm or decay; protecting from loss or from being used up.

con sist en cy (kən sis′tən sē) *noun.* Degree of firmness or stiffness: *Frosting for a cake must be of the right* consistency *to spread easily without dripping.*

con spir a cy (kən spir′ə sē) *noun.* Secret planning with others to do something unlawful or wrong; plot. **conspiracies.**

con strain (kən strān′) *verb.* 1. To force to do something; compel: *I felt* constrained *to question them further.* 2. To confine; restrain: *The wild animal was* constrained. **constrained, constraining.**

con sum mate (kən sum′it) *adjective.* In the highest degree; complete; perfect: *The orchestra played with* consummate *skill.* —

consummately *adverb.*

con trol (kən trōl') *noun.* Individual or group serving as a standard of comparison for testing the results of a scientific experiment performed on a similar individual or group.

con verse ly (kən vėrs'lē) *adverb.* If turned the other way around: Six is more than five; *conversely,* five is less than six.

con vey ance (kən vā'əns) *noun.* Thing that carries people and goods; vehicle: Trains and buses are public *conveyances.*

co or di na tor (kō ôrd'nā'tər) *noun.* Person or thing that arranges in proper order, harmonizes, adjusts, etc.

cor nice (kôr'nis) *noun.* An ornamental molding along the top of a wall, pillar, or side of a building.

cor ru gat ed (kôr'ə gā'tid) *adjective.* Bent or shaped into wavy folds or ridges; wrinkled: *corrugated* paper.

coun te nance (koun'tə nəns) *noun.* 1. Expression of the face. 2. Face; features: a person with a noble *countenance.*

cra ni ot o my (krā nē o'tə mē) *noun.* The cutting or removal of part of the skull. **craniotomies.**

cre scen do (krə shen'dō) *noun.* A gradual increase in force or loudness, especially in music.

cringe (krinj) *verb.* Shrink from danger or pain; crouch in fear: I *cringed* when the nurse gave me a shot. **cringed, cringing.**

cro chet (krō shā') *verb.* To make (sweaters, lace, etc.) by looping thread or yarn into links with a single hooked needle. **crocheted, crocheting.**

crouch (krouch) *verb.* 1. To stoop low with bent legs as though ready to spring. 2. To shrink down in fear. **crouched, crouching.**

cul ture plate (kul'chər plāt) *noun.* A small glass dish in which scientists grow bacteria, molds, and other microscopic colonies to study their reactions to various drugs.

cun ning (kun'ing) *noun.* 1. Slyness in getting what one needs or wants or in deceiving one's enemies. 2. Skill, cleverness.

cur ry (kėr'ē) *noun.* 1. A peppery sauce or powder made from a mixture of spices, seeds, and vegetables. 2. Food flavored with it. —*verb.* Prepare or flavor (food) with curry. **curried, currying.**

D

dahl ia (dal'yə) *noun.* A tall plant with large, showy flowers of many colors and varieties that bloom in autumn.

dap ple (dap'əl) *verb.* To mark or become marked with spots. **dappled, dappling.**

dark ling (därk'ling) *adjective.* Dark; in the dark.

de bris (də brē') *noun.* Scattered fragments; ruins; rubbish: The street was covered with broken glass, stone, and other *debris* from the explosion.

de cree (di krē') *noun.* Something ordered or settled by authority; official decision; law: The new state holiday was declared by a *decree* of the governor.

de fault (di fôlt') *verb.* Fail to do something or appear somewhere when due: They *defaulted* in the tennis tournament. **defaulted, defaulting.**

def er ence (def'ər əns) *noun.* Respect for the judgment, opinion, wishes, etc., of another: People often show *deference* to others who are older and wiser.

de i ty (dē'ə tē) *noun.* 1. God or goddess: Juno was the queen of the ancient Roman *deities.* 2. Divine nature; being a god; Christians believe in the *deity* of Jesus. **deities.**

de lib er ate (di lib'ər it) *adjective.* 1. Carefully thought out beforehand; made or done on purpose; intended: Their excuse was a *deliberate* lie. 2. Slow and careful in deciding what to do: *Deliberate* persons do not make up their minds quickly. —**deliberately** *adverb.*

de mise (di mīz') *noun.* Death.

de prive (di prīv') *verb.* 1. To take away from by force. 2. To keep from having or doing. **deprived, depriving.**

de tox i fi ca tion (dē tok'sə fə

kā'shən) *noun.* The removal of poison or the effects of poison.

de vise (di vīz') *verb.* Think out; plan or contrive; invent: She *devised* a way of raising boards up to her tree house by using a pulley. **devised, devising.**

di a be tes (dī'ə bē'tis or dī'ə bē'tēz) *noun.* Disease in which a person's system cannot properly absorb normal amounts of sugar and starch because the pancreas fails to secrete enough insulin.

di a tom (dī'ə tom) *noun.* Any of numerous microscopic, one-celled algae that have hard shells.

dis ci pli nar i an (dis'ə plə ner'ē ən) *noun.* Person who enforces discipline or who believes in strict discipline.

dis con cert (dis'kən sėrt') *verb.* To disturb the self-possession of; embarrass greatly; confuse. **disconcerted, disconcerting.**

dis crim i na tion (dis krim'ə nā'shən) *noun.* A difference in attitude or treatment shown to a particular person, class, etc.: Racial or religious *discrimination* in hiring employees is against the law.

dis en gage (dis'en gāj') *verb.* Free or release from anything that holds; detach; loosen: He *disengaged* his hand from that of the sleeping child.

dis tress (dis tres') *noun.* Great pain or sorrow; anxiety; trouble. **distresses.**

di vert (də vėrt') *verb.* 1. To turn aside. 2. To amuse, entertain. **diverted, diverting.**

don (don) *verb.* To put on (clothing, etc.). **donned, donning.**

douse (dous) *verb.* 1. Plunge into water or any other liquid. 2. Throw water over; drench: We quickly *doused* the flames. **doused, dousing.**

dove tail (duv' tāl') *verb.* Fit together exactly: The various pieces of evidence *dovetailed* so completely that the mystery was solved at once. **dovetailed, dovetailing.**

drach ma (drak'mə) *noun.* Unit of money of modern Greece, worth about 3½ cents.

dray (drā) *noun.* A low, strong cart

for carrying heavy loads.

drudg er y (druj′ər ē) *noun.* Work that is hard, tiresome, or disagreeable.

dur a bil i ty (dùr′ə bil′ə tē *or* dyùr′ə bil′ə tē) *noun.* Lasting quality; ability to withstand wear.

dy nam ic (dī nam′ik) *adjective.* Of energy or force in motion.

E

eer ie (ir′ē) *adjective.* Causing fear because of strangeness or weirdness: a dark and *eerie* old house. **eerier, eeriest.** —**eerily** *adverb.*

ef fer ves cent (ef′ər ves′nt) *adjective.* Giving off bubbles of gas; bubbling: Ginger ale is *effervescent.*

e lec tri fy (i lek′trə fī) *verb.* 1. Charge with electricity. 2. Excite; thrill. **electrified, electrifying.**

e lec tro plate (i lek′trə plāt) *verb.* Cover (silverware, printing plates, etc.) with a coating of metal by means of electrolysis. **electroplated, electroplating.**

el e va tion (el′ə vā′shən) *noun.* A raised place; high place.

ell (el) *noun.* An extension of a building built at right angles to the main structure, forming an L-shaped floor plan.

E man ci pa tion Proc la ma tion. (i man′sə pā′shən prok′lə mā′shən) Statement issued by Abraham Lincoln on January 1, 1863, declaring free all persons held as slaves in any state then in armed rebellion against the United States.

em bed (em bed′) *verb.* Enclose in a surrounding mass; fasten or fix firmly: Precious stones are often found *embedded* in rock. **embedded, embedding.**

em ber (em′bər) *noun.* Piece of wood or coal still glowing in the ashes of a fire.

e merge (i mėrj′) *verb.* Come into view; come out; come up: The sun *emerged* from behind a cloud.

en case (en kās′) *verb.* 1. Put into a case. 2. Cover completely; enclose: A cocoon *encased* the caterpillar. **encased, encasing.**

en deav or (en dev′ər) *verb.* Make

an effort; try hard; attempt strongly: Each time she *endeavored* to do better than before. **endeavored, endeavoring.**

en grave (en grāv′) *verb.* 1. To cut deeply in; carve in an artistic way. 2. To cut (a picture, design, map, etc.) in lines on a metal plate, block of wood, etc. for printing. 3. To print from such a plate, block, etc. 4. To fix firmly. **engraved, engraving.**

en gross (en grōs′) *verb.* To occupy wholly; take up all the attention of. **engrossed, engrossing.**

en hance (en hans′) *verb.* Make greater; add to; heighten: The gardens *enhanced* the beauty of the house. **enhanced, enhancing.**

en light en (en līt′n) *verb.* To give truth and knowledge to; inform; instruct. **enlightened, enlightening.**

en mi ty (en′mə tē) *noun.* The feeling that enemies have for each other; hostility or hatred. **enmities.**

e nor mi ty (i nôr′mə tē) *noun.* Extreme, outrageous: The *enormity* of the crime made it likely that the criminal was not sane.

en thrall (en thrôl′) *verb.* To hold captive by beauty or interest; fascinate; charm. **enthralled, enthralling.**

en thu si ast (en thü′zē ast) *noun.* Person who is filled with interest or zeal.

en tice (en tīs′) *verb.* Attract by arousing hopes or desires; tempt: The smell of food *enticed* the hungry children into the house. **enticed, enticing.** —**enticingly** *adverb.*

e nu me rate (i nü′mə rāt′ *or* i nyü′mə rāt′) *verb.* Name one by one; list: She *enumerated* the capitals of the European countries.

en vi rons (en vī′rənz) *noun.* Surrounding districts; suburbs: We visited Boston and its *environs.*

en vi sion (en vizh′ən) *verb.* To picture in one's mind. **envisioned, envisioning.**

ep ic (ep′ik) *noun.* A long poem that tells the adventures of one or more great heroes. —*adjective.* Of or like an epic; grand, heroic.

ep i sode (ep′ə sōd) *noun.* A single happening or group of happenings in real life or in a story: Being named the best athlete of the year was an important *episode* in the baseball player's life.

e qui lib ri um (ē′kwə lib′rē əm) *noun.* Balance: The gymnast maintained *equilibrium* on a balance beam.

et i quette (et′ə ket) *noun.* The customary rules for behavior in polite society.

e volve (i volv′) *verb.* Develop gradually; unfold: Buds evolve into flowers. **evolved, evolving.**

ex ag ge ra tion (eg zaj′ə rā′shən) *noun.* A saying or thinking something is greater than it is; goes beyond the truth.

ex as pe ra tion (eg zas′pə rā′shən) *noun.* Extreme annoyance; irritation; anger.

ex ec u tive (eg zek′yə tiv) *noun.* Person who carries out or manages affairs.

ex plor a to ry (ek splôr′ə tôr′ē) *adjective.* Of exploration.

ex po si tion (ek′spə zish′ən) *noun.* 1. A public show or exhibition. 2. A detailed explanation. 3. Speech or writing explaining a process, thing, or idea.

ex tinc tion (ek stingk′shən) *noun.* Bringing to an end; wiping out; destruction: Physicians are working toward the *extinction* of many serious diseases.

ex tract (ek strakt′) *verb.* 1. Pull out or draw out, usually with some effort: *extract* a tooth. 2. Obtain by pressing, squeezing, etc.: *extract* oil from olives. **extracted, extracting.** — (ek′strakt) *noun.* A concentrated preparation of a substance: Vanilla *extract,* made from vanilla beans, is used as flavoring.

ex u ber ant (eg zü′bər ənt) *adjective.* Abounding in health and high spirits; overflowing with good cheer: I was in an *exuberant* mood all day. —**exuberantly** *adverb.*

F

fa cil i ty (fə sil′ə tē) *noun.* (Usually plural) Something that makes an action easy; aid; convenience. **facilities.**

fal la cy (fal'ə sē) *noun.* Mistake in reasoning; misleading or unsound argument. **fallacies.**

fa nat i cal (fə nat'ə kəl) *adjective.* Unreasonably enthusiastic; extremely zealous. **—fanatically** *adverb.*

fe line (fē'līn) *noun.* Cat. *—adjective.* 1. Of a cat. 2. Like that of a cat.

fe roc i ty (fə ros'ə tē) *noun.* Great cruelty; savageness; fierceness: The wolves fought with great *ferocity.* **ferocities.**

fet id (fet'id) *adjective.* Smelling very bad; stinking.

fi as co (fē as'kō) *noun.* A complete or ridiculous failure; humiliating breakdown: The play was a *fiasco* and closed after only three performances. **fiascos** or **fiascoes.**

fiend (fēnd) *noun.* 1. An evil spirit; devil. 2. A very wicked or cruel person.

fleet ing (flē'ting) *adjective.* Passing swiftly; soon gone: a *fleeting* smile. **—fleetingly** *adverb.*

floe (flō) *noun.* Field or sheet of floating ice.

flour ish (flėr'ish) *noun.* A waving about: He removed his hat with a *flourish.* **flourishes.**

fo li age (fō'lē ij) *noun.* Leaves of a plant.

fo rage (fôr'ij) *noun.* Hay, grain, or other food for horses, cattle, etc. *—verb.* Hunt or search for food: Rabbits *forage* in our garden. **foraged, foraging.**

fore most (fôr'mōst) *adjective.* 1. First: I am *foremost* in line. 2. Chief; leading: one of the *foremost* scientists of this century.

fore run ner (fôr'run'ər) *noun.* 1. Person who is sent ahead to prepare for and announce another's coming; herald. 2. Sign or warning that something is coming: Black clouds are *forerunners* of a storm. 3. Predecessor; ancestor.

fore shad ow (fôr shad'ō) *verb.* Indicate beforehand; be a warning of: Those dark clouds *foreshadow* a storm. **foreshadow, foreshadowing.**

fore warn (fôr wôrn') *verb.* To warn beforehand. **forewarned,** forewarning.

for go (fôr gō') *verb.* Do without; give up: She decided to *forgo* the concert and do her lessons. **forgone, forgoing.**

for mi da ble (fôr'mə də bəl) *adjective.* Hard to overcome; hard to deal with; to be dreaded: a *formidable* opponent. **—formidably** *adverb.*

for ni ca tion (fôr nə kā'shən) *noun.* Sexual intercourse between people who are not married.

fri a ble (frī'ə bəl) *adjective.* Easily crumbled.

func tion al (fungk'shə nəl) *adjective.* Having a usefulness; working; acting: The *functional* wings of an insect are those used for flying. **—functionally** *adverb.*

fur tive (fėr'tiv) *adjective.* Done quickly and with stealth to avoid being noticed. **—furtively** *adverb.*

fu tile (fyü'tl) *adjective.* Not successful; useless: He fell down after making *futile* attempts to keep his balance.

fu til i ty (fyü til'ə tē) *noun.* 1. Uselessness. 2. Unimportance. **futilities.**

G

ga ble (gā'bəl) *noun.* End of a ridged roof, with the three-cornered piece of wall that it covers.

gag gle (gag'əl) *noun.* A flock of geese.

gam bol (gam'bəl) *noun.* A running and jumping about in play; frolic.

gan gly (gang'glē) *adjective.* Awkwardly tall and slender; lank and loosely built.

gasp (gasp) *verb.* 1. Try hard to get one's breath with open mouth. 2. Utter with gasps: "Help! Help!" *gasped* the drowning man.

ge ne al o gy (jē'nē al'ə jē *or* jē'nē ol'ə jē) *noun.* Account of the descent of a person or family from an ancestor or ancestors.

Gen tile (jen'tīl) *noun.* Person who is not a Jew. *—adjective.* Not Jewish.

ges ture (jes'chər) *noun.* Movement of any part of the body to help express an idea or a feeling: Speakers often make *gestures* with their hands to stress something that they are saying.

glad i a tor (glad'ē ā'tər) *noun.* Slave, captive, or paid fighter who fought at the public shows in the arenas in ancient Rome.

gorge (gôrj) *verb.* Eat greedily until full; stuff with food: I *gorged* myself with cake at the party. **gorged, gorging.**

gos ling (goz'ling) *noun.* A young goose.

Goth ic (goth'ik) *noun.* Style of architecture using pointed arches, flying buttresses, and high, steep roofs. *—adjective.* Of this kind of architecture.

grid (grid) *noun.* 1. A pattern of evenly spaced vertical and horizontal lines. 2. Framework of parallel iron bars with spaces between them; grating; gridiron.

gus to (gus'tō) *noun.* Hearty enjoyment; keen relish.

H

hack le (hak'əl) *noun.* 1. One of the long, slender feathers on the neck of a rooster, pigeon, peacock, etc. 2. (Plural) Hairs on the back of a dog's neck that can become erect.

hal i but (hal'ə bət) *noun.* A large flatfish, much used for food. **halibuts** or **halibut.**

hal low (hal'ō) *verb.* 1. Make holy; make sacred. 2. Honor as holy or sacred: "*Hallowed* be Thy name." **—hallowed, hallowing.**

ham let (ham'lit) *noun.* A small village.

ham per (ham'pər) *verb.* To hold back; hinder. **hampered, hampering.**

hap haz ard (hap haz'ərd) *adjective.* Not planned; random: *Haphazard* answers are often wrong. **—haphazardly** *adverb.*

hap less (hap'lis) *adjective.* Unlucky, unfortunate.

har ass (har'əs *or* hə ras') *verb.* Disturb; worry; torment: Heat and flies *harassed* the hikers. **harassed, harassing.**

har row ing (har'ō ing) *adjective.* Very painful or distressing: a *harrowing* experience.

har ry (har'ē) *verb.* 1. Raid; attack;

pillage. 2. To harass by constant or repetitive attack. **harried, harrying.**

head land (hed'lənd) *noun.* Point of high land jutting out into water; cape; promontory.

hearth (härth) *noun.* Stone or brick floor of a fireplace, often extending into the room.

heath (hēth) *noun.* 1. Open wasteland with heather or low bushes growing on it; moor. 2. A low bush growing on such land.

heir (er *or* ar) *noun.* Person who has the right to somebody's property or title after the death of its owner.

her bi vore (hėr'bə vôr) *noun.* Any animal that feeds mainly on plants.

hew (hyü) *verb.* 1. Cut with an ax, sword, etc.; chop: He *hewed* down the tree. 2. Cut into shape; form by cutting with an ax, etc.: *hew* stone for building. **hewed, hewed** or **hewn, hewing.**

hid e ous (hid'ē əs) *adjective.* Very ugly; frightful; horrible: a *hideous* crime. **—hideously** *adverb.*

hog wash (hog'wosh) *noun.* Worthless or nonsensical language.

horde (hôrd) *noun.* Multitude; crowd; swarm: *hordes* of grasshoppers.

hov er (huv'ər *or* hov'ər) *verb.* Stay in or near one place; wait nearby: The dogs *hovered* around the kitchen door at mealtime. **—hovered, hovering.**

I

im be cil i ty (im'bə sil'ə tē) *noun.* 1. Great stupidity. 2. A very stupid or foolish action, remark, etc. **imbecilities.**

im merse (i mėrs') *verb.* To dip or lower into a liquid until covered by it: I *immersed* my aching feet in a bucket of hot water. **—immersed, immersing. —immersion** (i mėr'zhən) *noun.*

im pact (im'pakt) *noun.* 1. A striking (of one thing against another); collision. 2. A forceful or dramatic effect.

im pair (im per' *or* im par') *verb.* To make worse; damage; harm;

weaken. **impaired, impairing.**

im pal a (im pal'ə) *noun.* A large brownish-bay antelope of Africa. **—impala** or **impalas** *plural.*

im pass i ble (im pas'ə bəl) *adjective.* Without feeling or emotion; unmoved; impassive: Her face was *impassible* when we told her the news.

im pel (im pel') *verb.* To drive or force; cause. **impelled, impelling.**

im per i al (im pir'ē əl) *adjective.* 1. Of an empire or its ruler. 2. Supreme; majestic. **—imperially** *adverb.*

im pla ca ble (im pla'kə bəl) *adjective.* Unable to be appeased; refusing to be reconciled; unyielding. **—implacably** *adverb.*

im pli ca tion (im'plə kā'shən) *noun.* Something implied; indirect suggestion; hint: She did not actually refuse, but the way that she frowned was an *implication* of her unwillingness.

im plic it ly (im plis'it lē) *adverb.* 1. Unquestioningly. 2. By implication.

im pound (im pound') *verb.* Enclose or confine within limits: A dam *impounds* water. **impounded, impounding.**

im print (im print') *verb.* To fix firmly in the mind. **imprinted, imprinting.**

in au gu rate (in ô'gyə rāt') *verb.* To make a formal beginning of; begin. **inaugurated, inaugurating.**

in can des cent (in'kən des'nt) *adjective.* 1. Glowing with heat; red-hot or white-hot: The embers of the fire were still *incandescent* even though the flames had disappeared. 2. Shining brightly; brilliant. **—incandescently** *adverb.*

in ces sant (in ses'nt) *adjective.* Never stopping; continual: The *incessant* noise from the factory kept me awake all night. **—incessantly** *adverb.*

in con sol a ble (in'kən sō'lə bəl) *adjective.* Not to be comforted; broken-hearted: The girl was *inconsolable* at the loss of her kitten.

in de ci sive (in'di sī'siv) *adjective.* Not deciding or settling the matter; without a clear result. **—indecisively** *adverb.*

in dig nant (in dig'nənt) *adjective.* Angry at something unworthy, unjust, or mean. **—indignantly** *adverb.*

in dig na tion (in'dig nā'shən) *noun.* Anger at something unworthy, unjust, or mean: Cruelty to animals aroused his *indignation.*

in ef fec tu al (in'ə fek'chü əl) *adjective.* Without effect; failing to have the effect wanted; useless; powerless. **—ineffectually** *adverb.*

in ert (in ėrt') *adjective.* Having no power to move or act; lifeless: A stone is an *inert* mass of matter.

in ex plic a ble (in'ik splik'ə bəl *or* in ek'splə kə bəl) *adjective.* Not able to be explained; mysterious. **—inexplicably** *adverb.*

in ex tri ca ble (in ek'strə kə bəl) *adjective.* Not able to be gotten out of: an *inextricable* maze. **—inextricably** *adverb.*

in fest (in fest') *verb.* Trouble or disturb frequently or in large numbers: Mosquitoes *infest* swamps. **—infested, infesting.**

in ge nu i ty (in'jə nü'ə tē *or* in'jə nyü'ə tē) *noun.* Skill in planning or making; cleverness: The girl showed *ingenuity* in making toys out of scraps of wood.

i ni ti a tion (i nish'ē ā'shən) *noun.* Admission into a group or society.

in no va tion (in'ə vā'shən) *noun.* Change made in the established way of doing things: The principal made many *innovations.*

in sa tia ble (in sā'shə bəl) *adjective.* Not able to be satisfied; extremely greedy: The boy had an *insatiable* appetite for candy. **—insatiably** *adverb.*

in su late (in'sə lāt) *verb.* 1. Keep from losing or transferring electricity, sound, etc., especially by covering, packing, or surrounding with a material that does not conduct electricity, heat, etc.: Telephone wires are often *insulated* by a covering of rubber. 2. Set apart; separate from others; isolate: Prisoners are *insulated* from the normal, everyday world. **insulated, insulating.**

in su lin shock. (in'sə lən shok) *noun.* Condition of illness leading to coma and caused by too much insulin in the bloodstream.

in ten sive (in ten'siv) *adjective.*
Deep and thorough. —**intensively**
adverb.

in tri cate (in'trə kit) *adjective.*
With many twists and turns; puz-
zling, entangled, or complicated:
An *intricate* knot is very hard to tie
or untie. —**intricately** *adverb.*

in tu i tive (in tü'ə tiv *or* in tyü'ə tiv)
adjective. Perceiving or understanding immediately and without
reasoning: an *intuitive* mind.

in val u a ble (in val'yü ə bəl *or* in
val'yə bəl) *adjective.* Valuable
beyond measure; very precious;
priceless: Good health is an *invaluable* blessing. —**invaluably**
adverb.

in var i a bly (in ver'ē ə blē *or* in
var'ə blē) *adverb.* Without change;
without exception: Spring *invariably* follows winter.

in vul ner a ble (in vul'nər ə bəl)
adjective. Not capable of being
wounded or injured; not open to
attack.

ir i des cent (ir'ə des'ənt) *adjective.*
Displaying changing colors;
change of color when moved or
turned.

i ro ny (ī'rə nē) *noun.* Event or
outcome which is the opposite of
what would naturally be expected.
—**ironic** *adjective.*

i so la tion (ī'sə lā'shən) *noun.* The
state of being set apart; separate
from others; kept alone.

J

jo vi al (jō'vē əl) *adjective.* Good-
hearted and full of fun; good-
humored and merry. —**jovially**
adverb.

K

keep sake (kēp'sāk') *noun.* Thing
kept in memory of the giver:
Before my friend went away, she
gave me her picture as a *keepsake.*

koo doo (kü'dü) *noun.* A large,
grayish-brown African antelope
with white stripes.

L

lan guish (lang'gwish) *verb.*
Become weak or wasted through
pain, hunger, etc.; suffer under
any unfavorable conditions: Wild
animals often *languish* in captivity.
—**languished, languishing.**

lapse (laps) *noun.* 1. A slight mistake or error: a *lapse* of memory.
2. A slipping by; a passing away:
A minute is a short *lapse* of time.
3. A slipping back; sinking down;
slipping into a lower condition:
War is a *lapse* into savage ways.
lapses. —*verb.* 1. Make a slight
mistake or error. 2. Slip by; pass
away: His interest in the dull story
soon *lapsed.* 3. Fall or pass into
any state: Our discussion *lapsed*
into silence. **lapsed, lapsing.**

la tent (lāt'nt) *adjective.* Present but
not active; hidden: The power of a
seed to grow into a plant remains
latent if it is not planted.

ledg er (lej' ər) *noun.* Book of
accounts in which a business
keeps a record of all money trans-
actions.

le git i mate (lə jit'ə mit) *adjective.*
1. Allowed or admitted by law;
rightful; lawful: a *legitimate* title or
right. 2. Valid; logical; acceptable:
Sickness is a *legitimate* reason for
being absent from school. —**legit-
imately** *adverb.*

li a na (lē ä'nə *or* lē an'ə) *noun.* A
climbing plant or vine. **lianas.**

loath some (lōŦн'səm) *adjective.*
Making one feel sick; disgusting: a
loathsome odor. —**loathsomely**
adverb.

lop sid ed (lop'sī'did) *adjective.*
Larger or heavier on one side
than the other; leaning to one
side.

lu nar (lü'nər) *adjective.* 1. Of the
moon. 2. Like the moon.

lurk (lėrk) *verb.* 1. Stay about without arousing attention; wait out of
sight; be hidden. 2. Move about in
a secret and sly manner. **lurked,
lurking.**

lymph gland. (limf' gland') *noun.*
Any of the small oval bodies that
filter harmful microorganisms from
the tissue fluid.

M

ma gen ta (mə jen'tə) *noun.* 1. A
purplish-red dye. 2. A purplish
red. —*adjective.* Purplish-red.

maim (mām) *verb.* Cut off or make
useless an arm, leg, ear, etc.;
cripple; disable: His foot was
maimed in the accident. **maimed,
maiming.**

ma lar i a (mə ler'ē ə *or* mə lar'ē ə)
noun. Disease characterized by
chills, fever, and sweating. Malaria
is caused by one-celled animals in
the blood and is transmitted by
certain mosquitoes.

ma ma ci ta (mä'mə sē'tə) *noun.*
Spanish for Little Mother.

man a cle (man'ə kəl) *noun.* (Usually plural) Fetter for the hands;
handcuff. **manacles.**

man i fest (man'ə fest) *adjective.*
Apparent to the eye or to the
mind; plain; clear: The error was
manifest. —*verb.* Show plainly;
reveal; display. **manifested, man-
ifesting.** —*noun.* A list of cargo of
a ship or aircraft.

ma ter i al ize (mə tir'ē ə līz) *verb.*
To appear or cause to appear in
material or bodily form. **materialized, materializing.**

mea ger *or* **mea gre** (mē'gər) *adjective.* 1. Poor or scanty. 2. Thin;
lean. —**meagerly** *or* **meagrely**
adverb.

meg a phone (meg'ə fōn) *noun.* A
large, funnel-shaped horn used to
increase the loudness of the voice
or the distance at which it can be
heard.

me ni al (mē'nē əl) *adjective.* Of or
suited to a servant; low; mean.

merge (mėrj) *verb.* 1. Cause to be
swallowed up or absorbed so as
to lose its own character or iden-
tity; combine or consolidate: The
big company *merged* various
small businesses. 2. Become
swallowed up or absorbed in
something else: The two railroads
merged into one. **merged, merg-
ing.**

me thod i cal (mə thod'ə kəl) *adjective.* 1. Done according to a
method; systematic, orderly. —
methodically *adverb.*

me tic u lous (mə tik'yə ləs) *adjective.* Extremely or excessively careful about small details. —**meticulously** *adverb.*

mil i tan cy (mil'ə tən sē) *noun.* Warlike behavior or tendency; militant spirit or policy.

min e stro ne (min'ə strō'nē) *noun.* A thick soup containing vegetables, vermicelli, etc.

min i mize (min'ə mīz) *verb.* Reduce to the least possible amount or degree: The polar explorers took every precaution to *minimize* the dangers of their trip. **minimized, minimizing.**

mi rage (mə räzh') *noun.* An optical illusion, usually in the desert, at sea, or on a paved road, in which some distant scene appears to be much closer than it actually is.

mock (mok) *adjective.* Not real; pretended, copying.

mode (mōd) *noun.* 1. Manner or way in which a thing is done: Riding on a donkey is a slow *mode* of travel. 2. Style, fashion, or custom that is current; the way most people are behaving, talking, dressing, etc.

mod ule (moj'ul) *noun.* A packaged functional assembly for use with other such assemblies.

mo men tous (mō men'təs) *adjective.* Very important: Choosing between peace and war is a *momentous* decision. —**momentously** *adverb.*

mon arch (mon'ərk) *noun.* 1. King, queen, emperor, etc.; ruler. 2. Person or thing like a monarch.

mon i tor (mon'ə tər) *verb.* 1. Check and listen to (radio or television transmissions, telephone messages, etc.) by using a receiver. 2. Check or watch anything closely. **monitored, monitoring.**

moor (mùr) *verb.* 1. Put or keep (a ship, etc.) in place by means of ropes or chains fastened to the shore or to anchors. 2. Fix firmly; secure. **moored, mooring.**

mor tar (môr'tər) *noun.* Mixture of lime, cement, sand, and water, for holding bricks or stones together.

musk y (mus'kē) *adjective.* Of or like the substance with a strong and lasting odor, used in making perfumes: a *musky* odor.

mu tu al (myü'chü əl) *adjective.* Done, said, felt, etc., by each toward the other; given and received: *mutual* promises.

N

nar cot ic (när kot'ik) *noun.* Any drug that produces drowsiness, sleep, dullness, or an insensible condition, and lessens pain by dulling the nerves. —*adjective.* 1. Having the properties and effects of a narcotic. 2. Of narcotics or their use.

niche (nich) *noun.* A suitable place or position; place for which a person is suited: I have yet to find my *niche* in life.

noc tur nal (nok tèr'nl) *adjective.* 1. Of the night: Stars are a *nocturnal* sight. 2. In the night: a *nocturnal* visitor. 3. Active in the night: The owl is a *nocturnal* bird. —**nocturnally** *adverb.*

non com mit tal (non'kə mit'l) *adjective.* Not committing oneself; not saying yes or no. —**noncommittally** *adverb.*

non plus (non plus' *or* non'plus) *verb.* Puzzle completely; make unable to say or do anything: We were *nonplused* to see two roads leading off to the left where we had expected only one. **nonplused** or **nonplussed, nonplusing** or **nonplussing.**

O

o blit e rate (ə blit'ə rāt') *verb.* To remove all traces of; wipe or blot out; destroy: The heavy rain *obliterated* the footprints. **obliterated, obliterating.**

ob scure (əb skyùr') *adjective.* 1. Not clearly expressed; hard to understand; vague. 2. Not well known; attracting no notice.

ol fac tor y (ol fak'tər ē) *adjective.* Having to do with smelling; of smell: The nose is an *olfactory* organ. —*noun.* An olfactory organ. **olfactories.**

om i nous (om'ə nəs) *adjective.* Unfavorable; threatening: Those black clouds look *ominous.* —**ominously** *adverb.*

om niv or ous (om niv'ər əs) *adjective.* 1. Eating every kind of food. 2. Eating both animal and vegetable food: Human beings are *omnivorous.*

or deal (ôr dēl') *noun.* A severe test or experience: I dreaded the *ordeal* of going to the dentist.

or phan age (ôr'fə nij) *noun.* Home for children whose parents are dead.

out rage (out'rāj) *noun.* An act showing no regard for the rights or feelings of others; overturning of the rights of others by force; act of violence; offense; insult: The tyrant was guilty of many *outrages.*

out ra geous (out rā'jəs) *adjective.* Very bad or insulting; shocking: *outrageous* language. —**outrageously** *adverb.*

o ver pro tec tive ness (ō'vər prə tek'tiv nis) *noun.* The act of shielding or protecting more than is necessary.

o ver ride (ō'vər rīd') *verb.* 1. To act in spite of: *override* advice or objections. 2. To ride over; trample on. **overrode, overridden, overriding.**

P

pains tak ing (pānz'tā'king) *adjective.* Very careful; particular; scrupulous: a *painstaking* painter. —**painstakingly** *adverb.*

pall (pôl) *noun.* 1. A heavy cloth of black, purple, or white velvet spread over a coffin, a hearse, or a tomb. 2. A dark, gloomy covering: A thick *pall* of smoke shut out the sun from the city.

pal let (pal'it) *noun.* Bed of straw; poor bed.

pan de mo ni um (pan'də mō'nē əm) *noun.* Wild uproar or confusion.

pang (pang) *noun.* A sudden, short, sharp pain: the *pangs* of a toothache.

pan o ram a (pan'ə ram'ə) *noun.* A wide, unbroken view of a surrounding region.

par ish (par'ish) *noun.* 1. District

that has its own church and clergyman. 2. People of a parish. 3. Members of the congregation of a particular church. 4. (In Louisiana) A county.

par lia ment (pär′lə mənt) *noun.* Council or congress that is the highest lawmaking body in some countries.

pa vil ion (pə vil′yən) *noun.* Part of a building higher and more decorated than the rest.

ped a go gy (ped′ə gō′jē) *noun.* Science or art of teaching.

pen sive (pen′siv) *adjective.* Thoughtful in a serious or sad way. **—pensively** *adverb.*

per ceive (pər sēv′) *verb.* 1. Be aware of through the senses; see, hear, taste, smell, or feel: Did you *perceive* the colors of that bird? 2. Take in with the mind; observe: I soon *perceived* that I could not make them change their minds. **perceived, perceiving. —perceivably** *adverb.*

per cep tive (pər sep′tiv) *adjective.* Able to perceive; intelligent: a *perceptive* audience. **—perceptively** *adverb.*

per func tor y (pər fungk′tər ē) *adjective.* Done merely for the sake of getting rid of the duty; done from force of habit; mechanical; indifferent.

per il ous (per′ə ləs) *adjective.* Full of peril; dangerous. **—perilously** *adverb.*

pe rim e ter (pə rim′ə tər) *noun.* 1. The outer boundary of a figure or area: the *perimeter* of a garden. 2. Distance around such a boundary.

per pet u al (pər pech′ü əl) *adjective.* 1. Lasting forever; eternal: the *perpetual* hills. 2. Lasting throughout life: a *perpetual* income. 3. Never ceasing; continuous: a *perpetual* stream of visitors. **—perpetually** *adverb.*

per sist ent (pər sis′tənt) *adjective.* 1. Not giving up, especially in the face of dislike, disapproval, or difficulties; persisting: a *persistent* salesperson. 2. Going on; continuing; lasting: a *persistent* headache that lasted for days. **—persistently** *adverb.*

pert (pèrt) *adjective.* Too forward or free in speech or action; saucy;

bold: a *pert* reply.

pes ti cide (pes′tə sīd) *noun.* Substance used to kill pests, such as mosquitoes.

pet tish (pet′ish) *adjective.* Peevish; cross. **—pettishly** *adverb.*

phe nom e nal (fə nom′ə nəl) *adjective.* Extraordinary: a *phenomenal* memory.

pho bi a (fō′bē ə) *noun.* A deep, irrational fear of a certain thing or group of things: a *phobia* about snakes.

phos pho res cence (fos′fə res′ns) *noun.* 1. Act or process of giving out light without burning or by very slow burning that seems not to give out heat: the *phosphorescence* of fireflies. 2. Light given out in this way.

phys i o log i cal (fiz′ē ə loj′ə kəl) *adjective.* Of physiology: Digestion is a *physiological* process. **—physiologically** *adverb.*

pid dle (pid′l) *verb.* To deal or work in a trifling or petty way; to act or concern one's self idly or inefficiently; to trifle; play; putter. **piddling.**

pi lot (pī′lət) *adjective.* Serving as a guiding or tracking device, or a trial or operation.

pin na cle (pin′ə kəl) *noun.* 1. A high peak or point of rock. 2. The highest point: at the *pinnacle* of one's fame. 3. A slender turret or spire.

pla cate (plā′kāt *or* plak′āt) *verb.* To soothe or satisfy the anger of; make peaceful; appease: *placate* a person one has offended. **placated, placating.**

plight (plīt) *noun.* Condition or situation, usually bad.

plow share (plou′sher′ *or* plou′shar′) *noun.* Blade of a plow; the part of a plow that cuts the soil.

plun der (plun′dər) *verb.* Rob by force; rob: The pirates entered the harbor and began to *plunder* the town. **plundered, plundering. —** *noun.* 1. Things taken in plundering; booty; loot: They carried off the *plunder* in their ships. 2. Act of robbing by force: In olden times soldiers often gained great wealth by *plunder* of a conquered city.

ply (plī) *verb.* 1. Keep up work on; work away at or on: to *ply* one's trade. 2. Supply with in a pressing manner: *ply* a person with food or drink. **plied, plying.**

pneu mo coc cus (nü′mə kok′əs) *noun.* The bacterium which causes pneumonia. **—pneumococci** (nu′mə kok′ī) *plural.*

pom mel *or* **pum mel** (pum′əl) *verb.* Strike or beat; beat with the fists.

pom pa dour (pom′pə dôr) *noun.* Arrangement of hair in which it is puffed high over the forehead or brushed straight up and back from the forehead.

pon der (pon′dər) *verb.* To consider carefully; think over. **pondered, pondering.**

port fo li o (pôrt fō′lē ō) *noun.* A portable case for loose papers, drawings, etc.; briefcase.

por ti co (pôr′tə kō) *noun.* Roof supported by columns, forming a porch or a covered walk. **porticoes** *or* **porticos.**

pre car i ous (pri ker′ē əs) *adjective.* Not safe or secure; uncertain; dangerous; risky.

pre ced ing (prē sē′ding) *adjective.* Going or coming before; previous: Turn back and look for the answer on the *preceding* page.

pre cept (prē′sept) *noun.* Rule of action or behavior; guiding principal.

pred a tor (pred′ə tər) *noun.* Animal or person that lives by preying upon others.

pred i cate (pred′ə kāt) *verb.* To found or base (a statement, action, etc.) on something. **predicated, predicating.**

preen (prēn) *verb.* 1. Smooth or arrange (the feathers) with the beak. 2. Dress or groom (oneself) carefully. **preened, preening.**

prem is es (prem′is əs) *noun.* House or building with its grounds.

prime (prīm) *adjective.* 1. First in rank; chief: The town's *prime* need is a new school. 2. First in time or order; primary: the *prime* causes of pollution.

primp (primp) *verb.* To dress (oneself) with excessive care; dress carefully. **primped, primping.**

pri va tion (prī vā′shən) *noun.* Lack

of the comforts or of the necessities of life.

priv y (priv'ē) *adjective.* Private. —*noun.* A small outhouse used as a toilet. **privies.**

pro cure (prə kyùr') *verb.* Get by care or effort; obtain; secure: *procure* a job in a bank.

pro di gious (prə dij'əs) *adjective.* 1. Very great; huge; vast: The ocean contains a *prodigious* amount of water. 2. Wonderful; marvelous. **—prodigiously** *adverb.*

prod i gy (prod'ə jē) *noun.* 1. A marvel; wonder: Mary's four-year-old brother, a musical *prodigy,* plays the piano. 2. A wonderful sign or omen: The brilliant comet seemed a *prodigy* to all who saw it. **prodigies.**

prof fer (prof'ər) *verb.* Offer for acceptance; present; tender: We *proffered* our regrets at having to leave so early. **proffered, proffering.** —*noun.* An offer made: Her *proffer* of advice was accepted.

prom i nent (prom'ə nənt) *adjective.* Easy to see: I hung the picture in a *prominent* place in the living room. **—prominently** *adverb.*

prom is so ry   note. (prom'ə sôr'e nōt) *noun.* A written promise to pay a stated sum of money to a certain person at a certain time.

prone (prōn) *adjective.* 1. Inclined or disposed; liable: He is *prone* to forget to do his chores. 2. Lying face down: be *prone* on the bed. 3. Lying flat: fall *prone* on the ground.

pro pose (prə pōz') *verb.* To put forward; suggest. **proposed, proposing.**

pro spec tive (prə spek'tiv) *adjective.* Likely to happen; probable, expected.

pro té gé (prō'tə zhā) *noun.* Person who has been taken under the protection or kindly care of a friend or patron.

pro trude (prō trüd') *verb.* Thrust forth; stick out. **protruded, protruding.**

quar ters (kwôr'tərz) *noun.* Place to live or stay.

quer y (kwir'ē) *noun.* A question; inquiry.

queue (kyu) *noun.* A line of people, automobiles, etc. —*verb.* To form or stand in a long line. **queued, queuing** or **queueing.**

R

ra bies (rā'bēz) *noun.* A virus disease that attacks the central nervous system of warm-blooded animals, causing mental disturbance, muscular spasms, and paralysis, usually transmitted by the bite of a rabid animal and fatal unless treated with serum.

ra di us (rā'dē əs) *noun.* 1. A line segment going straight from the center to the outside of a circle or a sphere. 2. The length of such a line segment: The *radius* of the circle is 6 centimeters. 3. A circular area measured by the length of its radius: The explosion could be heard within a *radius* of ten miles. **—radii** (rā'de ī) or **radiuses** *plural.*

ram ble (ram'bəl) *verb.* 1. Wander about: We *rambled* here and there through the woods. 2. Talk or write about first one thing and then another with no useful connections. **rambled, rambling.**

ram shack le (ram'shak'əl) *adjective.* Loose and shaky; likely to come apart.

rank (rangk) *adjective.* Growing in a thick, coarse way: a *rank* growth of weeds.

rap ture (rap'chər) *noun.* A strong feeling that absorbs the mind; very great joy: In *rapture* the child gazed at the toys in the shop window.

ra tion al ize (rash'ə nə līz') *verb.* To find (often unconsciously) an explanation or excuse for. **rationalized, rationalizing.**

rau cous (rô'kəs) *adjective.* Hoarse; harsh-sounding: the *raucous* caw of a crow. **—raucously** *adverb.*

rav en ous (rav'ə nəs) *adjective.* 1. Very hungry. 2. Greedy. **—ravenously** *adverb.*

re al ism (rē'ə liz'əm) *noun.* (In art and literature) The picturing of life as it actually is.

reap (rēp) *verb.* 1. To cut (grain). 2. To gather (a crop). 3. To get as a return or reward. **reaped, reaping.**

re cline (ri klīn') *verb.* Lean back; lie or lay down: *recline* on a couch. **reclined, reclining.**

rec ol lect (rek'ə lekt') *verb.* To call back to mind; remember. **recollected, recollecting.**

Ref or ma tion (ref'ər mā'shən) *noun.* The religious movement in Europe in the 1500s that aimed at reform within the Roman Catholic Church but led to the establishment of Protestant churches.

re gal (rē'gəl) *adjective.* 1. Belonging to a king or queen; royal: *regal* power. 2. Fit for a king or queen; stately; splendid; magnificent: a *regal* banquet. **—regally** *adverb.*

re ha bil i ta tion (rē'hə bil'ə tā'shən) *noun.* Restoration to a good condition or to a former standing.

rel ic (rel'ik) *noun.* 1. Thing left from the past: This ruined bridge is a *relic* of the Civil War. 2. Object having interest because of its age or its associations with the past; keepsake; souvenir.

rem i nisce (rem'ə nis') *verb.* Talk or think about past experiences or events. **reminisced, reminiscing.**

rem i nis cent (rem'ə nis'nt) *adjective.* Recalling past persons, events, etc.: *reminiscent* talk.

re morse (ri môrs') *noun.* Deep, painful regret for having done wrong: I felt *remorse* for hurting her feelings, so I apologized.

re mu ne ra tion (ri myü'nə rā'shən) *noun.* A reward; pay; payment.

re proof (ri prüf') *noun.* Words of blame or disapproval; rebuke.

re pulse (ri puls') *verb.* 1. Drive back; repel: Our soldiers *repulsed* the enemy. 2. Refuse to accept; reject: She *repulsed* my invitation. **repulsed, repulsing.**

re serve (ri zėrv') *noun.* A place where wild animals, fish, or trees and plants are protected: People are not allowed to hunt on that *reserve.*

res i den tial (rez'ə den'shəl) *adjective.* Of or suitable for homes or residences.

re strain (ri strān') *verb.* Hold back; keep down; keep in check; keep within limits.

re straint (ri strānt') *noun.* 1. A restraining or a being restrained: Violent people sometimes need *restraint.*

re tal i ate (ri tal'ē āt) *verb.* Pay back wrong, injury, etc.; return like for like, usually to return evil for evil: If we insult them, they will *retaliate.* **retaliated, retaliating.**

rev (rev) *verb.* (Informal) Increase the speed of (an engine or motor). **revved, revving.**

rev e la tion (rev'ə lā'shən) *noun.* 1. Act of making known: We all waited for the *revelation* of the winner's name. 2. The thing made known: Her true nature was a *revelation* to me.

rev er ie (rev'ər ē) *noun.* Dreamy thoughts; dreamy thinking of pleasant things.

re vive (ri vīv') *verb.* 1. Bring back or come back to life or consciousness: *revive* a half-drowned person. 2. Bring or come back to a fresh, lively condition: Flowers *revive* in water. **revived, reviving.**

re vulsed (ri vulst') *adjective.* To be disgusted or sickened.

rif fle (rif'l) *noun.* A ripple in a stream or current of water; also, a place where the water ripples or is set into violent commotion, as on rocks or in a shallow rapid.

rig or ous (rig'ər əs) *adjective.* Severe; strict: the *rigorous* discipline in the army.

rit u al (rich'ü əl) *noun.* 1. A form or system of rites. 2. Any regularly followed routine.

ro guish (rō'gish) *adjective.* Playfully mischievous.

ro man tic (rō man'tik) *adjective.* 1. Characteristic of romances or romance; appealing to fancy and the imagination: a *romantic* life in exotic lands. 2. Interested in adventure and love; having ideas or feelings suited to romance: The old couple reminisced about the days of their courtship, when they were young and *romantic.* 3. Of romanticism in literature, art, and music. 4. Not based on fact; fanciful; imaginary; unreal. 5. Not customary or practical; fantastic;

extravagant: *romantic* illusion. — **romantically** *adverb.*

S

sanc tion (sangk'shən) *verb.* Authorize; approve; allow: Her conscience does not *sanction* stealing. **sanctioned, sanctioning.**

sand bar (sand'bär') *noun.* Ridge of sand in a river or along a shore, formed by the actions of tides or currents.

sap phire (saf'īr) *noun.* 1. A clear, hard, usually blue, precious stone. —*adjective.* Bright-blue.

scav en ger (skav'ən jər) *noun.* Animal that feeds on decaying animal or plant matter.

scope (skōp) *noun.* 1. Distance the mind can reach; extent of view. 2. The area over which any activity extends.

scrag gly (skrag'lē) *adjective.* Rough or irregular; ragged.

scree (skrē) *noun.* 1. Heap of stones at the base of a cliff. 2. Landslide; debris from a landslide.

scribe (skrīb) *noun.* Person who copies manuscripts.

scrub (skrub) *noun.* Low, stunted trees or shrubs.

sear (sir) *verb.* 1. Burn or char the surface of: The fire *seared* the trunks of the trees. **seared, searing.**

se ren i ty (sə ren'ə tē) *noun.* Peace and quiet; calmness.

serge (sėrj) *noun.* Kind of cloth woven with slanting ridges in it.

set tle ment house. (set'l mənt hous) *noun.* Place in a poor, neglected neighborhood where work for its improvement is carried on.

sheen (shēn) *noun.* Brightness; luster.

si (sē) *adverb.* Spanish for yes.

si mul ta ne ous ly (sī'məl tā'nē əs lē) *adverb.* At once; at the same time; together.

sin u ous (sin'yü əs) *adjective.* Having many curves or turns; winding.

skua (skyü'ə) *noun.* A gull-like bird that lives in or near cold regions.

skulk (skulk) *verb.* 1. Keep out of sight to avoid danger, work, duty, etc.; hide or lurk in a cowardly way. 2. Move in a stealthy, sneak-

ing way. **skulked, skulking.**

slink (slingk) *verb.* Move in a sneaking, guilty manner; sneak. **slunk, slinking.**

slith er (sliŦH'ər) *verb.* Slide down or along a surface, especially unsteadily: Rocks *slithered* down the side of the hill.

sludge (sluj) *noun.* 1. Soft mud; mire; slush. 2. A soft, thick, muddy mixture, deposit, sediment, etc. 3. Small broken pieces of floating ice: In winter there is *sludge* on the sea near the shore.

slug gish (slug'ish) *adjective.* Slow-moving; not active; lacking energy or vigor: When I stay up late, I am often *sluggish* the next day.

smol der (smōl'dər) *verb.* To burn and smoke without flame. **smoldered, smoldering.**

smoth er (smuŦH'ər) *verb.* To make unable to get air; kill by keeping air from. **smothered, smothering.**

smug (smug) *adjective.* Too pleased with one's own goodness, cleverness, respectability, etc.; self-satisfied; complacent. — **smugness** *noun.* —**smugly** *adverb.*

snarl (snärl) *verb.* 1. To tangle or become tangled: The kitten *snarled* the yarn by playing with it. 2. Confuse. **snarled, snarling.**

so lid i fy (sə lid'ə fī) *verb.* Make or become solid; harden.

sparse (spärs) *adjective.* 1. Thinly scattered; occurring here and there: a *sparse* population. 2. Scanty; meager: a *sparse* diet. —**sparsely** *adverb.*

Spar tan (spärt'n) *adjective.* 1. Of Sparta or its people. 2. Like the Spartans; simple, frugal, and severe.

spat u la (spach'ə lə) *noun.* Tool with a broad, flat, flexible blade, used for mixing drugs, spreading paints or frostings, etc.

spec tral (spek'trəl) *adjective.* 1. Of or like a specter; ghostly: the *spectral* form of a ship on a foggy sea. 2. Of or produced by the spectrum: *spectral* colors. —**spectrally** *adverb.*

spec u la tion (spek'yə lā'shən) *noun.* Careful thought; reflection: *speculations* about the nature of the universe.

spew (spyü) *verb.* To throw out; cast forth. **spewed, spewing.**

spite (spīt) *noun.* Ill will; grudge: He broke my new radio out of *spite.*

spon ta ne ous (spon tā′nē əs) *noun.* Caused by natural impulse or desire; not forced or compelled; not planned beforehand: Both sides burst into *spontaneous* cheers at the skillful play.

stag nate (stag′nāt) *verb.* 1. Be stagnant; become stagnant. 2. Make stagnant. **stagnated, stagnating.**

stalk (stôk) *verb.* Approach or pursue without being seen or heard: The hungry lion *stalked* a zebra.

staph y lo coc cus (staf′ə lə kok′əs) *noun.* Any of a group of spherical bacteria that bunch together in irregular masses. — **staphylococci** (staf′ə lə kok′i) *plural.*

sta tus (stā′təs or stat′əs) *noun.* 1. Social or professional standing; position; rank: to seek *status.* 2. State; condition: Diplomats are interested in the *status* of world affairs.

stealth y (stel′thē) *adjective.* Done in a secret manner; secret; sly. **stealthier, stealthiest. —stealthily** *adverb.*

stench (stench) *noun.* A very bad smell; stink.

steppe (step) *noun.* A vast, treeless plain.

steth o scope (steth′ə skōp) *noun.* Instrument used by doctors to hear the sounds produced in the lungs, heart, etc.

stock tick er. (stok tik′ər) *noun.* A telegraphic instrument that prints stock-market reports or news on a paper tape.

sto i cism (stō′ə siz′əm) *noun.* Patient endurance; indifference to pleasure and pain.

stu por (stü′pər) *noun.* A dazed condition; loss or lessening of the power to feel.

sub lime (sə blīm′) *adjective.* Lofty or elevated in thought, feeling, language, etc.; noble; grand; exalted: *sublime* devotion.

sub lim i ty (sə blim′ə tē) *noun.* Lofty excellence; grandeur; majesty; exalted state.

sub se quent (sub′sə kwənt) *adjective.* Coming after; following, later. —**subsequently** *adverb.*

sub sid ence (səb sīd′ns or sub′sə dəns) *noun.* Act or process of subsiding: the *subsidence* of a flood.

sub spe cies (sub′spē shēz) *noun.* A subdivision of a species.

sub stance (sub′stəns) *noun.* 1. What a thing consists of; matter; material: Ice and water are the same *substance* in different forms. 2. The real, main, or important part of anything: The *substance* of an education is its effect on your life, not just learning lessons.

sub ter fuge (sub′tər fyüj) *noun.* Trick or excuse used to escape something unpleasant.

sub tle ty (sut′l tē) *noun.* 1. Subtle quality. 2. Something subtle. **subtleties.**

suc cu lent (suk′yə lənt) *adjective.* Juicy: a *succulent* peach. —**succulently** *adverb.*

suc cumb (sə kum′) *verb.* Give way; yield: I *succumbed* to temptation and ate the last piece of candy.

suf fice (sə fīs′) *verb.* Be enough; be sufficient: Fifty dollars will *suffice* to buy that coat.

sul pha drug. (sul′fə drug) *noun.* An antibacterial substance used to treat many types of infections.

su per fi cial (sü′pər fish′əl) *adjective.* Concerned with or understanding only what is on the surface; not thorough; shallow. —**superficially** *adverb.*

su per in tend (sü′pər in tend′) *verb.* Oversee and direct (work or workers); manage (a place, institution, etc.) **superintended, superintending.**

su per sede (sü′pər sēd′) *verb.* To take the place of; cause to be set aside; displace: Electric lights have *superseded* gaslights. **superseded, superseding.**

sure ty (shur′ə tē) *noun.* Security against loss, damage, or failure to do something.

surge (sėrj) *verb.* Rise and fall; move like waves: A great wave *surged* over us. **surged, surging.** —*noun.* 1. A swelling wave; sweep or rush of waves: Our boat

was upset by a *surge.* 2. Something like a wave: A *surge* of anger swept over him.

sy ringe (sə rinj′) *noun.* 1. A narrow tube fitted with a plunger or rubber bulb for drawing in a quantity of fluid and then forcing it out in a stream. 2. Hypodermic syringe. —*verb.* Clean, wash, inject, etc., by means of a syringe. **syringed, syringing.**

T

ta boo (tə bü′) *noun.* System or act of setting things apart as forbidden; prohibition; ban. —*adjective.* Forbidden by custom or tradition; prohibited; banned.

tact ful (takt′fəl) *adjective.* 1. Having the ability to say and do the right things. 2. Showing tact. —**tactfully** *adverb.*

tac tic (tak′tik) *noun.* 1. Detail of military tactics; maneuver. 2. Any skillful move; gambit.

tac ti cal (tak′tə kəl) *adjective.* 1. Of tactics; concerning tactics. 2. Relating to the disposal of military or naval forces in action against an enemy. —**tactically** *adverb.*

tal on (tal′ən) *noun.* Claw of an animal, especially a bird of prey.

tan dem (tan′dəm) *adverb.* One behind the other: drive horses *tandem.* —*adjective.* Having animals, seats, parts, etc., arranged one behind the other.

tap es try (tap′ə strē) *noun.* Fabric with pictures or designs woven in it, used to hang on walls, cover furniture, etc. **tapestries.**

taunt (tônt) *verb.* Jeer at; mock; reproach: My classmates *taunted* me for being teacher's pet. **taunted, taunting.** —*noun.* A bitter or insulting remark; mocking; jeering.

taut en (tôt′n) *verb.* To draw together tightly; to make tense. **tautened, tautening.**

teem (tēm) *verb.* Be full (of); abound; swarm: The swamp *teemed* with mosquitoes. **teemed, teeming.**

ten e ment (ten′ə mənt) *noun.* A building, especially in a poor section of a city, divided into sets of rooms occupied by separate families.

teth er (teᴛн'ər) *noun*. Rope or chain for fastening an animal so that it can graze or move only within a certain limit.

thresh (thresh) *verb*. 1. To separate the grain or seeds from (wheat, etc.). 2. To toss about; thrash. **threshed, threshing.**

throng (thrông) *noun*. A crowd; multitude. —*verb*. 1. To crowd; fill with a crowd: People *thronged* the gymnasium to see the basketball game. 2. Come together in a crowd; go or press in large numbers: The people *thronged* to see the king. **thronged, thronging.**

tink er (ting'kər) *noun*. Person who mends pots, pans, etc. —*verb*. 1. To mend; patch. 2. Work or repair in an unskilled or clumsy way: The children were *tinkering* with the clock and broke it. 3. Work or keep busy in a rather useless way: I was *tinkering* in my workshop. **tinkerer** (ting'kər ər) *noun*.

tol er ance (tol'ər əns) *noun*. 1. A willingness to be tolerant; a putting up with people whose opinions or ways differ from one's own. 2. The power of enduring or resisting the action of a drug, poison, etc. 3. Action of allowing or permitting: The principal's *tolerance* of their bad behavior surprised us.

tol er ate (tol'ə rāt') *verb*. 1. To allow or permit. 2. To bear; endure; put up with. **tolerated, tolerating.**

tra jec tor y (trə jek'tər ē) *noun*. The curved path of a projectile, comet, or planet.

trans fix (tran sfiks') *verb*. 1. To pierce through. 2. To make motionless (with amazement, terror, etc.). **transfixed, transfixing.**

trans for ma tion (tran'sfər mā'shən) *noun*. 1. A changing in form or appearance. 2. A changing in condition, nature, or character.

trep i da tion (trep'ə dā'shən) *noun*. Nervous dread; fear; fright.

trun dle (trun'dl) *verb*. 1. Roll along; push along: The worker *trundled* a wheelbarrow full of cement. **trundled, trundling.** —*noun*. Trundle bed.

tuft (tuft) *noun*. Bunch of feathers, hair, grass, etc., held together at one end: The goat had a *tuft* of hair on its chin.

tu mult (tü'mult *or* tyü'mult) *noun*. 1. Noise or uproar; commotion: The sailors' voices could not be heard above the *tumult* of the storm. 2. A violent disturbance or disorder: The cry of "Fire! Fire!" caused a *tumult* in the stadium.

tur moil (tér'moil) *noun*. State of agitation or commotion; disturbance; tumult: Unexpected guests put us in a *turmoil*.

twi light (twī'līt') *noun*. The faint light reflected from the sky before the sun rises and after it sets.

U

ul ti mate (ul'tə mit) *adjective*. Greatest possible. —**ultimately** *adverb*.

un ac cus tomed (un'ə kus'təmd) *adjective*. 1. Not accustomed. 2. Not familiar; unusual; strange.

un al ien a ble (un ā'lyə nə bəl) *adjective*. Inalienable; not able to be given or taken away.

un can ny (un kan'ē) *adjective*. 1. Strange and mysterious; weird. 2. So far beyond what is normal or expected as to have some special power.

un der grad u ate (un'dər graj'ü it) *noun*. Student in college or university who has not yet received a degree.

un der nour ished (un'dər nér'isht) *adjective*. Not having enough food.

un err ing (un ér'ing *or* un er'ing) *adjective*. Making no mistakes; exactly right. —**unerringly** *adverb*.

un fath om a ble (un faᴛн'ə mə bəl) *adjective*. 1. Too deep to be measured. 2. Too mysterious to be understood.

un flinch ing (un flin'ching) *adjective*. Not drawing back from difficulty, danger, or pain; firm. — **unflinchingly** *adverb*.

un gain ly (un gān'lē) *adjective*. Awkward; clumsy: Long arms and large hands can give a person an ungainly appearance.

un in hib it ed (un'in hib'ə tid) *adjective*. Not held back; not hindered or restrained.

un nerve (un nérv') *verb*. Deprive of nerve, firmness, or self-control. **unnerved, unnerving.**

un pal at a ble (un pal'ə tə bəl) *adjective*. Not agreeable to the taste; unpleasant.

un prec e dent ed (un pres'ə den'tid) *adjective*. Having no precedent; never done before; never known before: An *unprecedented* event took place in 1961, when a human being traveled for the first time in outer space.

up surge (up'sérj') *noun*. A rising upward; rise; upturn.

ur sine (ér'sīn) *adjective*. Of or like a bear or as of a bear.

V

van tage (van'tij) *noun*. A better position or condition; advantage.

Vat i can (vat'ə kən) *noun*. 1. The collection of buildings grouped about the palace of the pope in Rome. 2. The government, office, or authority of the pope.

verge (vérj) *noun*. The point at which something begins or happens; brink: Their business is on the *verge* of ruin.

ver ti go (vér'tə gō) *noun*. Dizziness; giddiness.

ves ti bule (ves'tə byül) *noun*. 1. Passage or hall between the outer door and the inside of a building. 2. The enclosed space at the end of a railroad passenger car.

vet er i nar i an (vet'ər ə ner'ē ən) *noun*. Doctor or surgeon who treats animals.

vir tu al (vér'chü əl) *adjective*. Being something in effect, though not so in name; for all practical purposes; actual; real: The battle was won with so great a loss of soldiers that it was a *virtual* defeat. —**virtually** *adverb*.

vir tue (vér'chü) *noun*. 1. Moral excellence; goodness: a person of the highest *virtue*. 2. A good quality: She praised the *virtues* of her small car.

vis age (viz'ij) *noun*. Face or

appearance: a grim *visage.*

vis u al ize (vizh′ü ə līz) *verb.* To form a mental picture of.

vi tal (vī′tl) *adjective.* 1. Of life: Growth and decay are *vital* processes. 2. Necessary to life: Eating is a *vital* function. 3. Very important; basic: a *vital* question. 4. Causing death, failure, or ruin: a *vital* wound. 5. Full of life and spirit; lively: What a *vital* person she is—never idle, never dull! — **vitally** *adverb.*

vi tal i ty (vī tal′ə tē) *noun.* Strength, energy, vigor.

vol ley (vol′ē) *noun.* 1. Shower of stones, bullets, words, oaths, etc.: A *volley* of arrows rained down upon the attacking knights. 2. The discharge of a number of guns at once. 3. The hitting or return of a tennis ball before it touches the ground. —*verb.* 1. Discharge or be discharged in a volley: Cannon *volleyed* on all sides. 2. Hit or return (a tennis ball) before it touches the ground. 3. Hit a tennis ball back and forth over the net until someone misses or

faults. **volleyed, volleying.**

vo lu mi nous (və lü′mə nəs) *adjective.* Numerous, great in number.

vul ner a ble (vul′nər ə bəl) *adjective.* 1. Capable of being wounded or injured; open to attack: The army's retreat left the city *vulnerable.*

W

wal low (wol′ō) *verb.* Roll about; flounder. **wallowed, wallowing.** —*noun.* Place where an animal rolls about.

war i ly (wer′ə lē *or* war′ə lē) *adverb.* In a wary manner; cautiously; carefully: The hikers climbed *warily* up the dangerous path.

wa ver (wā′vər) *verb.* Be undecided; hesitate: We are still *wavering* between a picnic and a trip to the zoo. **wavered, wavering.**

wheel wright (hwēl′rīt′) *noun.* Person whose work is making or repairing wheels, carriages, and wagons.

wist ful (wist′fəl) *adjective.* Longing,

yearning. —**wistfully** *adverb.*

with er (wiŦH′ər) *verb.* Lose or cause to lose freshness; make or become dry and lifeless; dry up; fade; shrivel: The hot sun *withers* the grass. **withered, withering.**

woo (wü) *verb.* 1. Seek to marry. 2. Seek to win; try to get: Some people *woo* fame. 3. Try to persuade; urge. **wooed, wooing.**

wood cut (wùd′kut′) *noun.* 1. An engraved block of wood to print from. 2. A print from such a block.

Works Prog ress Ad min is tra tion. (wėrks prog′res ad min′ə strā′shən) *noun.* A program established in the U.S. in 1935 by President Franklin D. Roosevelt to provide work for persons without jobs. —**WPA** *abbreviation.*

Z

zest (zest) *noun.* 1. Keen enjoyment; relish: The hungry children ate with *zest.* 2. A pleasant or exciting quality, flavor, etc.: Wit gives *zest* to conversation.